CW01065122

Electromagnetism

Book 3

Electromagnetic waves

Edited by Nicholas Braithwaite

SMT359 Course Team

Course Team Chair

Stuart Freake

Academic Editors

John Bolton, Nicholas Braithwaite,
Stuart Freake, Tom Smith

Authors

John Bolton, Nicholas Braithwaite,
Stuart Freake, Bob Lambourne,
Tom Smith, Mike Thorpe

Consultants

Derek Capper, Andrew Coates,
Andrew Conway, Alan Durrant,
Allister Forrest, David Grimes,
Ian Halliday, Craig McFarlane,
Robin Preston, Gillian Stansfield,
Steve Swithenby, Stan Zochowski

Course Manager

Michael Watkins

Course Team Assistant

Tracey Woodcraft

LTS, Project Manager

Rafael Hidalgo

Editors

Peter Twomey, Alison Cadle,
Rebecca Graham

TeX Specialist

Jonathan Fine

Graphic Design Advisors

Mandy Anton, Sarah Hofton

Graphic Artists

Roger Courthold (Lead artist),
Steve Best, Sarah Hack

Picture Researchers/Copyrights

Lydia Eaton, Martin Keeling

Software Designers

Fiona Thomson, Will Rawes

Video Producers

Owen Horn, Martin Chiverton

External Assessor

Don Davis (University College, London)

The editor wishes to thank the following for their contributions to this book: Chapters 3 and 4, Ian Halliday; Chapter 5, Derek Capper; Chapter 6, Andrew Conway; and Tom Smith, who was the book editor and main author until his retirement in 2005.

This publication forms part of an Open University course SMT359 Electromagnetism. The complete list of texts which make up this course can be found at the back. Details of this and other Open University courses can be obtained from the Student Registration and Enquiry Service, The Open University, PO Box 197, Milton Keynes, MK7 6BJ, United Kingdom: tel. +44 (0)870 333 4340, email general-enquiries@open.ac.uk

Alternatively, you may visit the Open University website at http://www.open.ac.uk where you can learn more about the wide range of courses and packs offered at all levels by The Open University.

To purchase a selection of Open University course materials visit http://www.ouw.co.uk or contact Open University Worldwide, Michael Young Building, Walton Hall, Milton Keynes MK7 6AA, United Kingdom for a brochure. tel. +44 (0)1908 858785; fax +44 (0)1908 858787; email ouwenq@open.ac.uk

The Open University
Walton Hall, Milton Keynes
MK7 6AA

First published 2006. Copyright © 2006. The Open University

Edited and designed by The Open University.

Typeset at The Open University.

Printed and bound in the United Kingdom at the University Press, Cambridge.

ISBN 0 7492 6987 1

1.1

EMF

Contents

Introduction

Waves and electromagnetism

You can probably think of several situations in which oscillations at one place lead to oscillations, at the same frequency, somewhere else: musical notes from vibrating strings and speech formed from vibrations of vocal chords are easily heard across an auditorium; a duck dabbling at the edge of a pond creates ripples that spread away to the bank opposite (Figure 1); TV and radio broadcast signals are produced by the oscillation of electrical charges up and down in an aerial and can be detected miles away. In circumstances like these, the original oscillations generate waves. Figure 2 shows the bizarre spectacle of a 'Mexican wave' — an arm-raising disturbance that sometimes travels around sports grounds during lulls in the main entertainment.

Figure 1 Ducks causing ripples on water.

Figure 2 A Mexican wave.

All waves carry information from one place to another — strictly speaking, they transport energy and momentum. What is more, waves do not normally leave any permanent change in the space through which they have passed.

This book is concerned with electromagnetic waves, so Maxwell's equations are at the core of the story. It is assumed that you are familiar with these equations and the theory of electromagnetism that underpins them, and also with the mathematical language used to express this theory. The aim here is to use this prior knowledge to account for various phenomena associated with electromagnetic waves.

Even when restricted to a description of electric and magnetic fields in a vacuum, which is the simplest scenario we can envisage, there are solutions of Maxwell's equations that represent travelling waves. This suggests that electromagnetic waves are able to propagate through a vacuum, and this is one of their key characteristics.

The transmission of electromagnetic energy through a vacuum is a common experience: we have plenty of evidence that various types of energy (or information) get through the emptiness of space — ultraviolet, visible and infrared radiation reaches us from the Sun, and the solar system is bathed in gamma rays, X-rays, light and radio waves from hot or dense matter in and around stars (see

Figure 3). These are all examples of electromagnetic waves that are associated with a range of frequencies from over 10^{23} Hz to below 10^2 Hz (Figure 4).

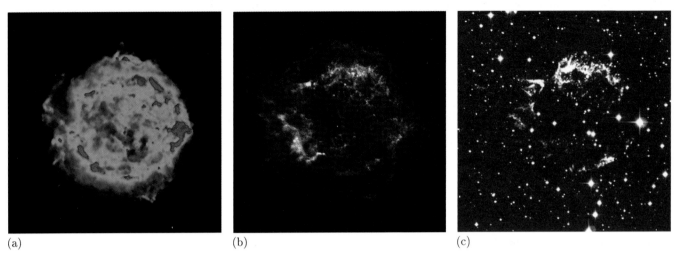

(a) (b) (c)

Figure 3 Images of the Cassiopeia A supernova remnant, produced by (a) radio waves, (b) X-rays and (c) light. The supernova is believed to have erupted about 300 years ago.

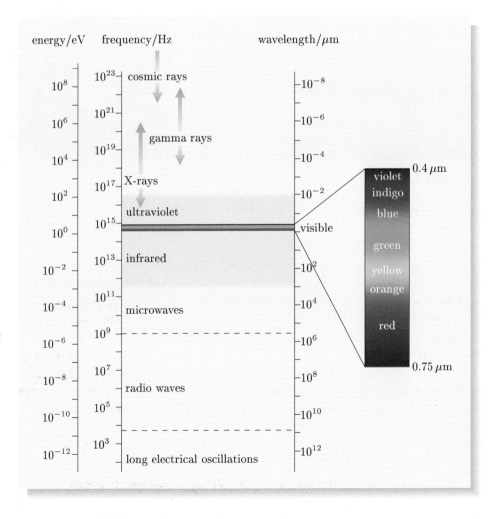

Figure 4 The electromagnetic spectrum. Light occupies the narrow range between about 4×10^{14} Hz (0.75 μm) and 7.5×10^{14} Hz (0.4 μm), and we place a disproportionately large significance on it chiefly because that is what our eyes have evolved to detect — and seeing is believing.

The spectrum in Figure 4 has a scale that shows the wavelength in free space (in micrometres) as an alternative to the classification by frequency. At one extreme the wavelength is subatomic, being fractions of picometres, while at the other end it is truly mountainous, being a few kilometres or so. It is from here that we get the radio terms 'long wave', 'medium wave', 'short wave' and 'microwave' (micro here implying 'even shorter' rather than meaning 10^{-6}).

The origin of electromagnetic waves

Figure 5 shows sources of electromagnetic waves that should be familiar to you. Light can originate from solids: an incandescent filament glows in response to thermal energy; a light-emitting diode (LED) radiates in response to electric current; the fluorescent coating on the walls of an energy-saving light bulb emits visible radiation when stimulated by the absorption of ultraviolet radiation. Gases can also be a source of electromagnetic waves: it is the ultraviolet radiation from an ionized gas that stimulates the fluorescent coating on the walls of an energy-saving light bulb; auroral glows are caused by high-energy electrons colliding with gas in the upper atmosphere; lightning flashes light up a dark sky and simultaneously cause a radio receiver to crackle.

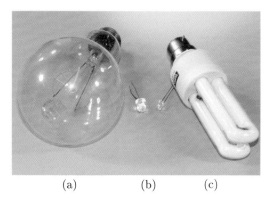

(a)   (b)   (c)   (d)   (e)

Figure 5   (a) A light bulb; (b) two LEDs; (c) a compact fluorescent energy-saving light bulb; (d) an aurora; (e) lightning.

Energy is transferred into electromagnetic waves in a wide variety of physical processes. Here are some further examples. Gamma rays arise when an electron and a positron recombine, *and* during spontaneous reconfiguration within an atomic nucleus. X-rays are generated when electrons are rapidly decelerated, *and* when an electron within an atom of a heavy element makes a transition from a high energy level down to a much lower energy level. The bending of high-energy electron beams produces intense radiation, particularly across the X-ray and ultraviolet ranges, *and* ultraviolet emission follows the relaxation of an excited atom's outer shell electrons to the ground state levels. Many of these emission processes are best explained by quantum mechanics.

In this book, we shall not be combining our ideas of electromagnetism with quantum mechanics, so we shall mostly restrict our discussion of electromagnetic radiation to what happens *after* it has left its source. However, the generation of radio waves by antennas and the scattering of light by atoms and molecules will be linked by a classical description to the spatial and temporal behaviour of currents and charges.

The properties of electromagnetic waves

In 1888 Heinrich Hertz (Figure 6) confirmed the link, that had been predicted from Maxwell's equations, between charges, currents and waves. In a series of ingenious experiments Hertz demonstrated that rapidly-changing currents associated with short sparks were a source of energy that behaved similarly to light. It was reflected and refracted when interacting with matter, it was diffracted at the edges of solid objects, and it was simply superposed when interacting with itself. Remarkably, the wavelength of the disturbance generated by the sparking circuit was about a million times longer than that of light. We can now identify these 'Hertzian' waves as belonging to the radio end of the electromagnetic spectrum.

Figure 6 Heinrich Hertz.

The video sequence *Hertz: putting Maxwell to the test* on the course DVD describes the experiments that led to the widespread acceptance of Maxwell's theory.

Some properties are common to all wave phenomena; others are more specific to electromagnetic waves. As Hertz knew well, all waves exhibit reflection, refraction, diffraction and interference — I shall assume that you have encountered these phenomena before, though not necessarily in connection with electromagnetic waves. The most familiar examples of reflection and refraction come from optical mirrors and lenses (Figure 7). The scale of optical diffraction and optical interference is smaller than we can easily see outside a laboratory, but water waves and sound waves conveniently show the same effects on a larger scale. Indeed, the radio waves that Hertz was experimenting with are also convenient for demonstrations of these common wave phenomena.

Figure 7 Mirrors and lenses used to reflect and refract high-power laser beams in a research project to develop a blue laser for large-area projection TV displays.

Some waves are said to be 'transverse' (as opposed to 'longitudinal') because the associated disturbances occur at right angles to the direction of propagation. The waves on stretched strings and on membranes are transverse; by contrast, sound waves in gases are inherently longitudinal. Through his pioneering studies of the energy radiated by sparks, Hertz established that his electromagnetic waves were transverse. For electromagnetic waves, the orientation of the electrical component is important in some circumstances because it tends to cause electrical polarization of a medium. Accordingly, the orientation of the electrical component of an electromagnetic wave is called its direction of polarization. Figure 8 includes two situations that exploit the direction of polarization of electromagnetic waves.

Electromagnetic waves are special in the way they are able to propagate through a vacuum: all electromagnetic waves will pass through empty space, and all do so at 'the speed of light *in vacuo*', which is $3.00 \times 10^8 \, \text{m s}^{-1}$. With the possible exception of gravity waves, no other waves can transport energy and momentum without there being some medium through which to travel.

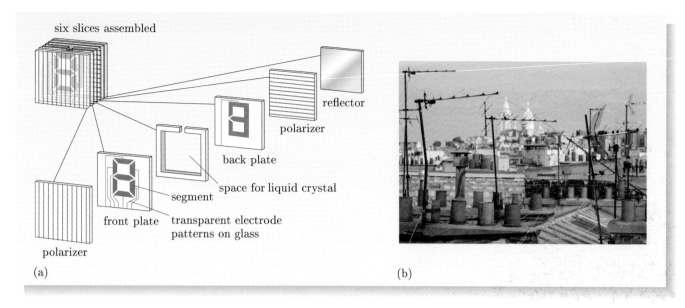

Figure 8 (a) A schematic of a liquid-crystal display element showing crossed polarizers. (b) Rooftop antennas all point towards the transmitter and have horizontal elements to detect the horizontally-polarized television signal.

When passing into matter, electromagnetic waves are slowed, or even completely turned back, because of the response of the medium to the electrical and magnetic disturbances that constitute the wave. It is this that gives rise to their refraction and reflection. The way in which electromagnetic waves are affected when they propagate through media is most starkly apparent at interfaces between different substances. In terms of electromagnetism there are two classes of media to consider: dielectrics (insulators) and conductors. The laws of refraction and reflection emerge as natural consequences of applying Maxwell's equations at the interface between two different 'transparent' dielectrics.

Propagation through matter does more than simply reducing the speed with which waves travel. Two more phenomena arise that need to be reconciled with the classical theory of electromagnetism. First, there is the fact that the speed of propagation is dependent on the frequency of the waves, so that information encoded across any range of frequency becomes dispersed in time and space as it propagates. Second, electromagnetic energy may be lost from a wave through absorption by the atoms of any material through which it travels. Understanding how optical signals are degraded in passing through glass fibres is the key to practical fibre-based telecommunication systems.

There are even more curious observations to be accounted for when electromagnetic waves encounter conducting media. Among them is the fact that electromagnetic waves barely penetrate good conductors, and the slight extent to which they do so is less the higher the frequency and the higher the conductivity.

Inspired by Hertz's findings, Guglielmo Marconi demonstrated wireless communications over distances first of a few metres in 1895, across the English Channel in 1898, and then across the Atlantic in 1901. This last feat involved low-frequency electromagnetic waves interacting with the charged particles in the ionosphere. This is a more complicated medium than simple dielectrics and conductors because the density of free charges changes from hour to hour. Large differences in conductivity arise between daytime and night-time, caused by photo-ionization of atoms and molecules in the atmosphere by light from the Sun. Ionized media are important environments for electromagnetic waves, not least because most matter in the Universe is ionized, that is, it is in the form of plasma. There is a rich variety of waves that can carry electromagnetic energy through plasmas, and these can be used to test the theory of electromagnetism.

One of the hallmarks of a good theory is that it can account for a wider range of phenomena than those for which it was originally conceived. Electromagnetism is one such theory. For instance, the topics discussed in Chapter 7 — the way in which biological tissue can be transparent and the peculiar resonances of electrical circuits — were unimaginable scenarios for Maxwell. Yet his equations, properly constrained by appropriate boundary conditions, will furnish solutions that enable us to develop a clear understanding of these and a whole host of other observations of the behaviour of electromagnetic waves.

Starting from Maxwell's equations

Together with equations governing the dynamics of particles, Maxwell's four equations can explain a great deal about the world we live in. Maxwell's decisive contribution, in the early 1860s, was to complete the theory by adding a link between time-dependent electric fields and the spatial structure of magnetic fields, namely the Ampère–Maxwell law. This had profound and far-reaching consequences. In particular, a momentous implication was the suggestion of the existence of electromagnetic waves, a prediction subsequently confirmed by Hertz. The way in which electric and magnetic fields work together to form propagating waves is embodied in Maxwell's equations, and they can be rearranged to reveal a wave equation even for the simplest case — that of empty space. You have already seen in Book 1 that simple expressions for travelling electric and magnetic waves are solutions of Maxwell's equations.

Maxwell's equations encompass the insights of Michael Faraday and others, and describe both steady-state and time-dependent electromagnetic phenomena. As you know, in order to deal with the electromagnetic properties of materials, the microscopic Maxwell's equations can be averaged over distances that are small on the scale of most measurements and observations, but large on an atomic scale. Maxwell's equations in media (see inside the front cover) provide a model that is sufficient to explain very well a vast range of physical phenomena.

The scope of this book

The general notation and terminology of waves is set out in Chapter 1. The wave equation is then derived from Maxwell's equations, and general solutions are constructed.

In Chapter 2 solutions of Maxwell's equations are found that are consistent with the generation of electromagnetic radiation by oscillating currents. The resulting model can be applied at the scale of metres to the generation of radio waves, and at the scale of nanometres to the scattering of light by particles as small as atoms.

Chapter 3 examines electromagnetic waves as they cross the boundary between two dielectric media, at normal incidence and at oblique angles. In the latter case the polarization of the waves plays an important role. Standard results from basic optics, such as the laws of refraction and reflection, emerge as the consequences of imposing appropriate conditions on the solutions of Maxwell's equations at the boundary.

Dispersion and absorption by dielectrics are described in Chapter 4. In particular, the complicated dielectric properties of water and silica are interpreted in terms of the classical theory of electromagnetism.

In Chapter 5 the conditions prevailing at conducting boundaries are imposed. The reflection of electromagnetic waves from, and their penetration through, conductors is explored. A brief account is given of how metallic structures can guide electromagnetic waves through otherwise empty space.

Electromagnetic waves in the ionosphere, and in other plasmas, are discussed in Chapter 6. The ionized gas that comprises a plasma presents a rich environment for electromagnetic phenomena.

Finally, Chapter 7 reviews two widely different cases involving electromagnetic waves. These are aspects of the transmission of light through biological tissue, specifically the cornea of the human eye, and a practically useful resonance of microwaves on a simple wire structure.

Chapter 1   Electromagnetic waves in empty space

1.1   About waves

It was shown in Book 1 that simple expressions for travelling waves satisfy
Maxwell's four differential equations for electric and magnetic fields in empty
space. This suggests that the equations can be combined into the standard form
of the wave equation. This is one of the main tasks in this chapter. First, the
basics of waves and the wave equation are set out. A wave equation for electric
and magnetic fields is then derived from Maxwell's equations, and the form of
a general solution is discussed. A convenient notation for travelling waves
is introduced based on complex exponential functions, and this notation is
used throughout this book. Finally, we quantify the energy associated with
electromagnetic waves.

1.1.1   The wave equation

The wave equation models the propagation of signals in many media. For
example, a wave equation can be derived for the local pressure in air, and
solutions of this equation represent sound waves, which travel at a characteristic
speed — the speed of sound. Starting from Maxwell's equations, we shall show in
Section 1.2 that similar wave equations apply to electric fields and magnetic
fields, and that these fields can propagate together at a characteristic speed even in
the absence of any medium whatsoever. First, however, we look at the nature of
the wave equation and its general solutions.

The wave equation for propagation of a quantity $A(z,t)$ in one dimension at a
constant speed v is

$$\frac{\partial^2}{\partial z^2} A(z,t) = \frac{1}{v^2} \frac{\partial^2}{\partial t^2} A(z,t).$$

It is useful sometimes to rearrange the form of the equation as follows:

$$\left(\frac{\partial^2}{\partial z^2} - \frac{1}{v^2} \frac{\partial^2}{\partial t^2} \right) A(z,t) = 0. \tag{1.1}$$

The essence of the **wave equation** is that it links the second derivative with
respect to space of the propagating quantity, $A(z,t)$, to the second derivative with
respect to time. For sound waves in air, for example, $A(z,t)$ represents pressure
disturbances moving through the air. In this book we shall be interested in electric
and magnetic fields propagating through empty space and within materials.

We can extend Equation 1.1 to three dimensions by including the other
second-order spatial derivatives:

$$\left(\left[\frac{\partial^2}{\partial x^2} + \frac{\partial^2}{\partial y^2} + \frac{\partial^2}{\partial z^2} \right] - \frac{1}{v^2} \frac{\partial^2}{\partial t^2} \right) A(x,y,z,t) = 0. \tag{1.2}$$

The wave equation is a second-order differential equation — that is, it contains
second derivatives. None of the derivatives is multiplied by anything other than a
simple constant, so it is a linear equation. It describes the general behaviour of a
wide selection of linear waves — that is, waves that do not change the properties
of the medium through which they pass.

1.1.2 Sinusoidal solutions of the wave equation

There is a whole class of solutions of Equation 1.1 that is based on sine and cosine functions. These sinusoidal waves have the form

$$A(z,t) = A_0 \cos(2\pi z/\lambda - 2\pi f t + \phi),$$

Since $\cos(\theta - \pi/2) = \sin\theta$, this equation covers both sine and cosine functions.

where z and t are independent variables representing space and time, respectively, and A_0, λ, f and ϕ are constant parameters that are illustrated in Figure 1.1 and defined below.

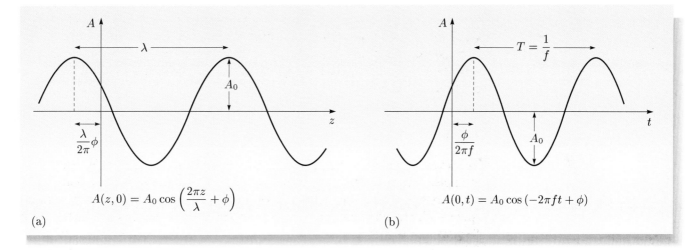

Figure 1.1 A sinusoidal wave $A(z,t) = A_0 \cos(2\pi z/\lambda - 2\pi f t + \phi)$.
(a) The wave profile as a function of position, shown at time $t = 0$.
(b) The wave profile as a function of time, shown at position $z = 0$.

- A_0 is the **amplitude** — this is the maximum value of the function $A(z,t)$.

- λ is the **wavelength**, which is the distance between successive maxima at an instant of time (Figure 1.1a).

- f is the **frequency**, which is the number of cycles of the wave that pass a fixed point in unit time. The SI unit of frequency is hertz (Hz). The reciprocal of the frequency is the **period**, $T = 1/f$, and this is the time between successive peaks of the wave passing a fixed point (Figure 1.1b).

- ϕ is an offset to the argument of the sinusoidal function; the argument of a periodic function is called its **phase**; accordingly, ϕ is a **phase shift** that applies at all places and at all times. Phase shifts are often given in the range $-\pi$ to $+\pi$.

It is convenient in the algebra of waves to use two different quantities in place of f and λ, absorbing the factors of 2π and tidying up the appearance thus:

$$A(z,t) = A_0 \cos(kz - \omega t + \phi). \tag{1.3}$$

In this expression,

- $\omega = 2\pi f$ is the **angular frequency** — this is a positive quantity, measured in s^{-1} to avoid confusion with the ordinary frequency f;

- $k = 2\pi/\lambda$ is called the **wavenumber** — this is a positive quantity, and its SI unit is m^{-1}.

Exercise 1.1 Determine the wavenumber and angular frequency for the waves in the following table, and complete the classification in the first column. ■

$k = 2\pi/\lambda$
$\omega = 2\pi f = 2\pi/T$
all given to 3 sig figs.

Wave type	Wavelength λ/m	Period T/s	Wavenumber k/m^{-1}	Angular frequency ω/s^{-1}
FM radio	3.00	10.0×10^{-9}	2.09	6.28×10^{8}
microwave	60.0×10^{-3}	0.200×10^{-9}	105	3.14×10^{10}
ultraviolet	120×10^{-9}	4.00×10^{-16}	5.24×10^{6}	1.57×10^{16}

Essential skill

Partial differentiation and working with solutions of the wave equation

---

Worked Example 1.1

Show that the function $A(z, t)$ in Equation 1.3 is a solution of the wave equation (Equation 1.1), and determine the speed of the wave represented by this function in terms of ω and k.

Solution

We need to evaluate the second partial derivatives of $A(z, t)$ with respect to t and with respect to z. The first partial derivative with respect to time is

$$\frac{\partial}{\partial t}\left(A_0 \cos(kz - \omega t + \phi)\right) = \omega A_0 \sin(kz - \omega t + \phi).$$

We repeat the process to obtain the second partial derivative, $\partial^2 A/\partial t^2 = \partial/\partial t(\partial A/\partial t)$:

$$\frac{\partial^2}{\partial t^2}\left(A_0 \cos(kz - \omega t + \phi)\right) = -\omega^2 A_0 \cos(kz - \omega t + \phi).$$

Likewise, the derivatives with respect to z are

$$\frac{\partial}{\partial z}\left(A_0 \cos(kz - \omega t + \phi)\right) = -kA_0 \sin(kz - \omega t + \phi),$$

$$\frac{\partial^2}{\partial z^2}\left(A_0 \cos(kz - \omega t + \phi)\right) = -k^2 A_0 \cos(kz - \omega t + \phi).$$

Substituting these results into Equation 1.1, we obtain

$$-k^2 A_0 \cos(kz - \omega t + \phi) - \frac{1}{v^2}(-\omega^2) A_0 \cos(kz - \omega t + \phi) = 0.$$

Thus $A_0 \cos(kz - \omega t + \phi)$ is a solution if $k^2 = \omega^2/v^2$. Since we defined ω and k to be positive quantities, the speed of the wave is $v = \omega/k$.

The wave represented by Equation 1.3 travels in the $+z$-direction, as we shall now show. At $t = 0$, the wave has the profile shown by the darker curve in Figure 1.2, and this is represented by the function $A(z, 0) = A_0 \cos(kz + \phi)$. At a short time Δt later, the profile will be represented by $A(z, \Delta t) = A_0 \cos(kz - \omega \Delta t + \phi)$, which can be rewritten as $A(z, \Delta t) = A_0 \cos\left(kz + (\phi - \omega \Delta t)\right)$. Thus the small increment of time Δt effectively reduces the phase shift ϕ, and this means that the wave profile is displaced in the direction of increasing z, as shown by the lighter curve in Figure 1.2.

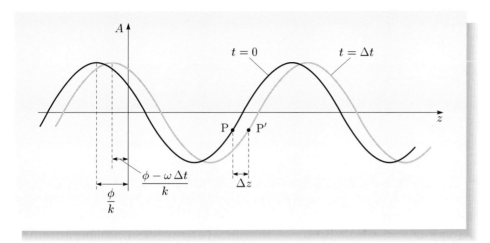

Figure 1.2 Profiles of a sinusoidal wave $A(z,t) = A_0 \cos(kz - \omega t + \phi)$ at times $t = 0$ (darker curve) and $t = \Delta t$ (lighter curve).

Now in the time interval Δt, the point labelled P on the wave travels a distance Δz to P'. These two points have the same phase, so the speed at which this point of constant phase travels is $v = \Delta z/\Delta t$. But for the phase to remain constant in Equation 1.3, we require $k\,\Delta z - \omega\,\Delta t = 0$. So we deduce that

$$v = \frac{\Delta z}{\Delta t} = \frac{\omega}{k}.$$

The speed that appears in the wave equation, $v = \omega/k$, is therefore called the **phase speed**, because it is the speed at which a point with constant phase travels.

This may also be familiar as $v = f\lambda = (2\pi f)(\lambda/2\pi)$.

Another sinusoidal solution of the wave equation is

$$A(z,t) = A_0 \cos(kz + \omega t + \phi).$$

You can see that this must represent a wave that travels in the opposite direction from that represented by Equation 1.3, since reversing the direction of time ($t \to -t$) in Equation 1.3 results in this new form. Alternatively, note that if a point of constant phase on this wave travels distance Δz in time Δt, then these quantities must be related by $k\,\Delta z + \omega\,\Delta t = 0$. In this case, $v = \omega/k = -\Delta z/\Delta t$. Since the speed v is positive, the displacement Δz must be negative, corresponding to the wave travelling in the negative z-direction.

If time were to run backwards, so too would the wave represented by Equation 1.3.

Yet another solution is

$$A(z,t) = A_0 \cos(-kz - \omega t + \phi).$$

In this case, if a point of constant phase travels distance Δz in time Δt, then $-k\,\Delta z - \omega\,\Delta t = 0$, and $v = \omega/k = -\Delta z/\Delta t$, so this also represents a wave travelling in the negative z-direction. Keep in mind that if the kz and ωt terms have opposite signs, the wave travels in the positive z-direction; if they have the same sign, the wave travels in the negative z-direction.

Here is a summary of what has just been established. Since ω and k are both positive, $\cos(kz - \omega t + \phi)$ represents a wave travelling in the positive z-direction, whereas $\cos(kz + \omega t + \phi)$ represents a wave travelling in the negative z-direction. The speed with which sinusoidal waves travel through space is given by the phase speed, $v = \omega/k$.

Exercise 1.2 Determine the speed and direction of travel of a sinusoidal wave that has frequency 1200 kHz and wavelength 250 m, and that has the form $A = A_0 \sin(kz - \omega t + \phi)$. ■

1.1.3   Linearity of the wave equation

Consider now an important property of the wave equation, corresponding to the everyday observation that light waves from two sources can propagate through a region of space without influencing each other. Indeed, any volume of space contains many coexisting electromagnetic waves which propagate without influencing each other.

Equation 1.1 is linear because the variable $A(z,t)$ occurs in it only to the first power. Linearity would be lost in a 'wave equation' that had some term like $A^2(z,t)$ in it.

This 'live and let live' behaviour is a consequence of the **linearity** of the wave equation. This means that if $A_1(z,t)$ and $A_2(z,t)$ are any two solutions of the wave equation, then any linear combination of these solutions, i.e. functions of the form $a_1 A_1(z,t) + a_2 A_2(z,t)$, where a_1 and a_2 are arbitrary constants, is also a solution. If the wave equations governing propagation of electromagnetic waves were not linear then, for example, radio (and TV) reception would depend on the instantaneous content of *all* broadcast signals in the neighbourhood. Common experience suggests that this is not the case — where inter-station interference does occur, it is due to non-linearity in the receiver rather than any lack of linearity during wave propagation.

Essential skill

Testing the linearity of an equation

Worked Example 1.2

Verify that the wave equation (Equation 1.1) is linear.

Solution

Take a linear combination of two functions, $A_1(z,t)$ and $A_2(z,t)$, that are known to be solutions, and see if this combination also satisfies the wave equation:

$$\left(\frac{\partial^2}{\partial z^2} - \frac{1}{v^2} \frac{\partial^2}{\partial t^2} \right) \left(a_1 A_1(z,t) + a_2 A_2(z,t) \right)$$

$$= a_1 \left(\frac{\partial^2}{\partial z^2} - \frac{1}{v^2} \frac{\partial^2}{\partial t^2} \right) A_1(z,t) + a_2 \left(\frac{\partial^2}{\partial z^2} - \frac{1}{v^2} \frac{\partial^2}{\partial t^2} \right) A_2(z,t)$$

$$= 0.$$

Both terms are independently zero because A_1 and A_2 are solutions of Equation 1.1. So the arbitrary linear combination of solutions A_1 and A_2 is also a solution.

1.1.4   General solutions of the wave equation

The property of linearity implies that there can be solutions of the wave equation that are not purely sinusoidal: arbitrary linear combinations of sinusoidal solutions of different frequencies are also solutions, and such linear combinations no longer have a simple sinusoidal form. Indeed, there is a very general form of solution of the wave equation, known as **d'Alembert's solution**. This solution has the form

$$g_1(z - vt) + g_2(z + vt),$$

where g_1 and g_2 are any functions that can be differentiated twice, and v is the wave speed.

Any periodic shape can be expressed as the sum of a discrete series of sinusoids using a mathematical technique known as *Fourier analysis*. Non-periodic shapes can similarly be represented as an integral over a continuous distribution of sinusoids. The linearity of the wave equation means that d'Alembert solutions are possible provided that all component sinusoids involved travel at the same speed.

Exercise 1.3   Show that *any* twice-differentiable functions of the form $g(z \pm vt)$ are solutions of Equation 1.1. ■

Two examples of d'Alembert solutions are shown in Figure 1.3. The solution $g(z - vt)$ represents a fixed wave profile travelling with speed v in the positive z-direction. To see this, note that the value of $g(z - vt)$ is the *same* for all combinations of z and t such that $z - vt$ has a particular value. Consider, for instance, the position $z = z_1$ and time $t = t_1$, indicated by the point labelled P in Figure 1.3b, where $z_1 - vt_1 = u_0$, so $g = g(u_0)$. Then g will be equal to $g(u_0)$ at some time Δt later, at the position P′ where $z - v(t_1 + \Delta t) = u_0$, that is, at $z = z_1 + v \Delta t$. The d'Alembert solution $g(z - vt)$ therefore represents a fixed shape moving with speed v in the positive z-direction. By similar reasoning, $g(z + vt)$ moves with speed v in the negative z-direction.

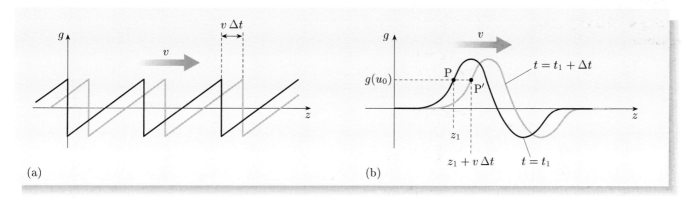

(a)   (b)

Exercise 1.4   Show that the function $A(z, t) = A_0 \cos(kz - \omega t + \phi)$ is a special case of d'Alembert's solution. ■

This section has established the foundations for our study of electromagnetic waves. The mathematics of waves is inevitably rather complicated, not least because it involves second derivatives in both space and time. You should be wary of short, neat lines of symbols that encapsulate several lines of verbal debate. Nevertheless, the notation is clearly an advantage when it enables relationships to be expressed succinctly. We have now rehearsed enough about the wave equation to set about extracting it from Maxwell's equations.

Figure 1.3   Examples of d'Alembert solutions of the wave equation: (a) a periodic function; (b) a non-periodic function.

1.2   Deriving a wave equation for empty space

Hertz's experiments with spark gaps demonstrated that the electric and magnetic fields associated with rapidly-varying currents appeared to propagate through space as waves. This quickly led to the general acceptance of Maxwell's theory. Maxwell would have thought of the waves as vibrations in a medium called the

The course DVD includes a video sequence *Hertz: putting Maxwell to the test* that describes Hertz's experiments.

'luminiferous ether'. Nowadays that view is considered invalid and we accept that electromagnetic waves propagate in vacuum, without any medium.

You have seen in Book 1 that electric and magnetic fields in the form of travelling waves do indeed satisfy Maxwell's equations. The goal of this section is to find how this comes about, by showing that Maxwell's equations can be combined into wave equations for the electric and magnetic fields, even in empty space.

1.2.1   Maxwell's equations in empty space

In empty space, there is (by definition) no matter, so there is no electric polarization and no magnetization, and therefore $\mathbf{D}(\mathbf{r}, t) = \varepsilon_0 \mathbf{E}(\mathbf{r}, t)$ and $\mathbf{B}(\mathbf{r}, t) = \mu_0 \mathbf{H}(\mathbf{r}, t)$. Also, in a region of empty space there are no charges and no particle currents, so $\rho_\mathrm{f} = 0$ and $\mathbf{J}_\mathrm{f} = 0$. Thus, in a vacuum, Gauss's law, the no-monopole law, Faraday's law and the Ampère–Maxwell law become, respectively,

$$\mathrm{div}\,\mathbf{E} = 0, \tag{1.4}$$

$$\mathrm{div}\,\mathbf{B} = 0, \tag{1.5}$$

$$\mathrm{curl}\,\mathbf{E} = -\frac{\partial \mathbf{B}}{\partial t}, \tag{1.6}$$

$$\mathrm{curl}\,\mathbf{B} = \varepsilon_0 \mu_0 \frac{\partial \mathbf{E}}{\partial t}. \tag{1.7}$$

Even in a vacuum, Maxwell's equations couple the vector components of $\mathbf{E}$ and $\mathbf{B}$ in complicated ways that are somewhat disguised by the elegant notation used in writing them. For example, within Equation 1.6, there are equations for three vector components. In Cartesian coordinates, the x-component is

$$\left(\frac{\partial E_z}{\partial y} - \frac{\partial E_y}{\partial z} \right) = -\frac{\partial B_x}{\partial t},$$

and there are similar equations for the y- and z-components. The notation of vector calculus will keep the mathematics tidy when we carry out further analysis in pursuit of the wave equation.

1.2.2   Revealing the wave equation

The wave equation is second order (it contains second derivatives) so we must consider derivatives of Maxwell's equations. Fortunately, there are general vectorial relations between the curl, grad and div operations that can be used to simplify matters.

Equations 1.6 and 1.7 are a pair of linear, coupled *first*-order vector differential equations for electric and magnetic fields. They can be combined to obtain separate equations for each field, though the price to be paid for achieving the separation is that the resulting equations are second order. That is acceptable as we are aiming to obtain a wave equation, and that too contains second derivatives. Here is how to extract a separate equation for the magnetic field alone.

- Take the curl of both sides of Equation 1.7 to obtain

$$\mathrm{curl}(\mathrm{curl}\,\mathbf{B}) = \mathrm{curl}\left(\varepsilon_0 \mu_0 \frac{\partial \mathbf{E}}{\partial t} \right).$$

- Recognize that

$$\mathrm{curl}\left(\varepsilon_0\mu_0\frac{\partial\mathbf{E}}{\partial t}\right) = \varepsilon_0\mu_0\frac{\partial}{\partial t}(\mathrm{curl}\,\mathbf{E}),$$

so that

$$\mathrm{curl}(\mathrm{curl}\,\mathbf{B}) = \varepsilon_0\mu_0\frac{\partial}{\partial t}(\mathrm{curl}\,\mathbf{E}).$$

- Use Equation 1.6 to eliminate $\mathrm{curl}\,\mathbf{E}$, giving

$$\mathrm{curl}(\mathrm{curl}\,\mathbf{B}) = \varepsilon_0\mu_0\frac{\partial}{\partial t}\left(-\frac{\partial\mathbf{B}}{\partial t}\right) = -\varepsilon_0\mu_0\frac{\partial^2\mathbf{B}}{\partial t^2}.$$

So now we have a second-order equation for the vector field $\mathbf{B}(\mathbf{r},t)$, namely

$$\mathrm{curl}(\mathrm{curl}\,\mathbf{B}) = -\varepsilon_0\mu_0\frac{\partial^2\mathbf{B}}{\partial t^2}. \tag{1.8}$$

This equation for $\mathbf{B}$ has been derived using only the information contained in Equations 1.6 and 1.7. We now make use of the vector identity (see inside the back cover)

$$\mathrm{curl}(\mathrm{curl}\,\mathbf{B}) = \mathrm{grad}(\mathrm{div}\,\mathbf{B}) - \nabla^2\mathbf{B},$$

where, in Cartesian coordinates, the *Laplacian operator* ∇^2 is

$$\nabla^2 = \frac{\partial^2}{\partial x^2} + \frac{\partial^2}{\partial y^2} + \frac{\partial^2}{\partial z^2}. \tag{1.9}$$

Since the no-monopole law (Equation 1.5) sets $\mathrm{div}\,\mathbf{B}$ equal to zero, this identity reduces to

$$\mathrm{curl}(\mathrm{curl}\,\mathbf{B}) = -\nabla^2\mathbf{B}.$$

Using this with Equation 1.8 gives the *vector* wave equation for the field $\mathbf{B}(\mathbf{r},t)$ in empty space,

$$\nabla^2\mathbf{B}(\mathbf{r},t) = \varepsilon_0\mu_0\frac{\partial^2\mathbf{B}(\mathbf{r},t)}{\partial t^2}. \tag{1.10}$$

Note that Equation 1.10 is a vector equation in three dimensions, that is, it contains three equations — one for each Cartesian component of the magnetic field. For each of these components we have the second derivative in space associated with the second derivative in time, which is the essence of a wave equation. Comparison with Equation 1.2 confirms that this is a three-dimensional version of the wave equation and that the product of the permittivity and permeability of free space, $\varepsilon_0\mu_0$, defines a phase speed: $c = \omega/k = 1/\sqrt{\varepsilon_0\mu_0}$.

The phase speed of electromagnetic waves in a vacuum is conventionally given the symbol c.

Exercise 1.5   Write out in Cartesian coordinates the three equations contained in Equation 1.10 to confirm its status as a vector wave equation. ∎

The equivalent equation for $\mathbf{E}(\mathbf{r},t)$ is

$$\nabla^2\mathbf{E}(\mathbf{r},t) = \varepsilon_0\mu_0\frac{\partial^2\mathbf{E}(\mathbf{r},t)}{\partial t^2}, \tag{1.11}$$

as you can show for yourself in the following exercise.

Exercise 1.6   Show that $\mathbf{E}(\mathbf{r},t)$ obeys Equation 1.11. Rather than copying the argument that leads to Equation 1.10 for $\mathbf{B}$, try to exploit the near symmetry of Maxwell's equations in free space: if you make the formal exchanges $\mathbf{B} \to -\varepsilon_0\mu_0\mathbf{E}$ and $\mathbf{E} \to \mathbf{B}$ in Maxwell's equations, then they are *unchanged*. ∎

1.3   Planar solutions of the wave equation

Solutions of Equations 1.10 and 1.11 for **E** and **B** must be consistent with *all four* of Maxwell's equations (1.4 to 1.7). There are usually many such solutions: one selects those that are appropriate to a given situation.

1.3.1   General plane wave solutions

In this chapter we focus on **plane wave** solutions, which are solutions that have a constant phase across infinite planes perpendicular to the direction of propagation. These solutions are very important because they are a good approximation to the radiation far from a source (Figure 1.4). In this distant region, the surfaces on which the phase of the wave is constant at any instant of time — known as **wavefronts** — are parallel planes.

Plane waves have wavefronts that are planar. The image they conjure up for me is a wide sheet of corrugated cardboard.

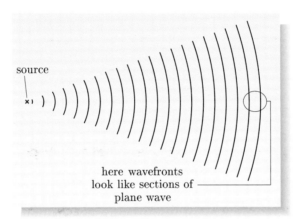

source

here wavefronts look like sections of plane wave

Figure 1.4   Far from a source, the radiated waves within a small region are effectively plane waves.

We can quite generally express solutions of Equation 1.11 in Cartesian coordinates as

$$\mathbf{E}(\mathbf{r}, t) = E_x(\mathbf{r}, t)\,\mathbf{e}_x + E_y(\mathbf{r}, t)\,\mathbf{e}_y + E_z(\mathbf{r}, t)\,\mathbf{e}_z.$$

A convenient case to consider is that of plane waves propagating along the z-axis. Then the disturbance must be uniform right across any plane on which z is constant. In particular, let us look for solutions that have an electric field directed along the x-axis, i.e. we are seeking solutions for which $E_y = 0$ and $E_z = 0$. Then E_x must satisfy

$$\left(\frac{\partial^2}{\partial x^2} + \frac{\partial^2}{\partial y^2} + \frac{\partial^2}{\partial z^2} \right) E_x(x, y, z, t) = \varepsilon_0 \mu_0 \frac{\partial^2 E_x(x, y, z, t)}{\partial t^2}. \tag{1.12}$$

This equation is still pretty complicated since it allows for dependence of E_x upon x, y, z and t. But for plane waves with wavefronts that correspond to planes with constant z, our solutions depend on z and t only, so Equation 1.12 reduces to

$$\frac{\partial^2 E_x(z, t)}{\partial z^2} = \varepsilon_0 \mu_0 \frac{\partial^2 E_x(z, t)}{\partial t^2}.$$

Now this is an equation that we know how to solve; it has exactly the form of Equation 1.1 with the phase speed $c = 1/\sqrt{\varepsilon_0 \mu_0}$. Then the general d'Alembert solution takes the form of a linear combination of waves travelling in opposite directions,

$$E_x(z, t) = a_1 \, g_1(z - ct) + a_2 \, g_2(z + ct), \qquad (1.13)$$

where a_1 and a_2 are arbitrary constants, and g_1 and g_2 are any twice-differentiable functions. You should recognize that the first term here represents a waveform moving at speed c in the direction of increasing z, and the second term is a waveform moving in the opposite direction.

As the direction of the z-axis and its origin are quite arbitrary — empty space is isotropic and homogeneous — the prediction made in the second half of the nineteenth century was that there could be electromagnetic excitations, or signals, moving in empty space, in any direction, at any location, at a universal speed c. Since ε_0 and μ_0 can be measured in the laboratory by means of simple experiments on static configurations of charges and currents, this theoretical prediction is remarkable.

To make such a breathtaking prediction, based on physical and/or mathematical insight, is the dream of all physicists — few succeed.

● Use data from inside the front cover to calculate the phase speed of plane electromagnetic waves.

○ $c = \dfrac{1}{\sqrt{\varepsilon_0 \mu_0}} = \sqrt{\dfrac{1}{8.85 \times 10^{-12} \, \text{C}^2 \, \text{N}^{-1} \, \text{m}^{-2} \times 4\pi \times 10^{-7} \, \text{N} \, \text{A}^{-2}}}$

$\qquad = 3.00 \times 10^8 \, \text{C}^{-1} \, \text{m} \, \text{A}.$

To get the right units of $\text{m} \, \text{s}^{-1}$, you need to identify amps with coulombs per second.

What Maxwell's equations stipulate about plane waves

As I have said, any pair $\mathbf{E}(\mathbf{r}, t)$ and $\mathbf{B}(\mathbf{r}, t)$ must be fully consistent with *all four* of Equations 1.4 to 1.7, and this condition intertwines their properties. This is something we should check, as in our search for a wave equation in the previous subsection we deliberately separated the electric and magnetic fields. To re-establish the link between them we need to invoke Maxwell's equations again.

Let us suppose that we have a solution of the wave equation for $\mathbf{E}$, as follows:

$$\mathbf{E}(z, t) = E_x(z, t) \, \mathbf{e}_x = g(z - ct) \, \mathbf{e}_x. \qquad (1.14)$$

This plane wave solution of Equation 1.11 represents a propagating electric field that is always parallel to the x-axis, and therefore perpendicular to the z-axis, which is the direction of propagation. It clearly satisfies Gauss's law for a vacuum, div $\mathbf{E} = 0$, since $E_x(z, t)$ is itself not a function of x, so

$$\text{div} \, \mathbf{E}(z, t) = \frac{\partial E_x(z, t)}{\partial x} = 0.$$

Gauss's law requires that the electric field for a plane wave is perpendicular to the direction of propagation: that is, the electric field is a *transverse* wave.

The no-monopole law leads to a similar conclusion for the magnetic field.

Maxwell's equations tell us that the time-dependent electric field in Equation 1.14 has a companion magnetic field. To find it, let us use Faraday's law for the empty space in which we are working, $\operatorname{curl}\mathbf{E} = -\partial\mathbf{B}/\partial t$. Since the electric field is $\mathbf{E}(z,t) = g(z - vt)\,\mathbf{e}_x$, we can write its curl as

$$\operatorname{curl}\mathbf{E} = \begin{vmatrix} \mathbf{e}_x & \mathbf{e}_y & \mathbf{e}_z \\ \dfrac{\partial}{\partial x} & \dfrac{\partial}{\partial y} & \dfrac{\partial}{\partial z} \\ g(z - ct) & 0 & 0 \end{vmatrix} = \left(\frac{\partial}{\partial z}\, g(z - ct) \right) \mathbf{e}_y = g'(z - ct)\,\mathbf{e}_y.$$

Then it follows that

$$g'(z - ct)\,\mathbf{e}_y = -\frac{\partial\mathbf{B}(z,t)}{\partial t},$$

which has the solution (check it!)

$$\mathbf{B}(z,t) = \frac{1}{c}\, g(z - ct)\,\mathbf{e}_y + \mathbf{C}(z),$$

where $\mathbf{C}(z)$ is any vector function of z that does not depend on t. In the present case we can ignore $\mathbf{C}(z)$, for it would correspond to a static background magnetic field, and not to a propagating electromagnetic disturbance. Then we have arrived at the following pair of solutions for $\mathbf{E}$ and $\mathbf{B}$:

$$\mathbf{E}(z,t) = g(z - ct)\,\mathbf{e}_x \quad \text{and} \quad \mathbf{B}(z,t) = \frac{1}{c}\, g(z - ct)\,\mathbf{e}_y. \tag{1.15}$$

The plane wave of the electric field is necessarily accompanied by a plane wave of magnetic field of similar shape, set perpendicular to it, as shown in Figure 1.5.

> Faraday's law requires that the magnetic field of an electromagnetic plane wave is perpendicular to the electric field and that the magnitudes of the fields are related by $|\mathbf{E}(z,t)| = c\,|\mathbf{B}(z,t)|$.

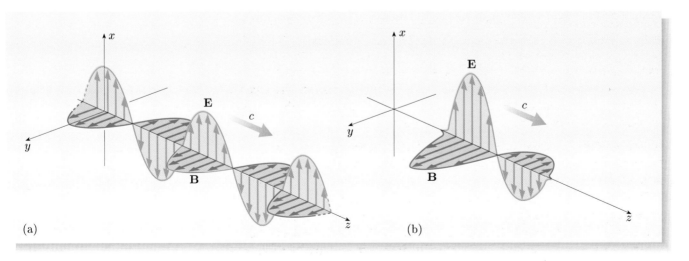

(a) (b)

Figure 1.5   (a) Sinusoidal and (b) non-sinusoidal pairs of $\mathbf{E}(z,t)$ and $\mathbf{B}(z,t)$ that are plane wave solutions of Maxwell's equations in a vacuum.

Worked Example 1.3

Show that the magnetic field in Equation 1.15 satisfies the no-monopole law and the Ampère–Maxwell law in free space.

Solution

First, since

$$\text{div}\,\mathbf{B} = \frac{\partial B_x}{\partial x} + \frac{\partial B_y}{\partial y} + \frac{\partial B_z}{\partial z}$$

and

$$\mathbf{B}(z,t) = B_y(z,t)\,\mathbf{e}_y,$$

we require that $\partial B_y(z,t)/\partial y = 0$, which is true because $B_y(z,t)$ is independent of y.

Second, we need to check the equation for $\text{curl}\,\mathbf{B}$:

$$\text{curl}\,\mathbf{B} = \begin{vmatrix} \mathbf{e}_x & \mathbf{e}_y & \mathbf{e}_z \\ \dfrac{\partial}{\partial x} & \dfrac{\partial}{\partial y} & \dfrac{\partial}{\partial z} \\ 0 & (1/c)\,g(z-ct) & 0 \end{vmatrix} = -\frac{1}{c}\,g'(z-ct)\,\mathbf{e}_x,$$

which should equal $\varepsilon_0\mu_0\,\partial\mathbf{E}/\partial t$, as indeed it does since

$$\varepsilon_0\mu_0\,\partial\mathbf{E}/\partial t = \varepsilon_0\mu_0(-c)\,g'(z-ct)\,\mathbf{e}_x$$

and $\varepsilon_0\mu_0 = 1/c^2$ as we have already established.

The Ampère–Maxwell law requires that the magnetic field is perpendicular to the electric field and that the phase speed is $c = 1/\sqrt{\varepsilon_0\mu_0}$.

The pair $(\mathbf{E},\mathbf{B})$ given by Equations 1.15 are *plane wave* solutions. They are proper solutions of the four Maxwell's equations in a vacuum, and are called *plane* waves because the fields do not depend upon position in any plane perpendicular to the axis of travel, which here is the z-axis. The plane wave solutions of Equation 1.15 are disturbances propagating along the z-axis, but with their electric and magnetic fields at right angles to it, and to each other — as illustrated in Figure 1.5; that is, they are transverse waves.

The fact that these solutions are not localized in directions perpendicular to the z-direction is an idealization, since actual electromagnetic disturbances, generated for instance by finite current sources, cannot extend out to infinity in any direction. However, plane waves are useful physical models for representing the radiation in regions that are small compared to the distance from a radiating source, as shown in Figure 1.4. In Chapter 2 we shall consider in detail the important example of radiation from an oscillating current dipole, and this will confirm the expectation that the waves are planar far from the source.

Exercise 1.7   Suppose that we have a wave $\mathbf{E}(z,t) = g(z+ct)\,\mathbf{e}_x$ propagating in the $-z$-direction. What is the corresponding magnetic field $\mathbf{B}(z,t)$? ∎

Coordinate-free expressions

The choice of the z-direction and the rotational orientation of the x- and y-axes about it are quite arbitrary. We shall now use these facts to obtain an expression relating the electric and magnetic fields which makes no reference to any particular coordinate system. Such expressions are called **coordinate-free expressions**. Their power is that they relate physical principles in the most general way. To derive a coordinate-free expression in the present case, note that in our chosen right-handed Cartesian system the three coordinate unit vectors are related by

$$\mathbf{e}_y = \mathbf{e}_z \times \mathbf{e}_x.$$

This allows us to relate the two fields in Equation 1.15 as

$$\mathbf{B}(z,t) = \frac{1}{c}\, g(z - ct)\, \mathbf{e}_y = \frac{1}{c}\, g(z - ct)\, (\mathbf{e}_z \times \mathbf{e}_x) = \frac{1}{c}\, \mathbf{e}_z \times \mathbf{E}(z,t).$$

But $\mathbf{e}_z$ is a unit vector in the direction of travel, and since the z-axis was arbitrarily chosen, we can say that plane wave solutions of Equations 1.4 to 1.7 obey the relation

$$\mathbf{B} = \frac{1}{c}\, \widehat{\mathbf{k}} \times \mathbf{E} \quad \text{or} \quad c\,\mathbf{B} = \widehat{\mathbf{k}} \times \mathbf{E}, \tag{1.16}$$

where $\widehat{\mathbf{k}}$ is a unit vector that defines the direction of travel (Figure 1.6).

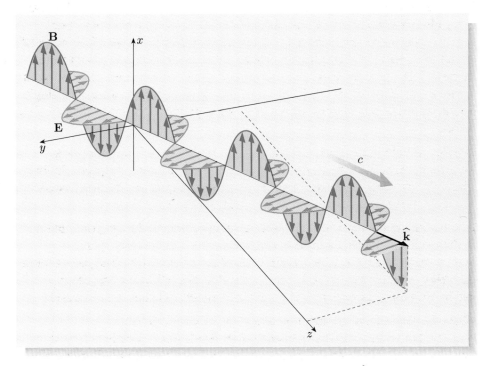

Figure 1.6   A plane wave travelling along the direction of $\widehat{\mathbf{k}}$. Note that the vector product $\mathbf{E} \times \mathbf{B}$ lies in the direction of propagation $\widehat{\mathbf{k}}$.

Although I have demonstrated this only for plane waves, Equation 1.16 is a general relation between the companion fields, $\mathbf{E}$ and $\mathbf{B}$, of any electromagnetic signal in empty space. It is true in any coordinate system, that is, it is coordinate-free. Thus $\mathbf{E}$, $\mathbf{B}$ and $\widehat{\mathbf{k}}$ lie at right angles to each other (Figure 1.7) in a right-handed, mutually orthogonal trio.

From Equation 1.16 and Figure 1.7 we deduce that for all electromagnetic waves in empty space,

$$\mathbf{E} = c\,\mathbf{B} \times \widehat{\mathbf{k}}. \tag{1.17}$$

The solution to Exercise 1.7 is consistent with this relationship.

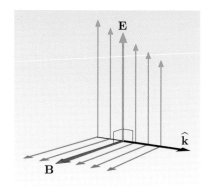

Figure 1.7 Relating $\mathbf{E}$, $\mathbf{B}$ and $\widehat{\mathbf{k}}$.

1.3.2 Linearly polarized monochromatic plane waves

So far we have established that Maxwell's equations allow wave propagation in empty space. In particular, plane waves of electric and magnetic fields are consistent with Maxwell's equations. These electromagnetic waves have similarly-shaped electric and magnetic fields, varying in space and time, oriented perpendicular to each other and perpendicular to the direction of travel. In this subsection, concentrating on waves of a single frequency, I shall introduce a convenient notation for waves that uses complex exponential functions and complex numbers. Then I shall re-examine the relative directions of the fields and the directions in which they propagate. The results will be derived for the specific case of propagation in empty space, but they are directly relevant to electromagnetic waves in any medium.

Plane electromagnetic waves can take just about any shape. In practice, however, many electromagnetic waveforms are well approximated by sinusoids. For instance, when you tune your radio to a particular station you are adjusting an LC circuit to resonate at a specific frequency — that of the station you wish to hear. In the visible spectrum, a single frequency corresponds to a pure colour between red (4×10^{14} Hz) and violet (7.5×10^{14} Hz). Electromagnetic waves of a single frequency are said to be **monochromatic** (see Figure 4 in the Introduction to this book).

Monochromatic plane electromagnetic waves will figure often in this book. They are characterized by a specific frequency and they move at speed c in free space. A wave with frequency f has angular frequency $\omega = 2\pi f$, wavelength $\lambda = c/f = 2\pi c/\omega$, and wavenumber $k = 2\pi/\lambda = \omega/c$.

In a medium, an electric field displaces bound charges, leading to polarization of the medium. Even though here we are concerned with empty space, we borrow that effect to describe the direction of the electric field. The **polarization direction** of an electromagnetic wave is the direction of the electric field vector, and in unbounded free space it is always transverse to the direction of travel.

When the direction of polarization of a plane electromagnetic wave is constant, the wave is said to be **linearly polarized**. For a linearly polarized, monochromatic, plane wave travelling in the z-direction and polarized in the x-direction, the electric field can be written as

$$\mathbf{E}(z, t) = E_{0x} \cos[kz - \omega t + \phi]\,\mathbf{e}_x,$$

where E_{0x} is the amplitude of the electric field and ϕ is an arbitrary phase shift.

Because of the way our eyes work, when two or more pure colours of light are mixed together, we perceive a single colour. So the description 'monochromatic' is potentially misleading. However, the scientific meaning of monochromatic is 'single frequency'.

The universal convention is to define the polarization direction as the direction of $\mathbf{E}$.

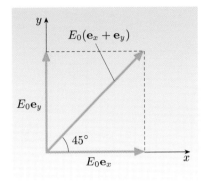

Figure 1.8 A linear combination of polarized waves can be viewed as a single equivalent wave by a vector addition.

● Write down a linear combination of two electric fields, travelling in the z-direction and polarized in the x-direction and the y-direction respectively, that describes a monochromatic plane wave polarized at $45°$ to the x- and y-axes.

○ The two fields must have the same angular frequency, the same amplitude and the same phase shift, so the combined field is

$$\mathbf{E}(z,t) = E_0 \cos[kz - \omega t + \phi]\, \mathbf{e}_x + E_0 \cos[kz - \omega t + \phi]\, \mathbf{e}_y$$
$$= E_0 \cos[kz - \omega t + \phi]\, (\mathbf{e}_x + \mathbf{e}_y).$$

The polarization is in the direction of $\mathbf{e}_x + \mathbf{e}_y$, which is at $45°$ to the x- and y-axes, as illustrated in Figure 1.8.

1.3.3   Complex exponential notation

In this subsection, I introduce a notation for waves that is based on complex exponential functions. The complex number relationships that will be used in this book are summarized in Table 1.1.

Table 1.1   Summary of complex number relationships used in this book.

complex number	z	$x + iy$
real part	$\mathrm{Re}\{z\}$	x
imaginary part	$\mathrm{Im}\{z\}$	y
square root of -1	$\sqrt{-1}$	i
complex conjugate	z^*	$x - iy$
magnitude (or modulus)	$\|z\| = \sqrt{zz^*}$	$\sqrt{x^2 + y^2}$
argument	$\arg z$	$\tan^{-1}(y/x)$
Euler's relation	$r \exp i\theta$	$r \cos\theta + ir \sin\theta$

The last entry in this table, Euler's relation, is particularly useful in the mathematical description of waves. It follows from the Taylor expansion for the exponential function,

$$\exp x = 1 + x + \frac{x^2}{2!} + \frac{x^3}{3!} + \frac{x^4}{4!} + \cdots ,$$

rewritten with an imaginary argument, $i\theta$:

$$\exp i\theta = 1 + i\theta - \frac{\theta^2}{2!} - \frac{i\theta^3}{3!} + \frac{\theta^4}{4!} + \cdots .$$

Grouping real and imaginary terms gives

$$\exp i\theta = \left(1 - \frac{\theta^2}{2!} + \frac{\theta^4}{4!} + \cdots\right) + i\left(\theta - \frac{\theta^3}{3!} + \cdots\right).$$

The terms in the first bracket are the Taylor expansion for $\cos\theta$, and those in the second bracket are the expansion for $\sin\theta$, so

$$\exp i\theta = \cos\theta + i\sin\theta.$$

As you have seen, we often have to take derivatives of the expressions we use for monochromatic waves. Derivatives of sines become cosines, and derivatives of cosines become negative sines. The Euler relation gives a compact way to handle the changes from sine to cosine, and vice versa, that accompany differentiation. Since

$$r \exp i\theta = r \cos\theta + ir \sin\theta,$$

where r and θ are real numbers, the *real part* of $r \exp i\theta$ embodies the cosine function. It is usually signalled by writing Re, so

$$\mathrm{Re}\{\exp i\theta\} = \cos\theta.$$

Taking derivatives with respect to θ, the *real part* of the result is

$$\mathrm{Re}\left\{\frac{\mathrm{d}}{\mathrm{d}\theta} \exp i\theta\right\} = \mathrm{Re}\{i \exp i\theta\}$$
$$= \mathrm{Re}\{i(\cos\theta + i\sin\theta)\}$$
$$= -\sin\theta$$
$$= \frac{\mathrm{d}}{\mathrm{d}\theta}(\cos\theta).$$

The complex exponential notation makes light work of the derivatives, with the 'i' in the argument of the exponential working with any 'i' in the rest of the expression to associate sine or cosine terms with the real part of the result. So we can use the complex exponential form, provided that we recognize that it is the real part of any result that represents what we need. In effect, in this complex representation the extra baggage of the imaginary part takes care of the switching between sine and cosine that arises on differentiation of sinusoidal functions.

Then the physical fields of a typical monochromatic electromagnetic wave moving along the positive z-direction and linearly polarized in the x-direction can be identified with the *real parts* of the following complex quantities:

$$\mathbf{E}(z,t) = E_{0x} \exp[i(kz - \omega t + \phi)]\,\mathbf{e}_x \tag{1.18}$$

and

$$\mathbf{B}(z,t) = \frac{E_{0x}}{c} \exp[i(kz - \omega t + \phi)]\,\mathbf{e}_y. \tag{1.19}$$

When an expression contains a complex exponential, it is a complex quantity, and physical quantities are conventionally identified with the real part of the expression. The complex exponential $\exp[i(kz - \omega t + \phi)]$ is effectively a linear combination of $\sin(kz - \omega t + \phi)$ and $\cos(kz - \omega t + \phi)$, and we have already established that linear combinations of solutions are also solutions of the wave equation. The complex exponential functions in Equations 1.18 and 1.19 are therefore also solutions of the wave equation.

We shall use this complex notation often, but not always. The complex representation simplifies the algebra, but the use of sine and cosine functions is always correct, though often algebraically more complicated.

It must always be understood that electric and magnetic fields are *real* quantities: the physical fields are given by the *real* parts of any complex expressions (Figure 1.9). To emphasize this important point, I shall use the subscript 'phys' on fields that are the real part of a complex exponential.

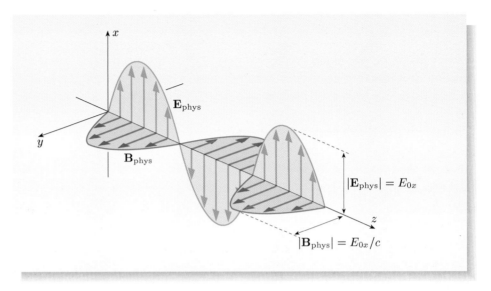

Figure 1.9   The electric and magnetic fields for a monochromatic plane wave travelling in the z-direction and polarized in the x-direction. The fields $\mathbf{E}_{\mathrm{phys}}$ and $\mathbf{B}_{\mathrm{phys}}$ are the real parts of complex expressions defined in Equations 1.18 and 1.19.

1.3.4   Plane waves moving in arbitrary directions

Equations 1.18 and 1.19 are plane wave solutions of Maxwell's equations for a specific choice of axes. This is all very well if we are free to so choose a coordinate system. But this is not always possible. For instance, we might need to deal with *two* waves propagating at some arbitrary angle and/or with arbitrary polarizations with respect to each other. In that case it is possible to choose coordinates such that one wave, or the other, moves along a chosen axis, but not both. We need to be able to represent plane waves travelling in any direction with any polarization.

A general monochromatic plane wave solution is embodied in the real part of the complex expression

$$\mathbf{E}(\mathbf{r}, t) = \mathbf{E}_0 \exp[\mathrm{i}(\mathbf{k} \cdot \mathbf{r} - \omega t + \phi)], \tag{1.20}$$

where $\mathbf{k}$ is called the **propagation vector** and has magnitude $k = \omega/c$. The direction of propagation is given by the unit vector $\widehat{\mathbf{k}} = \mathbf{k}/k$. Note that planes of constant phase for these waves are given by $\mathbf{k} \cdot \mathbf{r} - \omega t = $ constant, where any particular plane is specified by the value of the constant. Using $\mathbf{k} = (\omega/c)\widehat{\mathbf{k}}$ in this gives $\widehat{\mathbf{k}} \cdot \mathbf{r} = ct +$ another constant. This means that if $\mathbf{r}$ is the position vector of any point on a particular plane of constant phase, then its projection, $\widehat{\mathbf{k}} \cdot \mathbf{r}$, along the propagation direction (specified by the unit vector $\widehat{\mathbf{k}}$) moves at speed c (Figure 1.10).

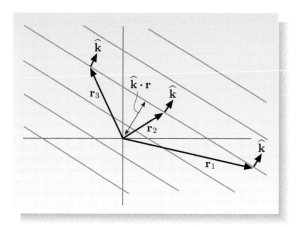

Figure 1.10 Wavefronts, which are planes of constant phase separated by 2π, travel in the direction $\widehat{\mathbf{k}}$ at speed c.

Equation 1.20 is the generalization of expressions like Equation 1.18, for which $\mathbf{k}$ is directed along the z-axis so that $\mathbf{k} = k_z\mathbf{e}_z = k\mathbf{e}_z$ and $\mathbf{k} \cdot \mathbf{r} = kz$.

Before adopting Equation 1.20 as our compact notation for linearly polarized, monochromatic, plane waves, travelling in an arbitrary direction, we shall demonstrate that it satisfies the wave equation and relevant Maxwell equations.

Worked Example 1.4

Show that Equation 1.20 is a solution of the wave equation (Equation 1.11), with $\varepsilon_0\mu_0 = 1/c^2$.

Essential skill

Using complex exponential notation

Solution

First, differentiate Equation 1.20 twice with respect to time:

$$\frac{\partial^2 \mathbf{E}(\mathbf{r}, t)}{\partial t^2} = (-\mathrm{i}\omega)^2 \mathbf{E}(\mathbf{r}, t) = -\omega^2 \mathbf{E}(\mathbf{r}, t).$$

Then, with $\mathbf{k} \cdot \mathbf{r} = k_x x + k_y y + k_z z$ in Equation 1.20, differentiate twice with respect to x:

$$\frac{\partial^2 \mathbf{E}(\mathbf{r}, t)}{\partial x^2} = (\mathrm{i}k_x)^2 \mathbf{E}(\mathbf{r}, t) = -k_x^2 \mathbf{E}(\mathbf{r}, t).$$

Since $\nabla^2 = \partial^2/\partial x^2 + \partial^2/\partial y^2 + \partial^2/\partial z^2$, it follows that

$$\nabla^2 \mathbf{E}(\mathbf{r}, t) = -(k_x^2 + k_y^2 + k_z^2)\mathbf{E}(\mathbf{r}, t) = -k^2 \mathbf{E}(\mathbf{r}, t).$$

Thus, in order for $\mathbf{E}$ to satisfy Equation 1.11, we must require that

$$-k^2 \mathbf{E}(\mathbf{r}, t) = \varepsilon_0\mu_0 \left(-\omega^2 \mathbf{E}(\mathbf{r}, t)\right),$$

and this is assured because $c = 1/\sqrt{\varepsilon_0\mu_0}$ is the phase speed, and $k^2 = \omega^2/c^2$.

Another test of acceptability for the complex exponential expression is that it can be used directly in Maxwell's equations. Let us try it in Equation 1.4 for the zero divergence of an electric field in a vacuum.

Essential skill

Using complex exponential
notation

Worked Example 1.5

Show that the electric field given by Equation 1.20 has zero divergence if the electric field is perpendicular to the propagation direction.

Solution

The constant amplitude $\mathbf{E}_0$ of the electric field can be written as

$$\mathbf{E}_0 = E_{0x}\mathbf{e}_x + E_{0y}\mathbf{e}_y + E_{0z}\mathbf{e}_z,$$

so

$$\text{div } \mathbf{E}(\mathbf{r}, t) = \left[E_{0x}\frac{\partial}{\partial x} + E_{0y}\frac{\partial}{\partial y} + E_{0z}\frac{\partial}{\partial z} \right] \exp[\mathrm{i}(\mathbf{k} \cdot \mathbf{r} - \omega t + \phi)].$$

Examining the derivative with respect to x:

$$E_{0x}\frac{\partial}{\partial x} \exp[\mathrm{i}(\mathbf{k} \cdot \mathbf{r} - \omega t + \phi)]$$

$$= E_{0x}\frac{\partial}{\partial x} \exp[\mathrm{i}(k_x x + k_y y + k_z z - \omega t + \phi)]$$

$$= \mathrm{i}k_x E_{0x} \exp[\mathrm{i}(\mathbf{k} \cdot \mathbf{r} - \omega t + \phi)].$$

Similar results hold for the y- and z-derivatives. Recognizing that $\mathrm{i}(k_x E_{0x} + k_y E_{0y} + k_z E_{0z}) = \mathrm{i}\mathbf{k} \cdot \mathbf{E}_0$, we can write div $\mathbf{E}$ in the compact form

$$\text{div } \mathbf{E}(\mathbf{r}, t) = \mathrm{i}\mathbf{k} \cdot \mathbf{E}_0 \exp[\mathrm{i}(\mathbf{k} \cdot \mathbf{r} - \omega t + \phi)].$$

To be consistent with Gauss's law in a vacuum, this divergence must vanish everywhere, so

$$\mathbf{k} \cdot \mathbf{E}_0 = 0. \tag{1.21}$$

This means that the electric field is perpendicular to the propagation direction.

The statement $\mathbf{k} \cdot \mathbf{E}_0 = 0$ is a generalization of what I asserted about the transverse nature of electromagnetic waves in Subsection 1.3.1 and confirms that the electric field of a monochromatic plane electromagnetic wave in vacuum is *always* polarized transverse to its direction of propagation (Figure 1.6). This is very important. Maxwell's equations for free space support *only* transverse waves — with their electric and magnetic vectors perpendicular to the direction of propagation.

The complex notation passes all the tests Maxwell's equations can throw up, so we shall henceforth use it with confidence. The equivalent complex expression for the magnetic field $\mathbf{B}$ associated with $\mathbf{E}$ must agree with the general coordinate-free expression in Equation 1.16. So, for this plane wave, the physical magnetic field will be the real part of

$$\mathbf{B}(\mathbf{r}, t) = \frac{1}{c}(\widehat{\mathbf{k}} \times \mathbf{E}_0) \exp[\mathrm{i}(\mathbf{k} \cdot \mathbf{r} - \omega t + \phi)]. \tag{1.22}$$

1.3.5 Circular polarization

The general plane waves that we have been considering have emerged as solutions of the wave equation extracted from Maxwell's equations. Earlier, I commented that non-sinusoidal and non-periodic waveforms can be constructed from linear combinations of a spectrum of waves of different frequencies. Here, I want to examine another possibility that arises when we have linear combinations of two monochromatic waves of the same frequency and travelling in the same direction but polarized at right angles and having different phase shifts. The polarization of the combination depends on the amplitudes and phases shifts of the two waves.

Suppose that we have a plane wave travelling in the z-direction and polarized in the x-direction, with a phase shift ϕ_x. We can write its electric field (compare Equation 1.18) as the real part of

$$\mathbf{E}(z,t) = E_{0x} \exp[\mathrm{i}(kz - \omega t + \phi_x)] \, \mathbf{e}_x, \tag{1.23}$$

where E_{0x} and ϕ_x are real quantities. But this choice of polarization is arbitrary. For instance, we might consider a plane wave (with the same angular frequency ω and therefore also the same wavenumber k) travelling in the z-direction but polarized in the y-direction, with phase shift ϕ_y. Its field is the real part of

$$\mathbf{E}(z,t) = E_{0y} \exp[\mathrm{i}(kz - \omega t + \phi_y)] \, \mathbf{e}_y, \tag{1.24}$$

where E_{0y} and ϕ_y might be different from E_{0x} and ϕ_x. Both waves, with their companion magnetic fields, are solutions of Maxwell's equations in free space, and of the wave equation. Since the wave equation is linear, an arbitrary linear combination of any two solutions is another solution. In particular, we might specify equal phases, so that $\phi_x = \phi_y \equiv \phi$, and add these two fields to obtain

$$\mathbf{E}^{(\mathrm{lin})}(z,t) = (E_{0x}\mathbf{e}_x + E_{0y}\mathbf{e}_y) \exp[\mathrm{i}(kz - \omega t + \phi)]. \tag{1.25}$$

Expression 1.25 is simply another linearly polarized plane wave travelling in the z-direction, but with its electric field vector polarized at an angle α to the x-axis, where $\tan \alpha = E_{0y}/E_{0x}$ (Figure 1.11).

The magnetic field associated with this wave can be obtained from Equation 1.16, which holds for all linearly polarized plane waves (or linear combinations of them), in this case with $\widehat{\mathbf{k}} = \mathbf{e}_z$.

Equation 1.25 is a particularly simple combination; it is a linearly polarized wave obtained by adding two other linearly polarized waves that have the *same* phase ϕ. There are many other possibilities, but here I shall consider only waves with **circular polarization**, for which the electric and magnetic field vectors each have a constant magnitude and remain perpendicular to each other and to the direction of propagation, but both rotate as the wave passes through a point. Expressions that describe circularly polarized, monochromatic, plane waves are obtained by adding the fields given by Equations 1.23 and 1.24 with equal amplitudes ($E_{0x} = E_{0y} \equiv E_0$) but a phase difference of $\pm\pi/2$, namely with either $\phi_y = \phi_x + \pi/2$ or $\phi_y = \phi_x - \pi/2$.

For example, setting $\phi_x = \phi$ and choosing $\phi_y = \phi + \pi/2$ gives an electric field that is the real part of

$$\begin{aligned} \mathbf{E}^{(\mathrm{circ})}(z,t) = {} & E_0 \exp[\mathrm{i}(kz - \omega t + \phi)] \, \mathbf{e}_x \\ & + E_0 \exp[\mathrm{i}(kz - \omega t + \phi + \pi/2)] \, \mathbf{e}_y. \end{aligned} \tag{1.26}$$

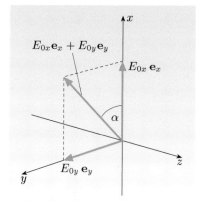

Figure 1.11 Polarization at an angle α to the x-axis.

But

$$\exp[i(kz - \omega t + \phi + \pi/2)] = \exp(i\pi/2)\exp[i(kz - \omega t + \phi)]$$
$$= i\exp[i(kz - \omega t + \phi)],$$

since $\exp(i\pi/2) = \cos(\pi/2) + i\sin(\pi/2) = i$. So we can equally well say that the real electric field corresponds with the real part of

$$\mathbf{E}^{(\text{circ})}(z,t) = E_0\exp[i(kz - \omega t + \phi)]\,(\mathbf{e}_x + i\mathbf{e}_y). \tag{1.27}$$

Note that since $\mathbf{E}^{(\text{circ})}$ is a linear combination of plane polarized waves, its associated magnetic field can be found by applying Equation 1.16.

Exercise 1.8   Show that the magnetic field corresponding to $\mathbf{E}^{(\text{circ})}$ is the real part of

$$\mathbf{B}^{(\text{circ})}(z,t) = \frac{E_0}{c}\exp[i(kz - \omega t + \phi)]\,(\mathbf{e}_y - i\mathbf{e}_x). \qquad\blacksquare$$

The properties of the physical electric field, $\mathbf{E}^{(\text{circ})}_{\text{phys}}$, are easily deduced by writing it down explicitly. For instance, Equation 1.27 gives

$$\mathbf{E}^{(\text{circ})}_{\text{phys}} = \text{Re}\{\mathbf{E}^{(\text{circ})}(z,t)\}$$
$$= E_0\cos(kz - \omega t + \phi)\,\mathbf{e}_x - E_0\sin(kz - \omega t + \phi)\,\mathbf{e}_y.$$

This electric field has the following properties.

- Its magnitude is the constant E_0.

- It propagates in the z-direction at speed $c = \omega/k$.

- At any fixed position z, the polarization rotates (hence the term *circularly polarized*) as time advances. For instance, in the $z = 0$ plane, the electric field is as follows (see also Figure 1.12):

$$\text{Re}\{\mathbf{E}^{(\text{circ})}(0,t)\} = E_0[\cos(-\omega t + \phi)\,\mathbf{e}_x - \sin(-\omega t + \phi)\,\mathbf{e}_y]$$
$$= E_0[\cos(\omega t - \phi)\,\mathbf{e}_x + \sin(\omega t - \phi)\,\mathbf{e}_y],$$

so when $\omega t = \phi$ the field is $E_0\mathbf{e}_x$, when $\omega t = \phi + \pi/2$ it is $E_0\mathbf{e}_y$, when $\omega t = \phi + \pi$ it is $-E_0\mathbf{e}_x$, and so on. The rotation of the polarization is shown in Figure 1.12. At a fixed time t, the electric field depends on position in the way illustrated in Figure 1.13.

Exercise 1.9   Another possible choice of phases for the two waves is $\phi_x = \phi$ and $\phi_y = \phi - \pi/2$. By deriving an expression that is the equivalent of Equation 1.27, show that this combined wave also has circular polarization. How does this wave differ from the one shown in Figures 1.12 and 1.13? $\blacksquare$

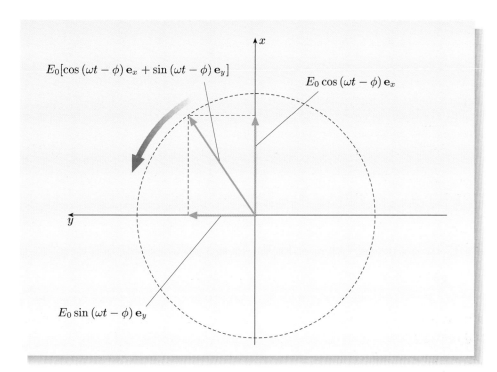

Figure 1.12 The rotating electric field in the plane $z = 0$ for a circularly polarized wave travelling in the z-direction.

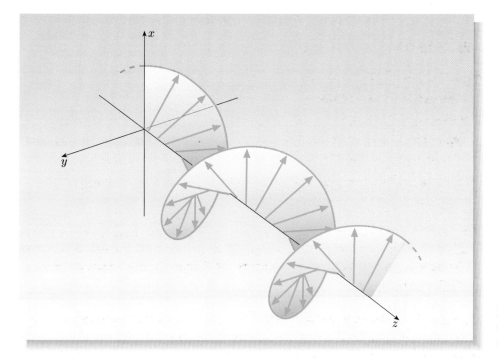

Figure 1.13 Rotation of the polarization direction of a circularly polarized wave travelling in the z-direction.

1.4 Energy transported by plane waves

One of the special features of electromagnetic waves is that they carry energy across empty space. To complete this chapter on electromagnetic waves in empty space, I shall derive an expression for the power per unit area that is associated with the passage of an electromagnetic wave. The SI unit of power per unit area is $W\,m^{-2}$, which is equivalent to $J\,m^{-2}\,s^{-1}$. By analogy with fluid flow, this is also known as the energy flux density. There is, for instance, a constant stream of energy passing from the Sun, to Earth and beyond, across the vacuum of space. By the time it arrives at the upper atmosphere, the flux density of solar radiation is about $1\,\mathrm{kW\,m^{-2}}$. That is something that can be fairly easily measured. In contrast, radio communications from space probes involve transmitted power levels of only a few watts, directed in a beam towards Earth. The beam inevitably diverges, and on arrival these signals are below a few $\mathrm{pW\,m^{-2}}$.

Let us consider a wave travelling along the z-axis, constituted by the pair

$$\mathbf{E}(z,t) = g(z - ct)\,\mathbf{e}_x \quad \text{and} \quad \mathbf{B}(z,t) = \frac{1}{c}\,g(z - ct)\,\mathbf{e}_y.$$

This waveform moves in the z-direction at speed c, unchanged in shape, and it transports energy. You can see that it must transport energy because it is comprised of electric fields and magnetic fields, both of which store energy. It was shown in Book 2 that the energy per unit volume associated with an electrostatic field is $\frac{1}{2}\mathbf{D} \cdot \mathbf{E}$, and that of a static magnetic field is $\frac{1}{2}\mathbf{B} \cdot \mathbf{H}$. The simplest examples to recall relate to static fields and storage of energy in capacitors and inductors. Here we have time-varying electromagnetic fields, but the principles are similar. To quantify the energy transport, let us examine an infinitesimal region of space of thickness δz in the direction of propagation, the z-axis, and cross-sectional area δA perpendicular to this direction (Figure 1.14). If this region is located at z_1, then at some time t the field energy within it is

$$\delta U(z_1, t) = \delta z\,\delta A\left[\tfrac{1}{2}\mathbf{B}(z_1, t) \cdot \mathbf{H}(z_1, t) + \tfrac{1}{2}\mathbf{D}(z_1, t) \cdot \mathbf{E}(z_1, t)\right].$$

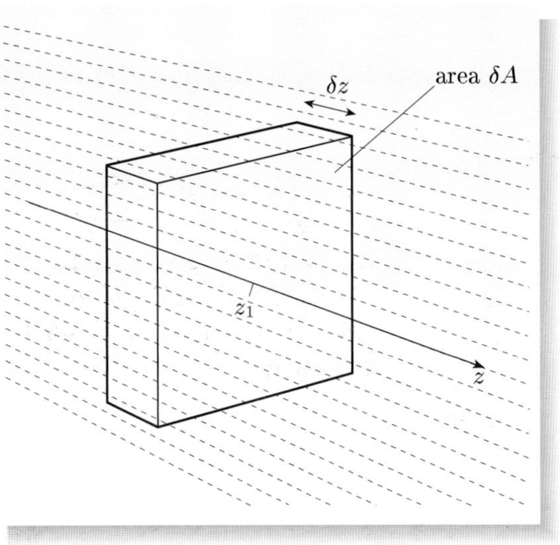

Figure 1.14 An electromagnetic wave passing through a small volume in a direction normal to the faces that have area δA.

At this point we need to be careful: here we are *multiplying* fields $\mathbf{E}$ with $\mathbf{D}$, and $\mathbf{B}$ with $\mathbf{H}$. We must use the *real* parts of complex expressions like those in Equations 1.20 and 1.22: that is, we should use $\mathbf{D}_{\mathrm{phys}}$, $\mathbf{E}_{\mathrm{phys}}$, $\mathbf{B}_{\mathrm{phys}}$ and $\mathbf{H}_{\mathrm{phys}}$.

Multiplication of variables is inevitably non-linear. In order to obtain a correct expression for the energy δU, we must extract the true (i.e. real) fields from expressions involving complex exponentials *before* we multiply them together.

Since in free space $\mathbf{D}_{\mathrm{phys}} = \varepsilon_0\mathbf{E}_{\mathrm{phys}}$ and $\mathbf{B}_{\mathrm{phys}} = \mu_0\mathbf{H}_{\mathrm{phys}}$, we can write

$$\delta U(z_1, t) = \delta z\,\delta A\left[\frac{1}{2\mu_0}B_{\mathrm{phys}}^2(z_1, t) + \frac{\varepsilon_0}{2}E_{\mathrm{phys}}^2(z_1, t)\right], \tag{1.28}$$

since $B_{\mathrm{phys}}^2 = \mathbf{B}_{\mathrm{phys}} \cdot \mathbf{B}_{\mathrm{phys}}$, and similarly $E_{\mathrm{phys}}^2 = \mathbf{E}_{\mathrm{phys}} \cdot \mathbf{E}_{\mathrm{phys}}$.

The first term in Equation 1.28 is the energy of the magnetic field within the volume, and from the expression in Equation 1.15 we can say

$$B_{\mathrm{phys}}^2(z_1, t) = \frac{1}{c^2}E_{\mathrm{phys}}^2(z_1, t) = \varepsilon_0\mu_0 E_{\mathrm{phys}}^2(z_1, t). \tag{1.29}$$

So the magnetic field's contribution to δU is the same as that of the electric field. So in total,

$$\delta U(z_1, t) = \delta z\,\delta A\,\varepsilon_0 E_{\mathrm{phys}}^2(z_1, t).$$

This energy is carried by the fields as they cross the volume at speed c. So, in the time interval $\delta t = \delta z/c$, an energy δU will have traversed the volume. Therefore the energy passing through the $z = z_1$ plane per unit area per unit time is

$$N(z_1, t) = \frac{\delta U}{\delta A\,\delta t} = c\,\varepsilon_0 E_{\mathrm{phys}}^2(z_1, t).$$

$N(z_1, t)$ is the **energy flux density** — the energy passing through unit area normal to the propagation direction in unit time — at the point z_1. So we can write the vector energy flux density at any general point z as

$$\mathbf{N}(z, t) = c\,\varepsilon_0 E_{\text{phys}}^2(z, t)\,\mathbf{e}_z. \tag{1.30}$$

A more general, coordinate-free result can be obtained with a little more manipulation. We know that $E_{\text{phys}}(z, t) = cB_{\text{phys}}(z, t)$, which in turn equals $c\mu_0 H_{\text{phys}}(z, t)$. So we can also write

$$\mathbf{N}(z, t) = (c\varepsilon_0 E_{\text{phys}}(z, t))(c\mu_0)H_{\text{phys}}(z, t)\,\mathbf{e}_z.$$

Now we chose axes with $\mathbf{E}_{\text{phys}} = E_{\text{phys}}\mathbf{e}_x$ and $\mathbf{H}_{\text{phys}} = H_{\text{phys}}\mathbf{e}_y$. So recalling the relation $\mathbf{e}_x \times \mathbf{e}_y = \mathbf{e}_z$, we can write the energy flux density $\mathbf{N}$, which is generally known as the **Poynting vector**, in a coordinate-free form as follows:

$$\mathbf{N} = \mathbf{E}_{\text{phys}} \times \mathbf{H}_{\text{phys}}. \tag{1.31}$$

The Poynting vector gives the directed energy flux density. Its SI unit is watts per square metre, W m^{-2} (or $\text{J m}^{-2}\,\text{s}^{-1}$), and its direction — the direction of energy flow — is perpendicular to both the electric and magnetic fields. When evaluating the Poynting vector, it is important to remember to use real physical expressions for the fields.

The vector that quantifies the energy flux density of an electromagnetic wave is named after John Poynting (1852–1914), who established this result.

Time-averaged Poynting vector for monochromatic plane waves

It is often important to know the power transported by plane monochromatic waves. For instance, consider the pair of waves given by Equation 1.18, for $\mathbf{E}$, and Equation 1.19, for $\mathbf{B}$. Their real parts are, respectively,

$$\mathbf{E}_{\text{phys}} = E_{0x}\cos(kz - \omega t + \phi)\,\mathbf{e}_x$$

and

$$\mathbf{B}_{\text{phys}} = \frac{E_{0x}}{c}\cos(kz - \omega t + \phi)\,\mathbf{e}_y.$$

Now $\mathbf{H} = \mathbf{B}/\mu_0$, so for this wave,

$$\mathbf{N}(z, t) = \mathbf{E}_{\text{phys}} \times \mathbf{B}_{\text{phys}}/\mu_0 = \frac{(E_{0x})^2}{\mu_0 c}\cos^2(kz - \omega t + \phi)\,(\mathbf{e}_x \times \mathbf{e}_y).$$

But $\mathbf{e}_x \times \mathbf{e}_y = \mathbf{e}_z$, and $c^2 = 1/\varepsilon_0\mu_0$, so the energy flux density for these waves can be written

$$\mathbf{N}(z, t) = \varepsilon_0(E_{0x})^2 c\cos^2(kz - \omega t + \phi)\,\mathbf{e}_z. \tag{1.32}$$

Notice that every term here is non-negative, so $\mathbf{N}$ represents a net energy flow per unit area in the z-direction, at right angles to both $\mathbf{E}$ and $\mathbf{B}$. Note also that the Poynting vector depends upon both t and z: it specifies the instantaneous energy flux density at time t and at a specific location z. However, when the frequency ω is relatively high, it is usually sensible to calculate the *time-average* of the flux density. The time-average of $\cos^2(kz - \omega t + \phi)$ at any fixed position z is $\frac{1}{2}$. So for any value of z, the time-average of the energy flux density, $\overline{\mathbf{N}}$, is

$$\overline{\mathbf{N}} = \tfrac{1}{2}\varepsilon_0(E_{0x})^2 c\,\mathbf{e}_z. \tag{1.33}$$

For a wave with propagation vector $\mathbf{k}$ and electric field amplitude E_0, we can write the time-averaged Poynting vector in the following coordinate-free form:

$$\overline{\mathbf{N}} = \tfrac{1}{2}\varepsilon_0 E_0^2 c\,\widehat{\mathbf{k}}. \tag{1.34}$$

Exercise 1.10   Calculate the electric field strength of a radio signal from a satellite if the magnitude of the time-averaged Poynting vector is $1\,\mathrm{pW\,m^{-2}}$.   ■

The video sequence *Plane polarized waves* on the course DVD presents animations of the spatial- and time-dependence of the electric and magnetic fields for plane polarized waves. Also, the sequence *Hertz: putting Maxwell to the test* describes the experiments that led to the widespread acceptance of Maxwell's theory.

Summary of Chapter 1

Section 1.1   The wave equation in one dimension is

$$\frac{\partial^2}{\partial z^2}A(z,t) - \frac{1}{v^2}\frac{\partial^2}{\partial t^2}A(z,t) = 0,$$

where v is the speed of the waves. The plane wave solutions of this equation can be expressed in terms of linear combinations of sinusoidal functions, representing waves travelling in either the positive or negative z-direction. The general solutions proposed by d'Alembert have the form $g(z - vt)$ and $g(z + vt)$, and represent waves with fixed profiles travelling in the positive and negative z-directions, respectively.

Section 1.2   A three-dimensional wave equation,

$$\nabla^2\mathbf{B}(\mathbf{r},t) = \varepsilon_0\mu_0\frac{\partial^2\mathbf{B}(\mathbf{r},t)}{\partial t^2},$$

can be extracted from Maxwell's equations. In a vacuum, a universal speed of propagation emerges from the algebra: $c = 1/\sqrt{\varepsilon_0\mu_0}$.

Section 1.3   Far from a source, the solutions of the wave equation are plane waves. When only a single frequency is present, we talk about monochromatic waves. Gauss's law and the no-monopole law impose a requirement for the electric and magnetic fields to be transverse to the propagation direction. Faraday's law and the Ampère–Maxwell law ensure that the electric and magnetic fields are perpendicular to each other and that the ratio of their amplitudes is $c = 1/\sqrt{\varepsilon_0\mu_0}$. The wave solutions of Maxwell's equations consist of oscillating electric and magnetic fields synchronized exactly in phase. The result of the coupling of the electric and magnetic fields is that electromagnetic radiation can propagate through empty space.

Complex exponential notation provides a compact way of representing linearly polarized, monochromatic plane waves, and is particularly suitable for working with the differentials in Maxwell's equations. The fields are the real parts of complex expressions like

$$\mathbf{E}(z,t) = E_{0x}\exp[\mathrm{i}(kz - \omega t + \phi)]\,\mathbf{e}_x.$$

The complex notation is easily generalized to describe monochromatic waves travelling in arbitrary directions and with arbitrary polarizations. Linear combinations of electromagnetic waves, polarized at right angles to each other, with equal amplitudes, constitute a linearly polarized wave if they are in phase and a circularly polarized wave if they differ in phase by $\pi/2$.

Section 1.4 The energy flux density in an electromagnetic wave is given by the Poynting vector, $\mathbf{N} = \mathbf{E}_{\mathrm{phys}} \times \mathbf{H}_{\mathrm{phys}}$. The time-average of the Poynting vector is

$$\overline{\mathbf{N}} = \tfrac{1}{2}\varepsilon_0(E_{0x})^2 c\,\mathbf{e}_z.$$

Achievements from Chapter 1

After studying this chapter you should be able to do the following.

1.1 Explain the meanings of the newly defined (emboldened) terms and symbols, and use them appropriately.

1.2 Define angular frequency and wavenumber, and relate them to the frequency, wavelength, period and speed of waves and to the general sinusoidal and complex exponential expressions for waves.

1.3 Demonstrate that twice-differentiable functions of the form $g(z \pm vt)$ (and in particular sinusoidal functions) are solutions of a one-dimensional wave equation.

1.4 Recognize that the wave equation and Maxwell's equations are linear, and make use of this property to generate solutions that are the superposition of other solutions.

1.5 Combine the differential versions of Maxwell's equations, for a vacuum, into three-dimensional wave equations for $\mathbf{E}$ and for $\mathbf{B}$.

1.6 Use Maxwell's equations to show that in vacuum, linearly-polarized plane wave solutions must have electric and magnetic fields that

- are orthogonal,
- are perpendicular to the direction of travel,
- are in phase,
- propagate at phase speed $c = 1/\sqrt{\varepsilon_0\mu_0}$,
- have a ratio of amplitudes given by c.

1.7 Recall and use the relationship $\mathbf{E} = c\mathbf{B} \times \widehat{\mathbf{k}}$.

1.8 Use complex exponential notation for monochromatic plane waves, and extract expressions for physical fields from complex exponential functions.

1.9 Explain what is meant by linear and circular polarization of monochromatic plane waves.

1.10 Derive an expression for the Poynting vector, and use it to calculate the instantaneous and average energy flux density associated with an electromagnetic wave propagating in a vacuum.

Chapter 2   Generation of electromagnetic waves

In Chapter 1 we found plane wave solutions of Maxwell's equations that represent energy propagating through empty space. It was mentioned that such waves are generated by time-dependent densities of charge and current. In this chapter we shall use Maxwell's equations to establish expressions that describe the steady-state radiation emitted by a small oscillating current element.

Because Maxwell's equations are linear, one strategy for finding solutions is to build them up from parts that account for different aspects of the overall situation. We are going to do that here, drawing inspiration from the Biot–Savart law to build an expression for the magnetic field **B** of an *oscillating* current element. From this we shall find the associated electric field. Maxwell's equations provide the test of the validity of the particular solutions that we synthesize in this way.

The resulting model can be applied equally well at large and small scales, and can explain a number of phenomena. It describes the generation of radio waves with wavelengths of hundreds of metres by antennas on the scale of metres. It also accounts for the scattering of light with wavelengths of hundreds of nanometres by atoms that are themselves less than a nanometre in size — and we shall show that this scattering process accounts for the appearance of the daytime sky.

Figure 2.1   Antenna at Alexandra Palace, London, used for the first BBC television service transmissions in 1936. The studios beneath the transmitter were used to make the first Open University television programmes.

2.1   The inverse square law for radiation

You saw in Chapter 1 that electromagnetic radiation transports energy. Television antennas (Figure 2.1) and radio antennas radiate signals to far places, and the Sun sends life-giving energy to us through space.

Consider the Sun as a spherically-symmetric source of radiant energy. Neglecting absorption by interplanetary matter, *far* from the Sun the total radiation power passing through any spherical surface centred on the Sun will be the same. This means that the power per unit area — the energy flux density — must fall off as the inverse square of the distance from it. This must be so since, at any particular radial distance r, the total power is uniformly distributed over a surface of area $4\pi r^2$ (Figure 2.2a).

The energy flux density, which is power per unit area, is given by the Poynting vector (see Equation 1.31).

More generally, the flow of electromagnetic energy from a point source is directed radially, and the power per unit area is given by the Poynting vector, $\mathbf{N}(r, \theta, \phi)$. Note that we shall use spherical coordinates in this chapter because the energy flux density is in the radial direction, but since the source need not be spherically symmetric we shall allow for angular-dependence on θ and ϕ. The power radiated into a small range of angles, defined by $\delta\theta$ at angle θ and $\delta\phi$ at angle ϕ, can be evaluated at any radius r as the product of the magnitude of the local (radial) Poynting vector, $N(r, \theta, \phi)$, and the area element, $(r\,\delta\theta)(r\sin\theta\,\delta\phi) = r^2 \sin\theta\,\delta\theta\,\delta\phi$, that spans the range of angles (Figure 2.2b). In the absence of absorption, the same power must be found at any radius, so

Radiation is so named because it emerges *radially* from a point source.

$$N(r_1, \theta, \phi)\, r_1^2 \sin\theta\,\delta\theta\,\delta\phi = N(r_2, \theta, \phi)\, r_2^2 \sin\theta\,\delta\theta\,\delta\phi,$$

which is assured if the power per unit area is inversely proportional to the square of the radius, that is $N(r, \theta, \phi) \propto r^{-2}$.

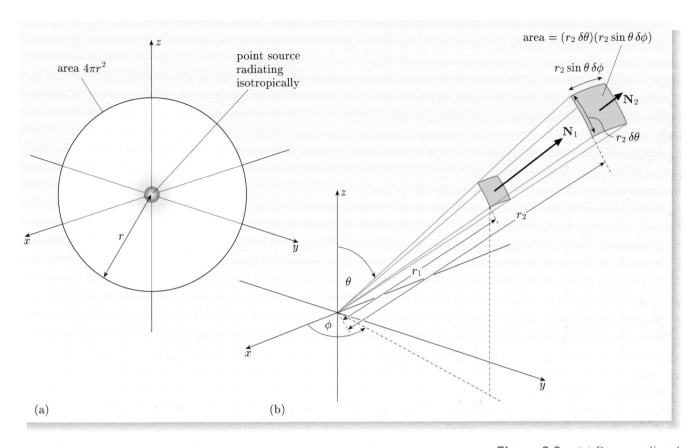

Figure 2.2 (a) Power radiated isotropically from a point source into a non-absorbing medium is spread uniformly over a spherical shell that has surface area proportional to radius squared. (b) Power radiated from a point source in a non-absorbing medium into any small range of angles is spread uniformly over surface elements that have areas proportional to radius squared.

● Summarize in a sentence the key points about the direction and radial-dependence of the flow of energy by radiation from a point source that is embedded in a non-absorbing medium.

○ The flow of energy is directed radially, and the energy per unit area per unit time falls as the inverse square of the radial distance.

In a radio or television transmitter, electrical charges are driven back and forth along the length of an antenna, and this leads to electromagnetic waves. From a distance, the antenna appears to be an electric dipole whose strength oscillates due to the displacement of electrical charges, and the oscillating dipole produces oscillating electric and magnetic fields around the antenna. Somehow, these oscillations are able to launch waves that carry energy away from the antenna. We know that *far* from the antenna the power per unit area in these radiated waves must be inversely proportional to the square of the radial distance from it.

However, just adding an oscillation to expressions for the fields produced by distributions of static charge or current does not predict the r^{-2}-dependence required for radiation. For instance, the electrostatic field from an electric dipole moment $\mathbf{p} = p\mathbf{e}_z$ located at the origin of spherical coordinates is

$$\mathbf{E}_{\text{dip}} = \frac{p}{4\pi\varepsilon_0 r^3}(2\cos\theta\,\mathbf{e}_r + \sin\theta\,\mathbf{e}_\theta), \quad \textit{(page 128 Book 1)} \qquad (2.1)$$

which has a magnitude proportional to r^{-3}. In Chapter 1 it was shown that Maxwell's equations link electric and magnetic fields in such a way that the radiated power in free space is proportional to the square of the fields. For example, for a plane wave travelling in the z-direction and polarized in the x-direction,

$$\overline{\mathbf{N}} = \frac{1}{2}\varepsilon_0(E_{0x})^2 c\,\mathbf{e}_z = \frac{1}{2\mu_0}(B_{0y})^2 c\,\mathbf{e}_z. \tag{2.2}$$

Thus, if the Poynting vector for radiation from a point source falls off as r^{-2}, the electric and magnetic fields must fall off as r^{-1}. So simply attaching a factor $\exp[\mathrm{i}(\mathbf{k}\cdot\mathbf{r} - \omega t)]$ to the electrostatic field in Equation 2.1 cannot account for radiation, since this field falls off much too quickly with increasing distance. Nevertheless, oscillating dipoles *do* radiate. The resolution lies with the way that time-varying electric and magnetic fields can sustain each other as electromagnetic waves.

The simplest model of a transmitting antenna is a small oscillating current element. In this chapter, we shall set out to find an expression for its radiated fields. To start the analysis, the following exercise considers the magnetic field that would result if we were merely to introduce an oscillating current into the magnetostatic expression of the Biot–Savart law. The result is not just a curiosity: we shall make use of it in the detailed calculations of Section 2.2.

Such a current element is equivalent to a small oscillating dipole, called a 'Hertzian' dipole, which is defined in Section 2.2.

Exercise 2.1   The Biot–Savart law gives the magnetic field $\delta\mathbf{B}(\mathbf{r})$ from an element $\delta\mathbf{l}$, carrying steady current I and located at the origin, as

$$\delta\mathbf{B}(\mathbf{r}) = \frac{\mu_0 I}{4\pi}\left(\frac{\delta\mathbf{l}\times\mathbf{r}}{r^3}\right). \tag{2.3}$$

Assume that the magnetic field from a sinusoidally oscillating current element is obtained by replacing I by $I_0\cos\omega t$ in this equation. Show that the power per unit area associated with the field $\delta\mathbf{B}(\mathbf{r}, t)$ is *not* consistent with the radiation of energy. ∎

According to Equation 2.2, if an oscillating current element is to radiate power, it must give rise to an oscillating magnetic field that falls off as r^{-1} at large distances, corresponding to a radiated power per unit area proportional to r^{-2}.

2.2   The magnetic field of a Hertzian dipole

An electric dipole is formed by a pair of charges, $\pm q$, separated by a short distance δl. If the strength of the charges oscillates with angular frequency ω, then the dipole moment is

$$\mathbf{p} = q\,\delta\mathbf{l} = q_0\,\delta\mathbf{l}\sin\omega t = \mathbf{p}_0\sin\omega t,$$

where $|\mathbf{p}_0| = p_0$ is the amplitude of the dipole moment. Now the oscillating charge can be produced by an oscillating current I flowing between the locations of the two charges, where

$$I = \frac{\mathrm{d}q}{\mathrm{d}t} = \frac{1}{\delta l}\frac{\mathrm{d}p}{\mathrm{d}t} = \frac{\omega p_0}{\delta l}\cos\omega t = I_0\cos\omega t,$$

and $I_0 = \omega p_0 / \delta l$ is the amplitude of the oscillating current. A **Hertzian dipole** is defined in terms of an oscillating current, $I_0 \cos \omega t$, flowing in a short element of length δl; it is presumed to have a length that is much smaller than the wavelength of any radiation that it produces, so $\delta l \ll \lambda$.

The Biot–Savart law is a useful source of inspiration for predicting the form of the magnetic field around a Hertzian dipole. However, it needs a little modification, and this will be guided by the following observations.

- The Biot–Savart field law applies strictly to *steady* current elements, but the overall form and symmetry of the magnetic field arise from the symmetry of the current element that is the source of the field.

- At any radial position, the magnetic field at a particular time must depend on what the current was at some earlier time; given the electromagnetic nature of the problem, it takes a time r/c for information about the current to reach a point that is at a distance r from the dipole. So the magnetic field must depend on what the current was some time earlier, and this takes account of the delay between a change in current occurring at the origin and the arrival of information about that change at a distant point. The time in our local equation for the field needs to be adjusted to deal with the propagation delay by making the substitution $t \rightarrow t - r/c$.

- The Biot–Savart field has a radial scaling of r^{-2}, but radiation fields must scale as r^{-1} if energy is to be conserved.

- The Biot–Savart law, with its r^{-2} scaling, must be recoverable from any modified form of the magnetic field when the frequency of the oscillating current is reduced to zero.

Let us look at these points in turn in more detail. In particular, we consider a Hertzian dipole — an oscillating current dipole of infinitesimal length — located at the origin of spherical coordinates, aligned with the z-axis, and surrounded by empty space. Our goal is to find the full functional dependence of the magnetic field on the magnitude of the current, its angular frequency of oscillation, the spatial coordinates and time, that is, to find an expression for $\mathbf{B}(I_0, \delta l, \omega, r, \theta, \phi, t)$. We shall use the symmetry of the problem, physical insight and knowledge of the form of the field in limiting cases, to build a feasible expression for the magnetic field. Once we have what appears to be a reasonable prediction for the field, we shall call on Maxwell's equations to validate it and to help us determine any unknown constants.

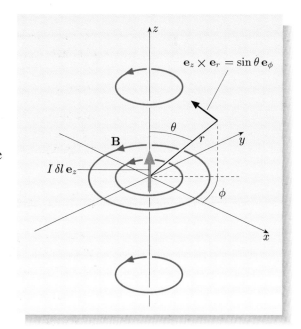

Figure 2.3   The form of the Biot–Savart field.

2.2.1   Dependence on angles and current

The first task is to mimic the general form of the Biot–Savart field. Figure 2.3 shows the form of the magnetic field due to a short, steady current element, located at the origin and lying along the z-axis.

We shall suppose that the angular-dependence of the magnetic field of an oscillatory current element, and its proportionality to current, are the same as in the Biot–Savart law (Equation 2.3). The spatial structure of the magnetic field depends on the vector product of $\delta\mathbf{l}$ and $\mathbf{r}$, where $\delta\mathbf{l} = \delta l\,\mathbf{e}_z$ is a vector length element for the Hertzian dipole:

$$\delta\mathbf{l} \times \mathbf{r} = (\delta l\,\mathbf{e}_z) \times (r\mathbf{e}_r) = \delta l\,r\sin\theta\,\mathbf{e}_\phi.$$

This means that on the z-axis ($\theta = 0$ or π) no magnetic field is generated by the current element. In fact, the field everywhere else is purely azimuthal, $\mathbf{B} = B_\phi\mathbf{e}_\phi$, circulating around the axis of the dipole, and having its maximum strength in the equatorial plane. The symmetry of the dipole means that the magnitude of the field is independent of ϕ.

The field is due to a short, oscillating current element, but the prefix δ in front of $\mathbf{B}$ is omitted as this expression now represents the total field under consideration.

Including explicitly the oscillatory nature of the current, the angular-dependence and the (as yet undetermined) radial-dependence, we can write B_ϕ as

$$B_\phi = \frac{\mu_0 I_0\,\delta l\,\cos\omega t}{4\pi}\sin\theta\,g(r),$$

where $g(r)$ describes the radial-dependence, which will be discussed in Subsection 2.2.3. To keep things tidy, it is convenient to group the first few terms together by defining a quantity η, such that

$$\eta = \frac{\mu_0 I_0\,\delta l}{4\pi}, \tag{2.4}$$

and to use complex exponential notation, so that

$$\cos\omega t = \mathrm{Re}\{\exp[-\mathrm{i}\omega t]\}.$$

Then the physical magnetic field will be based on the real part of

$$B_\phi = \eta\sin\theta\,g(r)\exp[-\mathrm{i}\omega t].$$

2.2.2   Retarded time

The magnetic field at a point at any particular time can only reasonably be based on information that has travelled out to it, from the origin of the field, at speed c — the characteristic speed of electromagnetic signals crossing empty space. So we need to modify the predicted form of the field by setting back, or 'retarding', the time at which the current is evaluated. At radius r, information takes time r/c to travel from the dipole at the origin, so the field at radius r and time t depends on the current at the origin at time $t - r/c$, and this is called the **retarded time**. The expression for the magnetic field at r therefore needs to be modified to be the real part of

In Chapter 1, to be as general as possible, I included a phase offset in the argument of the exponential. It is not needed here so I have effectively chosen it to be zero.

$$B_\phi = \eta\sin\theta\,g(r)\exp[-\mathrm{i}\omega(t - r/c)].$$

Remember that our goal is to establish a valid form for the magnetic field that will account for radiation from a Hertzian dipole. We have already appealed to wave propagation in the expression for retarded time, so we might as well build in the relationship between angular frequency, wavenumber and speed in a vacuum, namely $\omega = kc$. Then

$$-\mathrm{i}\omega(t - r/c) = -\mathrm{i}(\omega t - \omega r/c) = -\mathrm{i}(\omega t - kr) = \mathrm{i}(kr - \omega t),$$

and so

$$B_\phi = \eta\sin\theta\,g(r)\exp[\mathrm{i}(kr - \omega t)].$$

The dependence on ω is still not completely determined, as we shall see when we examine the dependence on r in the term $g(r)$.

2.2.3 Radial-dependence

The Biot–Savart law contains an inverse-square dependence on radius, but radiation requires a simple inverse-radial dependence. The inspired guess here is to allow both by writing

$$g(r) = \frac{a(\omega)}{r} + \frac{1}{r^2},$$

where $a(\omega)$ is a frequency-dependent factor, which will be discussed in the next subsection. The form of the magnetic field is now the real part of

$$B_\phi = \eta \sin\theta \left(\frac{a(\omega)}{r} + \frac{1}{r^2} \right) \exp[\mathrm{i}(kr - \omega t)].$$

Far from the source, the frequency-dependent $a(\omega)/r$ term dominates, but close to the source the $1/r^2$ term prevails (Figure 2.4).

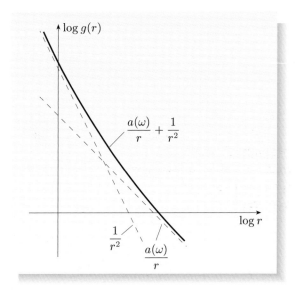

Figure 2.4 At sufficiently large distance, $a(\omega)r^{-1} > r^{-2}$, as illustrated in this log-log plot.

2.2.4 A constraint on the frequency-dependence

Notice first that as $\omega \to 0$, $\exp[-\mathrm{i}\omega t] \to 1$ and the oscillation ceases, leaving a steady current in the element. In practice, a steady current must flow to somewhere else, so such a current element cannot be entirely isolated — it must be part of a circuit. However, in the case of an oscillatory current, the Ampère–Maxwell law links the oscillation of current with the oscillation of electric and magnetic fields.

The final stage of construction of the magnetic field is to ensure that under steady conditions ($\omega = 0$), the expression for the magnetic field reduces to the Biot–Savart expression, with which we began. This means that we have to constrain $a(\omega)$, the coefficient of the new 'radiation component' that scales as r^{-1}. This term must vanish when $\omega = 0$ in order that only the Biot–Savart field remains when the current is steady. Other than that, $a(\omega)$ is the one parameter we can adjust to ensure that Maxwell's equations are satisfied.

So here is our prediction for the magnetic field of a Hertzian dipole: the physical field will be the real part of

$$B_\phi = \eta \sin\theta \left(\frac{a(\omega)}{r} + \frac{1}{r^2} \right) \exp[\mathrm{i}(kr - \omega t)], \tag{2.5}$$

with $a(\omega) = 0$ when $\omega = 0$, and $\eta = \mu_0 I_0\, \delta l / 4\pi$.

2.3 Testing with Maxwell's equations

We now have a prediction for the form of the magnetic field generated by an oscillating current element (a Hertzian dipole). If this magnetic field is a valid solution of Maxwell's equations, then it is just what we set out to obtain, since we have already built into it the necessary r^{-1} scaling at large distance that ensures the correct behaviour with regard to energy radiating from a point source.

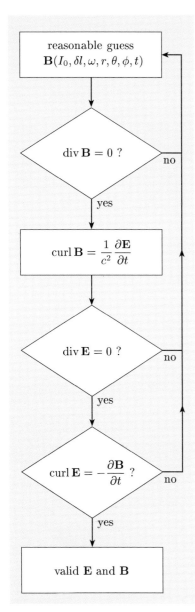

Figure 2.5 A flow chart showing the strategy for verifying and calibrating the electromagnetic fields of a Hertzian dipole.

$(\mathrm{curl}\,\mathbf{B})_r$ denotes the component of $\mathrm{curl}\,\mathbf{B}$ in the $\mathbf{e}_r$-direction.

The next four subsections test the predicted field with Maxwell's equations, suitably specialized for the free space that is assumed to surround the Hertzian dipole. These tests turn out to be important for two reasons. First, in doing these tests we obtain an expression for the electric field without appealing to further physical insight. Second, the form of the electric field naturally throws up an expression for $a(\omega)$, which we have so far been unable to prescribe, beyond its being equal to zero at zero frequency. In a sense, Maxwell's equations verify and calibrate the proposed magnetic field for a Hertzian dipole.

The procedure will be as illustrated in Figure 2.5. First we shall check that the divergence of the magnetic field is zero. Then we shall take its curl and use this with the Ampère–Maxwell law to establish the form of the associated electric field. Next we shall check the divergence of the electric field, which Gauss's law requires to be zero in empty space. Finally, we shall use Faraday's law to find under what circumstances the original magnetic field is exactly recovered.

2.3.1   The no-monopole law

The no-monopole law requires that all magnetic fields are divergence-free. Using the expression for the divergence in spherical coordinates from inside the back cover, we can write

$$\mathrm{div}\,\mathbf{B} = \frac{1}{r^2}\frac{\partial}{\partial r}\left(r^2 B_r\right) + \frac{1}{r\sin\theta}\frac{\partial}{\partial \theta}(\sin\theta\,B_\theta) + \frac{1}{r\sin\theta}\frac{\partial B_\phi}{\partial \phi}.$$

The expression proposed for $\mathbf{B}$ has $B_r = B_\theta = 0$, and B_ϕ independent of ϕ (Equation 2.5), so each term on the right-hand side is assuredly zero. Thus the proposed magnetic field meets the requirement that it is divergence-free.

2.3.2   The Ampère–Maxwell law

In a vacuum, the Ampère–Maxwell law requires that

$$\mathrm{curl}\,\mathbf{B} = \varepsilon_0\mu_0\frac{\partial \mathbf{E}}{\partial t} = \frac{1}{c^2}\frac{\partial \mathbf{E}}{\partial t}.$$

We do not yet know the electric field, but we can use this law to stipulate what its time derivative must be.

Since $\mathbf{B} = B_\phi\mathbf{e}_\phi$, the components of $\mathrm{curl}\,\mathbf{B}$ can be written (using the expression inside the back cover for curl in spherical coordinates) as follows:

$$(\mathrm{curl}\,\mathbf{B})_r = \frac{1}{r\sin\theta}\frac{\partial}{\partial \theta}(\sin\theta\,B_\phi), \tag{2.6}$$

$$(\mathrm{curl}\,\mathbf{B})_\theta = -\frac{1}{r}\frac{\partial}{\partial r}(rB_\phi), \tag{2.7}$$

$$(\mathrm{curl}\,\mathbf{B})_\phi = 0. \tag{2.8}$$

The fact that $B_r = B_\theta = 0$ greatly simplifies the task of evaluating $\mathrm{curl}\,\mathbf{B}$, but, even so, the form of B_ϕ in Equation 2.5 will result in several terms. Evaluating the r- and θ-components of curl $\mathbf{B}$, we obtain

$$(\text{curl}\,\mathbf{B})_r = \frac{1}{r\sin\theta}\frac{\partial}{\partial\theta}\left(\eta\sin^2\theta\left(\frac{a(\omega)}{r}+\frac{1}{r^2}\right)\exp[\mathrm{i}(kr-\omega t)]\right) \qquad \frac{\partial}{\partial\theta}(\eta\sin^2\theta)=2\eta\sin\theta\cos\theta$$

$$= \frac{2\eta\cos\theta}{r}\left(\frac{a(\omega)}{r}+\frac{1}{r^2}\right)\exp[\mathrm{i}(kr-\omega t)]$$

$$= 2\eta\cos\theta\left(\frac{a(\omega)}{r^2}+\frac{1}{r^3}\right)\exp[\mathrm{i}(kr-\omega t)], \qquad (2.9)$$

$$(\text{curl}\,\mathbf{B})_\theta = -\frac{1}{r}\frac{\partial}{\partial r}\left(r\eta\sin\theta\left(\frac{a(\omega)}{r}+\frac{1}{r^2}\right)\exp[\mathrm{i}(kr-\omega t)]\right)$$

$$= -\frac{\eta\sin\theta}{r}\left(\mathrm{i}ka(\omega)+\frac{\mathrm{i}k}{r}-\frac{1}{r^2}\right)\exp[\mathrm{i}(kr-\omega t)]$$

$$= \eta\sin\theta\left(-\frac{\mathrm{i}ka(\omega)}{r}-\frac{\mathrm{i}k}{r^2}+\frac{1}{r^3}\right)\exp[\mathrm{i}(kr-\omega t)]. \qquad (2.10)$$

The Ampère–Maxwell law can now be invoked to enable the electric field to be deduced by equating the components of its time derivative to the components of curl $\mathbf{B}$. For example, equating the r-components,

$$(\text{curl}\,\mathbf{B})_r = \frac{1}{c^2}\frac{\partial E_r}{\partial t}. \qquad (2.11)$$

Since we have an oscillatory time-dependence expressed through the complex exponential, and no other time-dependence to worry about, we can let the implicit exponential notation deal with the time derivative. Since $\mathbf{B}$ depends on time through $\exp[-\mathrm{i}\omega t]$, then inevitably the electric field must have a similar time-dependence, so $E_r = E_{r0}\exp[-\mathrm{i}\omega t]$ and

$$\frac{\partial E_r}{\partial t} = (-\mathrm{i}\omega)E_r. \qquad (2.12)$$

Similarly,

$$\frac{\partial E_\theta}{\partial t} = (-\mathrm{i}\omega)E_\theta. \qquad (2.13)$$

Substituting the expression for $(\text{curl}\,\mathbf{B})_r$ from Equation 2.9 for the left-hand side of Equation 2.11, and the expression for $\partial E_r/\partial t$ from Equation 2.12 for the right-hand side, and multiplying through by $c^2/(-\mathrm{i}\omega)$, leads to

$$E_r = \frac{2c^2\eta\cos\theta}{(-\mathrm{i}\omega)}\left(\frac{a(\omega)}{r^2}+\frac{1}{r^3}\right)\exp[\mathrm{i}(kr-\omega t)]. \qquad (2.14)$$

Following the reasoning in Section 2.1, this component cannot be associated with radiation as it has no part that falls off as r^{-1}.

The θ-component of the electric field is found in a similar way,

$$E_\theta = \frac{c^2\eta\sin\theta}{(-\mathrm{i}\omega)}\left(-\frac{\mathrm{i}ka(\omega)}{r}-\frac{\mathrm{i}k}{r^2}+\frac{1}{r^3}\right)\exp[\mathrm{i}(kr-\omega t)], \qquad (2.15)$$

and $E_\phi = 0$ since $(\text{curl}\,\mathbf{B})_\phi = 0$.

Viewing the terms according to their radial-dependence shows that there are three aspects to the electric field. The radiation field is evidently the part of E_θ that scales as r^{-1}, and it is this term that will remain at large r, long after the r^{-2} and r^{-3} terms in E_r and E_θ have become vanishingly small.

Notice that we have now established that the *radiation* fields generated by the oscillating dipole are $B_\phi \mathbf{e}_\phi$ and $E_\theta \mathbf{e}_\theta$. Just as we found for plane waves in Chapter 1, the electric and magnetic components of electromagnetic radiation are orthogonal.

The next step is to check that this electric field is divergence-free.

2.3.3   Gauss's law

To see that all is well with the deduced form of the electric field, we shall check that its divergence in the empty space around the Hertzian dipole is zero, as required by Gauss's law. The algebra is not quite as simple as for the divergence of the magnetic field, since now there are several more complicated terms. Here is what the divergence of **E** looks like after setting E_ϕ to zero:

$$\operatorname{div}\mathbf{E} = \frac{1}{r^2}\frac{\partial}{\partial r}\left[r^2\frac{2c^2\eta\cos\theta}{(-i\omega)}\left(\frac{a(\omega)}{r^2}+\frac{1}{r^3}\right)\exp[i(kr-\omega t)]\right]$$
$$+\frac{1}{r\sin\theta}\frac{\partial}{\partial\theta}\left[\frac{c^2\eta\sin^2\theta}{(-i\omega)}\left(-\frac{ika(\omega)}{r}-\frac{ik}{r^2}+\frac{1}{r^3}\right)\exp[i(kr-\omega t)]\right].$$

Doing the differentiation leads to the following result:

$$\operatorname{div}\mathbf{E} = \frac{2c^2\eta\cos\theta}{(-i\omega)r^2}\left[ik\left(a(\omega)+\frac{1}{r}\right)-\frac{1}{r^2}\right]\exp[i(kr-\omega t)]$$
$$+\frac{2c^2\eta\cos\theta}{(-i\omega)r}\left[-\frac{ika(\omega)}{r}-\frac{ik}{r^2}+\frac{1}{r^3}\right]\exp[i(kr-\omega t)].$$

On comparing the coefficients of terms in r^{-2}, r^{-3} and r^{-4} it can be seen that that they conveniently pair up and cancel. Thus $\operatorname{div}\mathbf{E}$ is zero. So far so good.

2.3.4   Faraday's law

The last stage of checking that Equations 2.5, 2.14 and 2.15 represent valid forms for the magnetic and electric fields around a Hertzian dipole is to check their consistency with Faraday's law, $\operatorname{curl}\mathbf{E} = -\partial\mathbf{B}/\partial t$. If the fields pass this test, then we have succeeded in building the form of electric and magnetic fields around a Hertzian dipole.

The components of $\operatorname{curl}\mathbf{E}$, when E_ϕ is zero, are as follows:

$$(\operatorname{curl}\mathbf{E})_r = -\frac{1}{r\sin\theta}\frac{\partial E_\theta}{\partial\phi},$$
$$(\operatorname{curl}\mathbf{E})_\theta = \frac{1}{r\sin\theta}\frac{\partial E_r}{\partial\phi},$$
$$(\operatorname{curl}\mathbf{E})_\phi = \frac{1}{r}\left(\frac{\partial}{\partial r}(rE_\theta)-\frac{\partial E_r}{\partial\theta}\right).$$

Because E_θ and E_r are not functions of ϕ, only the ϕ-component of $\operatorname{curl}\mathbf{E}$ remains. This is expected, since $\operatorname{curl}\mathbf{E}$ must be in the same direction as **B**. The remaining differentiation is straightforward, but it pays to be methodical:

$$\frac{1}{r}\left(\frac{\partial}{\partial r}(rE_\theta)\right) = \frac{c^2\eta\sin\theta}{(-\mathrm{i}\omega)r}\frac{\partial}{\partial r}\left[\left(-\mathrm{i}ka(\omega) - \frac{\mathrm{i}k}{r} + \frac{1}{r^2}\right)\exp[\mathrm{i}(kr - \omega t)]\right]$$

$$= \frac{c^2\eta\sin\theta}{(-\mathrm{i}\omega)r}\left[\mathrm{i}k\left(-\mathrm{i}ka(\omega) - \frac{\mathrm{i}k}{r} + \frac{1}{r^2}\right) + \left(\frac{\mathrm{i}k}{r^2} - \frac{2}{r^3}\right)\right]$$
$$\times \exp[\mathrm{i}(kr - \omega t)]$$

$$= \frac{c^2\eta\sin\theta}{(-\mathrm{i}\omega)}\left[\mathrm{i}k\left(\frac{-\mathrm{i}ka(\omega)}{r} - \frac{\mathrm{i}k}{r^2} + \frac{1}{r^3}\right) + \left(\frac{\mathrm{i}k}{r^3} - \frac{2}{r^4}\right)\right]$$
$$\times \exp[\mathrm{i}(kr - \omega t)]$$

and

$$-\frac{1}{r}\frac{\partial E_r}{\partial\theta} = \frac{2c^2\eta\sin\theta}{(-\mathrm{i}\omega)}\left(\frac{a(\omega)}{r^3} + \frac{1}{r^4}\right)\exp[\mathrm{i}(kr - \omega t)].$$

Then curl $\mathbf{E}$, which is directed along $\mathbf{e}_\phi$, has a value for $(\mathrm{curl}\,\mathbf{E})_\phi$ that is the sum of these two expressions. Now there are terms in r^{-1}, r^{-2}, r^{-3} and r^{-4}, though given the r-dependence that we specified for B_ϕ in Equation 2.5, we are expecting only the first two of these. The higher-order terms must vanish if the Biot–Savart law is to be satisfied.

Look first at the terms in r^{-4}: there are two terms with equal magnitude and opposite signs, so the r^{-4}-dependence does indeed vanish. Next examine the r^{-3} ← *it does 'if $a(\omega) = -\mathrm{i}k$* terms, which must also vanish, so

$$\frac{c^2\eta\sin\theta}{(-\mathrm{i}\omega)}(2\mathrm{i}k) + \frac{2c^2\eta\sin\theta}{(-\mathrm{i}\omega)}a(\omega) = 0,$$

which simplifies to $a(\omega) = -\mathrm{i}k$. But for electromagnetic waves in free space, $k = \omega/c$, so

$$a(\omega) = -\frac{\mathrm{i}\omega}{c}.$$

Here at last is an expression for $a(\omega)$, the coefficient of the extra term that we introduced into the Biot–Savart law. Notice that it behaves in the way we specified in Subsection 2.2.4, in that $a(\omega) \to 0$ as $\omega \to 0$.

Now we just have to check that the two remaining terms in the expressions that contribute to $(\mathrm{curl}\,\mathbf{E})_\phi$ give all that we require, which is that $(\mathrm{curl}\,\mathbf{E})_\phi = -\partial B_\phi/\partial t$. We have

$$(\mathrm{curl}\,\mathbf{E})_\phi = \frac{c^2\eta\sin\theta}{(-\mathrm{i}\omega)}\left[\mathrm{i}k\left(-\frac{\mathrm{i}ka(\omega)}{r} - \frac{\mathrm{i}k}{r^2}\right)\right]\exp[\mathrm{i}(kr - \omega t)]$$

$$= \frac{k^2c^2\eta\sin\theta}{(-\mathrm{i}\omega)}\left(\frac{a(\omega)}{r} + \frac{1}{r^2}\right)\exp[\mathrm{i}(kr - \omega t)]$$

$$= \mathrm{i}\omega\eta\sin\theta\left(\frac{a(\omega)}{r} + \frac{1}{r^2}\right)\exp[\mathrm{i}(kr - \omega t)].$$

The predicted form for B_ϕ was

$$B_\phi = \eta\sin\theta\left(\frac{a(\omega)}{r} + \frac{1}{r^2}\right)\exp[\mathrm{i}(kr - \omega t)], \qquad \text{(Eqn 2.5)}$$

so

$$-\frac{\partial B_\phi}{\partial t} = -(-\mathrm{i}\omega)B_\phi = \mathrm{i}\omega\eta\sin\theta\left(\frac{a(\omega)}{r} + \frac{1}{r^2}\right)\exp[\mathrm{i}(kr - \omega t)],$$

which is identical to the expression we obtained for $(\mathrm{curl}\,\mathbf{E})_\phi$.

The checks are complete — the electric field that we have found is indeed related to the magnetic field exactly as required by Faraday's law.

2.3.5   Validated forms for fields due to a Hertzian dipole

In this section we have constructed and validated solutions of Maxwell's equations for the fields due to an oscillating current element in otherwise empty space. The physical magnetic field is the real part of

$$\mathbf{B} = \eta\sin\theta\left(\frac{(-\mathrm{i}\omega/c)}{r} + \frac{1}{r^2}\right)\exp[\mathrm{i}(kr - \omega t)]\,\mathbf{e}_\phi. \qquad (2.16)$$

The physical electric field is the real part of

$$\mathbf{E} = \frac{2c^2\eta\cos\theta}{(-\mathrm{i}\omega)}\left(\frac{(-\mathrm{i}\omega/c)}{r^2} + \frac{1}{r^3}\right)\exp[\mathrm{i}(kr - \omega t)]\,\mathbf{e}_r$$
$$+ \frac{c^2\eta\sin\theta}{(-\mathrm{i}\omega)}\left(-\frac{(-\mathrm{i}\omega/c)(\mathrm{i}k)}{r} - \frac{\mathrm{i}k}{r^2} + \frac{1}{r^3}\right)\exp[\mathrm{i}(kr - \omega t)]\,\mathbf{e}_\theta. \qquad (2.17)$$

Grouping the terms by r-dependence rather than vector component shows that there are essentially three contributions to the electric field produced by a Hertzian dipole. The r^{-3} terms are effectively the *electrostatic field*,

$$\frac{c^2\eta}{(-\mathrm{i}\omega)}\exp[\mathrm{i}(kr - \omega t)]\left(\frac{2\cos\theta}{r^3}\,\mathbf{e}_r + \frac{\sin\theta}{r^3}\,\mathbf{e}_\theta\right)$$

— they have the same dependence on r and θ as the field of a steady electric dipole (compare Equation 2.1). The r^{-2} terms give rise to what is called the *induction field*, and the *radiation field* is the single term in r^{-1}.

We already know from Chapter 1 that Maxwell's equations can be manipulated into wave equations for $\mathbf{E}$ and $\mathbf{B}$. Indeed, we have already appealed to electromagnetic waves in setting up the retarded time in Subsection 2.2.2. So the next task is to see what sort of wave is involved. Given the spherical geometry, something more than a simple plane wave is expected.

2.4   Spherical waves radiating from a Hertzian dipole

2.4.1   The far fields

The radiation fields in Equations 2.16 and 2.17 are described by the terms in r^{-1}. We can neglect the other contributions at sufficiently large distances from the current element. Just how far can be specified by comparing the magnitudes of the various terms.

In Equation 2.16, the radiation term will predominate where

$$\frac{\omega/c}{r} \gg \frac{1}{r^2},$$

which simplifies to

$$r \gg \frac{\lambda}{2\pi}. \qquad (2.18)$$

A double inequality generally requires the ratio of terms on opposite sides to be at least one order of magnitude.

Since $2\pi \simeq 6$, this inequality is satisfied even for radial distances as short as 2λ. This means that, beyond a couple of wavelengths from the source, the magnetic field looks to all intents and purposes like the radiation term alone. The same is true for the electric field, as you will be able to show in the next exercise. Remember that a Hertzian dipole is short compared with the wavelength of radiation associated with it, so when the criterion $r \gg \lambda/2\pi$ is fulfilled, the dipole will already appear to be a point source. Radiation fields are often referred to as **far fields** (Figure 2.6).

Exercise 2.2   Use Equation 2.17 to obtain criteria for the radiation term to predominate in the expression for the electric field of a Hertzian dipole.   ■

At distances more than a couple of wavelengths from the source, the physical fields that are generated by a Hertzian dipole are essentially the real parts of the r^{-1} terms in Equations 2.16 and 2.17. A superscript 'rad' will be used from now on to indicate that these are the physical radiation fields.

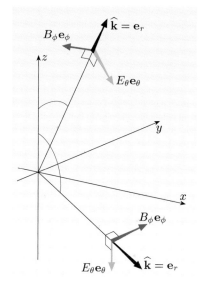

Figure 2.6   In the far field region, where the radiation field dominates, the Hertzian dipole appears to be a point source, and $\mathbf{B} = B_\phi \mathbf{e}_\phi$ and $\mathbf{E} = E_\theta \mathbf{e}_\theta$.

Radiation fields generated by a Hertzian dipole

$$\mathbf{B}^{(\mathrm{rad})} = \frac{\omega\eta}{c}\frac{\sin\theta}{r}\sin(kr - \omega t)\,\mathbf{e}_\phi, \qquad (2.19)$$

$$\mathbf{E}^{(\mathrm{rad})} = \omega\eta\frac{\sin\theta}{r}\sin(kr - \omega t)\,\mathbf{e}_\theta, \qquad (2.20)$$

where $\eta = \mu_0 I_0\,\delta l/4\pi$ (Equation 2.4).

There are a number of things to notice about these expressions for the radiation fields.

- Taking the real parts has picked out $\sin(kr - \omega t)$ from the complex exponential.

- The electric and magnetic fields are in phase with one another.

- The electric and magnetic fields are perpendicular to one another.

- The amplitudes of the electric and magnetic fields increase in proportion to the frequency and the magnitude of the oscillating current element (through η).

- $\mathbf{E}^{(\mathrm{rad})}$ and $\mathbf{B}^{(\mathrm{rad})}$ represent waves that travel in the direction of increasing r, that is $\widehat{\mathbf{k}} = \mathbf{e}_r$, and this direction is perpendicular to $\mathbf{E}^{(\mathrm{rad})}$ and $\mathbf{B}^{(\mathrm{rad})}$.

- The phase speed (or speed of propagation) is $c = \omega/k$.

- The phases of $\mathbf{E}^{(\mathrm{rad})}$ and $\mathbf{B}^{(\mathrm{rad})}$ at an instant of time have the same value at any point on the surface of a sphere centred on the Hertzian dipole, which means that these fields are **spherical waves**.

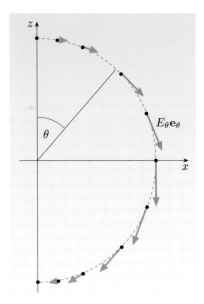

Figure 2.7   The electric field $\mathbf{E}^{(\mathrm{rad})}$ for various values of θ, at constant r and ϕ. The lengths of the field vectors correspond with the magnitude of the field.

- The pair $\mathbf{E}^{(\mathrm{rad})}$ and $\mathbf{B}^{(\mathrm{rad})}$ constitutes a polarized electromagnetic wave, with the polarization direction (the direction of the electric field) in the $\mathbf{e}_\theta$ direction (Figure 2.7).

- As we found for plane waves, $\mathbf{E}^{(\mathrm{rad})} = c\,\mathbf{B}^{(\mathrm{rad})} \times \widehat{\mathbf{k}}$.

- Unlike plane waves, the amplitudes of the spherical waves, $\mathbf{E}^{(\mathrm{rad})}$ and $\mathbf{B}^{(\mathrm{rad})}$, diminish as they propagate because of the $1/r$ scaling.

- The $\sin\theta$ factor is constant along the (radial) direction of propagation, and this factor gives an angular-dependence to the wave amplitudes, which we shall consider in the next subsection.

Exercise 2.3   Use Equation 2.20 to show that, far away from the source, several cycles of the spherical wave illustrated in Figure 2.8 will appear very similar to a plane wave.   ■

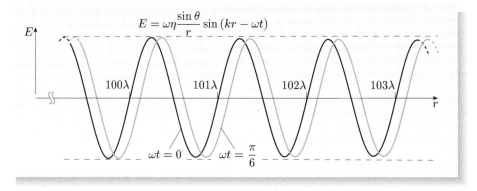

Figure 2.8   In the far field, the amplitude of the wave does not change significantly over several cycles, though it falls steadily with overall distance.

2.4.2   The spherical wave equation

The far field radiation that has emerged from our analysis is already qualifying for the description 'spherical wave'. In Chapter 1 it was shown that a three-dimensional wave equation could be derived from Maxwell's equations:

$$\nabla^2 \mathbf{B}(\mathbf{r}, t) = \frac{1}{c^2}\frac{\partial^2 \mathbf{B}(\mathbf{r}, t)}{\partial t^2}. \tag{2.21}$$

For plane waves, a Cartesian coordinate system is a natural choice, and that leads to Equation 2.21 being readily resolved into three scalar equations for the three Cartesian components of $\mathbf{B}(x, y, z, t)$.

Warning: the expressions inside the back cover for the Laplacian operator in cylindrical and spherical coordinates apply only for operating on a *scalar* quantity. You cannot use these formulas to evaluate $\nabla^2\mathbf{B}$.

For radiation from a point source, spherical coordinates are the sensible choice. However, that inevitably leads to complications in unravelling Equation 2.21 because the Laplacian operating on a vector in spherical geometry is complicated by the fact that the unit vectors $\mathbf{e}_r$, $\mathbf{e}_\theta$ and $\mathbf{e}_\phi$ are not constant in direction and so cannot be taken outside differential operators. The safest way to proceed is to go back to the vector identity for $\mathrm{curl}(\mathrm{curl}\,\mathbf{B})$ that was used to obtain Equation 2.21 in the first place:

$$\mathrm{curl}(\mathrm{curl}\,\mathbf{B}) = \mathrm{grad}(\mathrm{div}\,\mathbf{B}) - \nabla^2\mathbf{B}.$$

Using this identity, together with the no-monopole law, allows us to rewrite the general three-dimensional wave equation for the magnetic field (Equation 2.21) as

$$-\operatorname{curl}(\operatorname{curl}\mathbf{B}) = \frac{1}{c^2}\frac{\partial^2 \mathbf{B}(\mathbf{r},t)}{\partial t^2}. \tag{2.22}$$

Checking that Equations 2.16 and 2.17 are solutions to this general three-dimensional wave equation is rather messy (I know because I have done it!). There are two ways forward. The first is to use an algebra-solving computer program, such as *Mathematica* or *Mathcad*. Such a program can readily derive an expression for the electric field (Equation 2.17) that is associated with the predicted magnetic field (Equation 2.16), can confirm that these expressions for the fields are consistent with all four of Maxwell's equations, and can check that these fields are solutions of three-dimensional wave equations. Figure 2.9 overleaf shows an example of the output that is obtained when this is done.

We shall take a different approach. Because $\mathbf{B}^{(\mathrm{rad})}$ has the form shown in Equation 2.19, it turns out that the full three-dimensional wave equation can be greatly simplified to

$$\frac{1}{r}\frac{\partial^2}{\partial r^2}\left(r\,\mathbf{B}^{(\mathrm{rad})}\right) = \frac{1}{c^2}\frac{\partial^2}{\partial t^2}\mathbf{B}^{(\mathrm{rad})}. \tag{2.23}$$

This is an equation for spherical waves.

Worked Example 2.1

Show that Equation 2.19 is a solution of Equation 2.23.

Essential skill

Working with the equation for spherical waves

Solution

Substituting the expression for $\mathbf{B}^{(\mathrm{rad})}$ in the left-hand side of Equation 2.23,

$$\frac{1}{r}\frac{\partial^2}{\partial r^2}\left(r\left[\frac{\omega\eta}{c}\frac{\sin\theta}{r}\sin(kr-\omega t)\,\mathbf{e}_\phi\right]\right) = \frac{1}{r}\frac{\partial^2}{\partial r^2}\left[\frac{\omega\eta}{c}\sin\theta\sin(kr-\omega t)\,\mathbf{e}_\phi\right]$$

$$= \frac{-k^2}{r}\left[\frac{\omega\eta}{c}\sin\theta\sin(kr-\omega t)\,\mathbf{e}_\phi\right]$$

$$= -k^2\,\mathbf{B}^{(\mathrm{rad})}.$$

The second derivative of $\mathbf{B}^{(\mathrm{rad})}$ with respect to time is $-\omega^2\,\mathbf{B}^{(\mathrm{rad})}$, and substituting this and the expression for the spatial derivative into Equation 2.23 leads to

$$-k^2\,\mathbf{B}^{(\mathrm{rad})} = -\frac{\omega^2}{c^2}\,\mathbf{B}^{(\mathrm{rad})}.$$

This leads us to conclude that in order for Equation 2.19 to be a solution of Equation 2.23, we require that $\omega^2 = k^2 c^2$. This is the standard confirmation that we have been dealing with a wave equation and its solution.

2.4.3 Calculating the radiated power

As you saw in Chapter 1, the power per unit area at any point $\mathbf{r}$ and time t is given by the Poynting vector,

$$\mathbf{N}(\mathbf{r},t) = \mathbf{E}_{\mathrm{phys}}(\mathbf{r},t)\times\mathbf{H}_{\mathrm{phys}}(\mathbf{r},t) = \mathbf{E}_{\mathrm{phys}}(\mathbf{r},t)\times\mathbf{B}_{\mathrm{phys}}(\mathbf{r},t)/\mu_0.$$

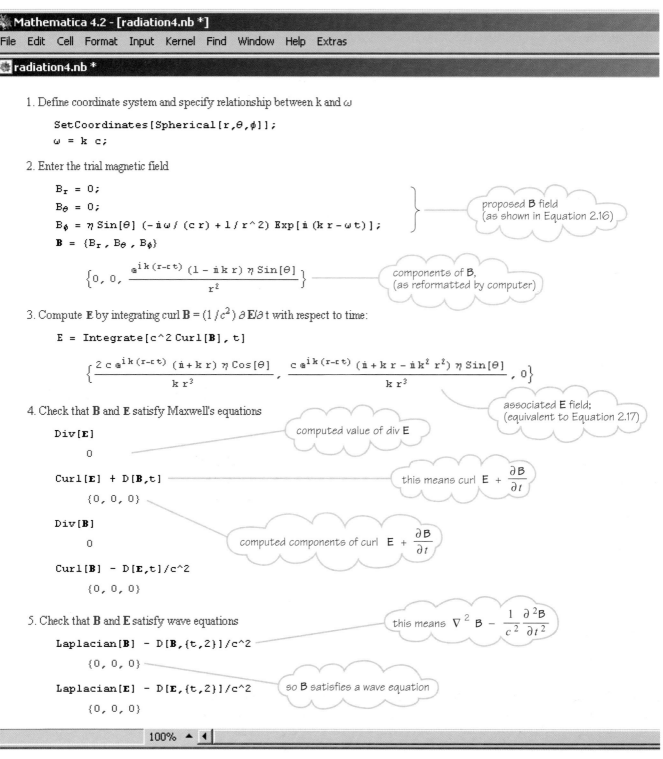

Figure 2.9   An annotated printout from the software package *Mathematica*, which was programmed to test whether proposed solutions for the fields produced by a Hertzian dipole were consistent with Maxwell's equations and the wave equation. The numbered lines of text describe steps in the process, black text is information and instructions input to the program, and red text is output from the program.

This is the directed energy flux density transported by the field. Here, we are interested in the energy radiated by the small oscillating dipole, so we shall assume that $r \gg \lambda$ and use the radiation fields $\mathbf{E}^{(\mathrm{rad})}$ and $\mathbf{B}^{(\mathrm{rad})}$.

In order to calculate the total power W radiated by a small oscillating current dipole, we need first to find the power radiated through an element of the spherical surface, radius r and centred on the dipole (Figure 2.10). This is

$$\delta W = \mathbf{N}(\mathbf{r},t) \cdot \delta\mathbf{S} = \big(\mathbf{N}(\mathbf{r},t)\cdot\mathbf{e}_r\big)\, r^2 \sin\theta\, \delta\theta\, \delta\phi.$$

This scalar quantity can then be integrated over a complete spherical surface to find the total power radiated by the Hertzian dipole.

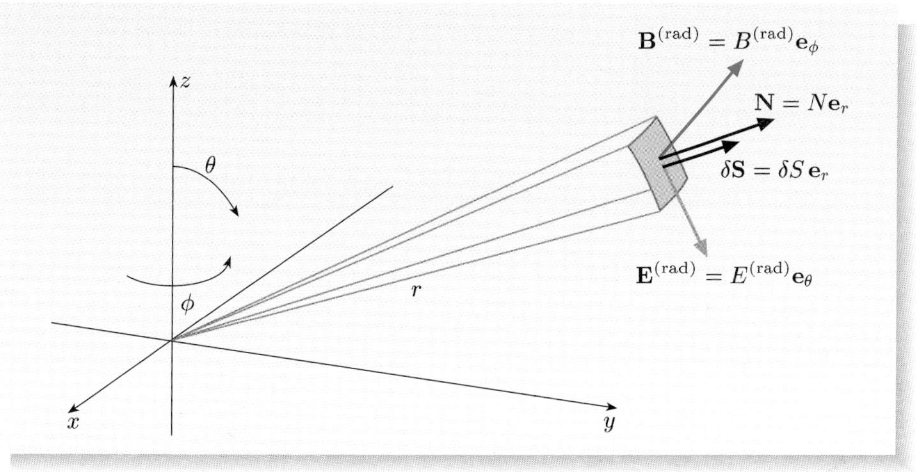

Figure 2.10 The power radiated through $\delta\mathbf{S}$ is $\mathbf{N}\cdot\delta\mathbf{S}$. In this case the direction of $\mathbf{N}$ lies along $\mathbf{e}_r$.

We must be careful here because the Poynting vector $\mathbf{N}$ is given by the *product* of two fields. So, in order to obtain the correct (real, physical) vector field for the power radiated through unit area, we must use expressions for the physical fields (Equations 2.19 and 2.20). Thus

$$\mathbf{N}^{(\mathrm{rad})}(\mathbf{r},t) = \mathbf{E}^{(\mathrm{rad})}(\mathbf{r},t) \times \left(\frac{\mathbf{B}^{(\mathrm{rad})}(\mathbf{r},t)}{\mu_0}\right)$$

$$= \left(\frac{\omega\eta}{r}\right)\left(\frac{\omega\eta}{c\mu_0 r}\right)\sin^2\theta\,\sin^2(kr-\omega t)\,\mathbf{e}_\theta \times \mathbf{e}_\phi.$$

But $\mathbf{e}_\theta \times \mathbf{e}_\phi = \mathbf{e}_r$, so

$$\mathbf{N}^{(\mathrm{rad})}(\mathbf{r},t) = \frac{\omega^2\eta^2}{c\mu_0 r^2}\sin^2\theta\,\sin^2(kr-\omega t)\,\mathbf{e}_r. \qquad (2.24)$$

As anticipated, the radiated power flows out along the radius vector $\mathbf{r}$, away from the source. Owing to the factor $\sin^2\theta$, the power per unit area is zero at $\theta = 0$ and $\theta = \pi$, and is a maximum at $\theta = \pi/2$. Note that $\mathbf{N}^{(\mathrm{rad})}$ does not depend on the azimuthal angle ϕ, which makes sense because the source is aligned along the z-axis, and this physical set-up is symmetrical with respect to the angle ϕ. So the power flowing through the surface element at time t is

$$\delta W = \mathbf{N}^{(\mathrm{rad})}\cdot\delta\mathbf{S} = \frac{\omega^2\eta^2}{c\mu_0}\sin^3\theta\,\sin^2(kr-\omega t)\,\delta\theta\,\delta\phi.$$

As expected, the power flowing through the element of area does not fall off with increasing r, although it does oscillate. But $\sin^2(kr-\omega t)$ is never negative, so the

$\sin^2\theta = \frac{1}{2}(1-\cos 2\theta)$
so $\sin^2 0 = \frac{1}{2}(1-1) = 0$
$\sin^2\pi = \frac{1}{2}(1-1) = 0$
$\sin^2\pi/2 = \frac{1}{2}(1-(-1)) = 1$

flow of energy is always outwards. We can express the time-average of δW, the power through the area element, by replacing $\sin^2(kr - \omega t)$ with its time-average, which is $\frac{1}{2}$. The time-average of δW is therefore

$$\overline{\delta W} = \frac{\omega^2 \eta^2}{2c\mu_0} \sin^3 \theta \, \delta\theta \, \delta\phi.$$

Finally, the overall time-averaged power radiated by a small Hertzian dipole is obtained by integrating over all directions of θ and ϕ:

$$\overline{W} = \frac{\omega^2 \eta^2}{2c\mu_0} \int_0^{2\pi} \mathrm{d}\phi \int_0^{\pi} \sin^3 \theta \, \mathrm{d}\theta$$

$$= \frac{\omega^2 \eta^2}{2c\mu_0} (2\pi) \int_0^{\pi} \sin^3 \theta \, \mathrm{d}\theta$$

$$= \frac{\omega^2 \eta^2}{2c\mu_0} (2\pi) \left(\tfrac{4}{3}\right).$$

$$\int_{\theta=0}^{\pi} \sin^3 \theta \, \mathrm{d}\theta$$
$$= \int_{\cos\theta=1}^{\cos\theta=-1} (\cos^2 \theta - 1) \, \mathrm{d}(\cos\theta)$$
$$= \left[\tfrac{1}{3}\cos^3 \theta - \cos\theta\right]_{\cos\theta=1}^{\cos\theta=-1}$$
$$= \tfrac{4}{3}.$$

Then using Equation 2.4 to substitute for η gives the following result.

> **Average power radiated by an oscillating current element**
>
> $$\overline{W} = \frac{\mu_0 \omega^2 I_0^2 (\delta l)^2}{12\pi c}. \tag{2.25}$$

In the description of the Hertzian dipole given in Section 2.2, the current amplitude, I_0, depends upon angular frequency ω, the amplitude of the oscillating dipole moment p_0, and the dipole length δl, according to the relationship

$$I_0 \, \delta l = \omega p_0. \tag{2.26}$$

Using this to substitute for $I_0 \, \delta l$ in Equation 2.25 gives the average power that is radiated in terms of the dipole moment, and this scales with the square of p_0 and the fourth power of ω:

> **Average power radiated by an oscillating dipole**
>
> $$\overline{W} = \frac{\mu_0 p_0^2 \omega^4}{12\pi c} = \frac{p_0^2 \omega^4}{12\pi \varepsilon_0 c^3}. \tag{2.27}$$

The strong frequency-dependence of the power radiated by an oscillating dipole has important consequences for the appearance of the Earth's atmosphere. This is discussed in the next section.

As we noted in Subsection 2.4.1, the electric field radiated by a Hertzian dipole aligned along the z-axis varies as $\sin\theta/r$, and is independent of the azimuthal angle ϕ. This dependence on θ is shown in Figure 2.11. Note that a radio transmitter that has the form of a vertical dipole transmits its maximum amplitude in the horizontal plane, and the field has zero amplitude in the vertical direction.

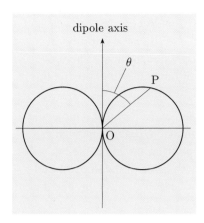

dipole axis

θ

P

O

Figure 2.11 Radiation pattern that shows the dependence of the electric field strength on θ at a fixed radius $r \gg \lambda$ in a plane through the axis of a Hertzian dipole. The distance from the origin O to point P on the curve is proportional to $\sin\theta$ and therefore proportional to the magnitude of the electric field at that angle θ. A three-dimensional version of this radiation pattern, which emphasizes the independence of ϕ, is obtained by rotating the two circles about the vertical axis.

Exercise 2.4   A Hertzian dipole of length 0.10 m is excited by a current of amplitude $I_0 = 1.0$ A at a frequency $\omega/2\pi = 13.56$ MHz. Estimate (a) the distance beyond which the radiation fields dominate, and (b) the average power radiated by the dipole.

13.56 MHz is a radio frequency that has been set aside for industrial use.

Exercise 2.5   With reference to Figures 2.7 and 2.11, suggest why the TV antennas in Figure 8b in the Introduction to this book are so deliberately co-aligned.

■

2.5   Scattering of light by the atmosphere

2.5.1   Scattering cross-section

Thus far we have established that a small oscillating dipole element radiates power according to Equation 2.27. But where does this energy come from? It comes, of course, from whatever agency keeps the dipole oscillating, perhaps a signal generator and amplifier.

But there is another way to generate dipole radiation: simply immerse a neutral molecule in an electromagnetic radiation field, say from a candle, a light bulb, a laser, a transmitting antenna, or the Sun. Then the electric field radiated from such a source will *induce* an oscillating dipole moment in the molecule, so causing it to radiate spherical waves with power depending on direction as shown in Figure 2.11. Should the incident waves be monochromatic with angular frequency ω (and not too intense), then this re-radiation of power will also be monochromatic at the same angular frequency, and described by Equations 2.19, 2.20 and 2.27. Thus the molecule takes incident radiation of well-defined frequency and direction, and scatters it into other directions. The scattering of light by molecules, or by particles that are small compared with the wavelength, is called **Rayleigh scattering**.

When an electric field $\mathbf{E}$ acts on a neutral molecule, a dipole moment $\mathbf{p}$ is induced in it. We shall here consider that the scattering molecule is in a gas that is not particularly dense, so the electric field is simply that of the incident field, $\mathbf{E}(\mathbf{r}, t)$. Because the field oscillates, it causes a slight oscillating redistribution of the molecule's electron cloud, giving rise to a corresponding oscillating dipole moment. Provided that the field is not too strong, the relationship between dipole moment and field is linear, with $\mathbf{p} = \varepsilon_0\alpha\mathbf{E}$, where α is called the **molecular** polarizability. But the electrons in molecules are capable of rather complicated internal motions when perturbed by outside forces. So the polarizability α generally depends on the angular frequency ω of the incident field. There are classical, or, better, quantum mechanical, models of molecules that predict this frequency-dependence, but we shall not discuss them here.

Suppose, then, that an incident monochromatic plane wave perturbs a molecule's structure at angular frequency ω, but not to such an extent that the molecule becomes ionized. Then the electrons will not escape from the molecule but will oscillate within the confines of a region essentially the size of the unperturbed molecule, and the induced dipole moment can then be treated as being like that of a Hertzian dipole.

If a plane wave $\mathbf{E}(z,t) = E_{0x}\cos(kz - \omega t)\,\mathbf{e}_x$ impinges on a molecule at the origin, then from Equation 1.33 the incident time-averaged power per unit area is

$$\overline{N} = \tfrac{1}{2}\varepsilon_0(E_{0x})^2 c. \tag{2.28}$$

The overall power scattered by the molecule is, by Equation 2.27,

$$\overline{W} = \frac{p_0^2 \omega^4}{12\pi\varepsilon_0 c^3},$$

where p_0 is the amplitude of the induced dipole moment, namely

$$p_0 = \varepsilon_0 \alpha E_{0x}. \tag{2.29}$$

It is convenient to associate with the scattering molecule an area, σ, called the (total) **scattering cross-section**, or just **cross-section**, such that the total scattered power, $\overline{W}$, from a molecule is equal to σ times the time-averaged incident power per unit area, $\overline{N}$. Then

$$\overline{W} = \sigma\overline{N}. \tag{2.30}$$

Although the actual scattering process is quite complicated, in simple terms the scattering cross-section acts like an area, σ, such that any light falling on it is removed by scattering from the forward beam.

● Combine Equations 2.28–2.30 to show that the cross-section for scattering at angular frequency ω is

$$\sigma(\omega) = \frac{\alpha^2 \omega^4}{6\pi c^4}. \tag{2.31}$$

○ Rearranging Equation 2.30, the cross-section is $\sigma = \overline{W}/\overline{N}$. Then substituting for $\overline{W}$, $\overline{N}$ and p_0, we obtain

$$\sigma = \frac{(\varepsilon_0 \alpha E_{0x})^2 \omega^4}{12\pi\varepsilon_0 c^3} \times \frac{2}{\varepsilon_0(E_{0x})^2 c} = \frac{\alpha^2 \omega^4}{6\pi c^4}.$$

Let us estimate the typical cross-section for a molecule in air. The dipole moment of an individual gas molecule has magnitude $p_0 = \varepsilon_0 \alpha E_{0x}$, so a gas in which the number of such molecules per unit volume is n will have a polarization of magnitude

$$P_0 = np_0 = n\varepsilon_0 \alpha E_{0x}.$$

But polarization and relative permittivity are related by

$$P_0 = (\varepsilon - 1)\varepsilon_0 E_{0x}.$$

Thus

$$n\alpha = \varepsilon - 1. \tag{2.32}$$

So, measurement of the relative permittivity at a given number density and frequency can give the polarizability, α, and, using Equation 2.31, a cross-section for scattering, averaged across the constituent particles. Air is made up of about 78% nitrogen (N_2) and 21% oxygen (O_2), with small, but sometimes important, amounts of argon, carbon dioxide, water vapour, dust, and trace gases.

At a temperature of 20 °C and one atmosphere pressure (about $1.0 \times 10^5 \, \mathrm{N \, m^{-2}}$), the relative permittivity of air at optical frequencies is measured to be 1.000 54. To estimate n, let us suppose that air behaves as a perfect gas of 'average air molecules', so that

$$P = nk_{\mathrm{B}}T, \tag{2.33}$$

where P is the pressure, n is the number density of molecules, T is the temperature in kelvin ($20\,°\mathrm{C} \simeq 293 \, \mathrm{K}$) and k_{B} is Boltzmann's constant ($1.38 \times 10^{-23} \, \mathrm{J \, K^{-1}}$). Using Equation 2.33 with Equation 2.32 gives

$$\alpha \simeq \frac{(\varepsilon - 1)}{n} = \frac{k_{\mathrm{B}}T}{P}(\varepsilon - 1).$$

Then since the relative permittivity for air is 1.000 54, $(\varepsilon - 1) \simeq 5.4 \times 10^{-4}$, and

$$\alpha_{\mathrm{air}} \simeq \frac{1.38 \times 10^{-23} \, \mathrm{J \, K^{-1}} \times 293 \, \mathrm{K} \times 5.4 \times 10^{-4}}{1.0 \times 10^5 \, \mathrm{N \, m^{-2}}} \simeq 2.2 \times 10^{-29} \, \mathrm{m^3}.$$

Exercise 2.6   Use the value for α_{air} calculated above to estimate the cross-section σ for air, at one atmosphere and 293 K, for green light with wavelength $\lambda = 520 \, \mathrm{nm}$. ■

From measurements of the diffusion of nitrogen molecules among other nitrogen molecules, the diameter of the molecules has been estimated and corresponds with a physical cross-section for molecule–molecule collisions of about $5 \times 10^{-19} \, \mathrm{m^2}$. Compared with this, the scattering cross-section for light is very small. This is fortunate for life on Earth, since sunlight must penetrate some tens of kilometres of the atmosphere to nurture life. However, over such distances there are numerous molecules that scatter the sunlight from its incident direction.

To quantify the extent to which light is scattered by the atmosphere, consider a slab of thickness δz in a rectangular column of air of cross-section A, which is illuminated from above, as shown in Figure 2.12. If the number density of molecules is n, then the total number of scattering targets in this slab is $nA\,\delta z$ (I am ignoring any variations of pressure and temperature in the column). Each scattering target presents a scattering area of σ, so the power scattered from the beam of light by the molecules in the thin slab is

$$\delta W = (nA\,\delta z) \times \sigma \overline{N(z)},$$

where $\overline{N(z)}$ is the magnitude of the time-average of the Poynting vector $\mathbf{N}(z)$ at the position of the slab. So the change $\delta \overline{N}$ in the magnitude of the Poynting vector as a result of the scattering in the slab is

$$\delta \overline{N} = -\delta W/A = -n\,\delta z\,\sigma \overline{N}.$$

To determine how the Poynting vector — the power per unit area — depends on the distance z travelled down the column, we need to integrate this expression.

Using a measured relative permittivity for air avoids having to make up a weighted average from reference data for pure gases.

Be careful: P is used here to indicate pressure, not polarization!

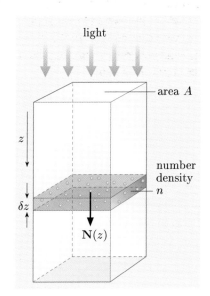

Figure 2.12   Molecules in a column of gas are 'seen' as scattering targets by incident radiation.

Thus

$$\int \frac{\mathrm{d}\overline{N}}{\overline{N}} = \int -n\sigma \, \mathrm{d}z,$$

and

$$\ln \overline{N} = -n\sigma z + \text{constant}.$$

If $\overline{N} = \overline{N_0}$ at $z = 0$, then this reduces to

$$\overline{N} = \overline{N_0} \exp(-n\sigma z) = \overline{N_0} \exp(-z/L_{\text{scat}}),$$

where

$$L_{\text{scat}} = \frac{1}{n\sigma} \qquad\qquad (2.34)$$

is known as the **scattering length**. Thus the radiated power decreases exponentially with distance travelled, and travelling a distance L_{scat} reduces the power by a factor of $e^{-1} = 0.37$.

At sea level, n is about 2.5×10^{25} m^{-3}. Using this value, and the estimate $\sigma \simeq 5 \times 10^{-31}$ m^2 from Exercise 2.6, gives a value for the scattering length, for green light ($\lambda = 520$ nm), as about 80 km. This is only a very rough estimate. For example, the number density of scatterers, n, varies with height, decreasing steadily to very low values at about 50 km above the surface. This reduces the average value of n and raises the estimate of L_{scat}.

Exercise 2.7   Estimate the scattering length for red light, with $\lambda = 650$ nm in a constant-density atmosphere with $n = 2.5 \times 10^{25}$ m^{-3}.   ∎

The spectrum of a beam of sunlight is modified by its passage through the atmosphere, with more of the blue components being removed by scattering from the forward direction than the red components. This is the reason why the sky looks blue during the daytime, for we then see a relatively large amount of the side-scattered bluer components. And the setting Sun in a clear sky appears red, for its forward beam has travelled over a long path close to the horizon and is heavily depleted of blue and green components, leaving only a weak red hue. Small amounts of dust, with dimensions smaller than the wavelength of light, contribute scattering targets that behave in much the same way as gas molecules, making the effect even more noticeable.

- ● The waxing and waning Moon, when visible in full daylight, is observed to be an incomplete sphere. What we readily call the region of shadow when viewed in a night-time sky, appears to be borderless blue sky in daylight (see Figure 2.13). Explain why it has this appearance.

- ○ The explanation is that blue light is preferentially scattered by the atmosphere that lies between the Moon and the observer. The bright part of the Moon's disk is reflecting sunlight through the blueness. The 'shadow' adds nothing to the blueness (nor does it takes anything from it), so the unlit part of the disk appears as blue as the surrounding sky.

Figure 2.13 Half-Moon seen in daytime. In the region of the half that is not illuminated by the Sun, the sky is as blue as elsewhere.

Figure 2.14 Early evening sky looking north: a polarizing filter shows that scattered sunlight from this direction is strongly polarized.

2.5.2 Polarization of sky light

If you examine the polarization of blue sky light from different regions of the sky using a piece of Polaroid or a lens from a pair of Polaroid sunglasses, you should find that sky light is partially polarized. The degree of polarization depends on the direction in which you look in relation to the direction of the Sun, with regions of the sky in directions at right angles to the direction of the incident sunlight showing the strongest degree of polarization. For example, in the early morning and late evening, the region that has a high degree of polarization is in a north–south arc (Figure 2.14), with regions to the east and west showing very little polarization.

It was discovered by Snyder and Pask in 1972 that bees make use of the polarization of scattered sunlight for navigational purposes. Unlike our eyes, those of a bee have a structure that has many individual segments, and many of the upward-looking segments are sensitive to polarization (Figure 2.15). In these segments, the molecules of the visual pigment rhodopsin are preferentially aligned in a particular direction and are maximally sensitive to light polarized parallel to this direction. In human eyes, the rhodopsin molecules are oriented randomly, and we are not sensitive to polarization.

Figure 2.15 Bees have segmented eyes (shown pink here) that are sensitive to polarization.

The fact that scattered radiation is generally polarized can be explained in terms of the $\sin\theta$-dependence of the amplitudes of the fields radiated by a Hertzian dipole. In Equation 2.20, the direction of polarization at any point is along the line defined by $\mathbf{e}_\theta$. We can use this fact to deduce the polarization of radiation produced by the dipoles induced in atoms and molecules in the upper atmosphere by the electric field of sunlight.

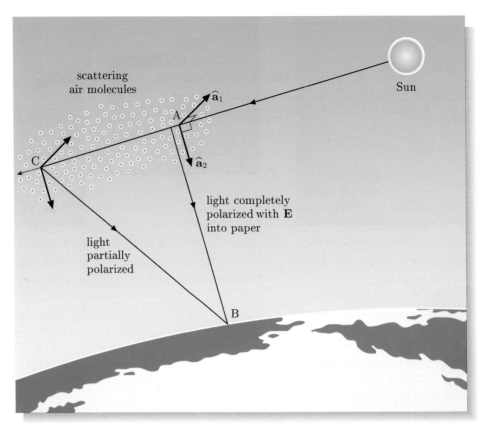

Figure 2.16   The polarization of sunlight scattered by molecules in the atmosphere.

Light from the Sun is unpolarized — it has no net polarization. However, any polarization can be resolved into components along two orthogonal directions that are both perpendicular to the propagation direction, and we shall resolve the instantaneous polarization of the sunlight into components in the two directions shown in Figure 2.16: the $\widehat{\mathbf{a}}_1$ direction is perpendicular to the plane containing the observer, the scattering molecules and the Sun (the plane of the diagram), and the $\widehat{\mathbf{a}}_2$ direction lies in the plane of the diagram. The dipoles induced in molecules by this sunlight can be resolved in the same way, into orthogonal dipole contributions along the $\widehat{\mathbf{a}}_1$ and $\widehat{\mathbf{a}}_2$ directions. An observer on the Earth at point B in Figure 2.16, looking at right angles to the incident rays of sunlight, will see nothing scattered from the dipole components in the $\widehat{\mathbf{a}}_2$ direction, because they do not radiate along their axes towards the observer due to the $\sin\theta$-dependence of the amplitude of the scattered radiation (see Equation 2.20 and Figure 2.11). Thus the observer sees light scattered only from the dipole components in the $\widehat{\mathbf{a}}_1$ direction, and this light will appear to be linearly polarized in that direction.

Looking at the sky in directions that are not perpendicular to the incident beam, such as along BC in Figure 2.16, the scattered light will appear only partially polarized. This is because the dipole components in the $\widehat{\mathbf{a}}_2$ direction at C will scatter light in the CB direction, and the polarization of this radiation will be perpendicular to the direction CB and in the plane of Figure 2.16.

Because light scattered from one molecule can be scattered again by other molecules, not all of the light scattered towards B by molecules at A comes from dipoles induced by light that was travelling directly away from the Sun. The observer at B will therefore receive a small proportion of light with polarization perpendicular to the $\hat{\mathbf{a}}_1$ direction. Such *multiple scattering* is part of the explanation of why the light from the sky is not completely polarized in directions at $90°$ to the line from the Sun to the observer.

2.5.3 Assumptions

We have made a particularly big assumption in our analysis of light scattering in the atmosphere. We used the cross-section for scattering from a *single* molecule to calculate the scattering from a distribution of many scatterers: we assumed that the total power scattered at some frequency is simply the power scattered by a single molecule multiplied by their total number. But Maxwell's equations are linear in the fields $\mathbf{E}$ and $\mathbf{B}$, and not in the intensity E^2 that appears in the expression for the radiated power. Although we may add fields that are solutions of the wave equation to obtain other valid solutions, strictly this addition does not extend to quantities that arise from products of fields. Because the spatial distribution of air molecules is essentially random and because air is not very dense, it turns out that we can deduce the power scattered from molecules in the atmosphere by adding separately the power scattered from individual molecules. Under these conditions, the electric fields scattered by different molecules do not, on average, interfere with each other: their scattered electric fields are said to be statistically incoherent.

Apart from mentioning multiple scattering briefly in Subsection 2.5.2, we have largely ignored the fact that light scattered from one molecule is to some extent re-scattered by other molecules. Because the scattering by air molecules is weak (i.e. they have quite a small cross-section), and because the density of air is not great, it is a good approximation to ignore multiple scattering. There are, however, many other situations where it is essential to include it. The calculation of the effects of multiple scattering in some materials can be very complicated, and is a topic of current research.

The assumption of *incoherence* is good here, but in Chapter 7 you will see that the cornea in the eye actually owes its transparency to a significant degree of scattering coherence.

Summary of Chapter 2

Section 2.1   Electric and magnetic fields that are associated with radiation from a point source must fall off in strength as r^{-1} in the absence of absorption, in order that energy is conserved as radiation spreads outwards.

Section 2.2   We can construct a magnetic field solution of Maxwell's equations for an oscillating current element (a Hertzian dipole) using the Biot–Savart field law to guide the dependence on ϕ, θ, current amplitude I_0 and dipole length δl; adding a term with r^{-1} scaling to the inherent r^{-2}-dependence of the Biot–Savart law to conform with the requirements of radiation fields; we must also retard the time ($t \to t - r/c$) to allow for propagation of information from the source to the observer.

Section 2.3   Maxwell's equations are used to calibrate and validate the predicted solution for the field from a Hertzian dipole. In this process, the $\mathbf{B}$ and $\mathbf{E}$ fields are confirmed as having terms with various radial-dependences.

Section 2.4   The terms with r^{-1}-dependences predominate when $r \gg \lambda$, and these terms form the radiation fields:

$$\mathbf{B}^{(\text{rad})} = \frac{\omega\eta}{c}\frac{\sin\theta}{r}\sin(kr - \omega t)\,\mathbf{e}_\phi,$$

$$\mathbf{E}^{(\text{rad})} = \omega\eta\,\frac{\sin\theta}{r}\sin(kr - \omega t)\,\mathbf{e}_\theta,$$

where $\eta = \mu_0 I_0\,\delta l/4\pi$.

The radiation fields satisfy a spherical wave equation. The fields correspond with electromagnetic waves that have a $\sin\theta$ angular-dependence, so that no power is radiated along the axis of the dipole and maximum power is radiated in the equatorial plane of the dipole. The total power radiated from an oscillating *current* dipole is

$$\overline{W} = \frac{\mu_0\omega^2 I_0^2(\delta l)^2}{12\pi c},$$

whereas in terms of an oscillating *charge*, the total radiated power is

$$\overline{W} = \frac{\mu_0 p_0^2\omega^4}{12\pi c} = \frac{p_0^2\omega^4}{12\pi\varepsilon_0 c^3}.$$

Section 2.5   The scattering of sunlight by the Earth's atmosphere can be understood in terms of radiation from dipoles induced in atoms and molecules by the electric field of electromagnetic radiation from the Sun. Owing to the ω^4 frequency-dependence of radiation scattered by an induced dipole, blue light is scattered much more effectively than red. This accounts for the blue appearance of clear skies. The $\sin\theta$-dependence of the amplitude of electromagnetic waves radiated from induced dipoles causes partial polarization of sky light, and this is strongest when viewed perpendicular to the incident sunlight.

Achievements from Chapter 2

After studying this chapter you should be able to do the following.

2.1   Explain the meanings of the newly defined (emboldened) terms and symbols, and use them appropriately.

2.2   State what is meant by a Hertzian dipole, and justify a predicted expression for the magnetic field produced by such a dipole.

2.3   Verify and calibrate solutions of Maxwell's equations for the electric and magnetic fields around a Hertzian dipole.

2.4   Explain what is meant by a spherical wave.

2.5   Calculate the power radiated into space by a Hertzian dipole.

2.6   Explain the direction of polarization of electromagnetic waves radiated by a Hertzian dipole.

2.7   Apply the Hertzian dipole model of light scattering to account for the intensity of light transmitted through the atmosphere, and for the blueness, redness and polarization of light from the sky under various conditions.

Chapter 3 Dielectrics: reflection and refraction

So far we have considered electromagnetic waves in empty space. The next thing to consider is what happens to these waves when they encounter dielectric materials. In this chapter and the next we shall use Maxwell's equations to derive various results that account for many optical phenomena that will be familiar to you from everyday observations. They apply equally well to electromagnetic radiation of longer wavelength. Central to the discussion will be the treatment of matter as a continuum, characterized by a permittivity and a permeability, with electric and magnetic effects averaged over millions of individual atoms. Such a model runs into difficulty as wavelengths approach the molecular scale (less than a few nm), so our findings cannot be applied to radiation with wavelengths that are much shorter than those of visible radiation.

Here are some observations to get us started. When I look at a pane of window glass, in addition to seeing through it to the other side I also see reflections of things on my side of the pane. The strength of the reflection increases the more obliquely I look at an area of the window pane. A slightly more sophisticated observation is that with Polaroid sunglasses, the intensity of the reflected image changes as I angle my head from side to side. Two even more sophisticated observations from the laboratories of my colleagues are as follows. For optical microscopy they use optical fibres to guide light to exactly where they want it on a specimen — in fact, I have come across surgeons guiding light to where they want it *within* a specimen (Figure 3.1). Windows set at curious angles are often to be seen on chambers whose gaseous contents are being probed by laser light (Figure 3.2). The goal of this chapter is to find explanations for all of these phenomena using Maxwell's equations.

Figure 3.1 (a) An optical microscope with illumination guided by fibre optics. (b) An endoscope, used in medicine for examinations of the digestive tract; fibre optics guide light to and from the area that is to be imaged. (c) An endoscope in use.

(a)

(b)

(c)

Figure 3.2 A pair of plane-parallel disc electrodes sealed in a quartz chamber. Angled windows are used for optimal light transmission.

3.1 Waves in transparent dielectrics

Electromagnetic radiation does not propagate at the same speed in all media: the refraction of light by water and glass, for example, results from the fact that light travels more slowly in these materials than in a vacuum. We shall soon show how the speed of light is related to the relative permittivity of a material, which we can use to 'explain' the phenomena of reflection and refraction. In this chapter we shall mainly study the propagation of electromagnetic waves in linear, isotropic, homogeneous (LIH) media that are also insulating (but polarizable) and transparent. There are various materials that come close to this ideal dielectric. For instance, glass and water are examples of LIH dielectric media that are transparent to light. The optical properties of isotropic materials, such as these, do not depend on direction. On the other hand, substances like Iceland spar and quartz, which are also transparent dielectrics, are not isotropic and exhibit a directional-dependence of their optical properties called *birefringence*.

Partially transparent dielectrics are discussed in Chapter 4, and conducting media in Chapter 5.

This is pronounced '*by-re-fringe-ence*'.

The first thing to get to grips with is how propagation of electromagnetic waves in LIH dielectric media differs from that in free space. What we need to know is how to write expressions for (i) the speed of propagation in a dielectric, (ii) the electric and magnetic components of an electromagnetic wave in a dielectric, and (iii) the power carried by a wave through a dielectric.

To generalize the free space results found in Chapter 1 to LIH media, we need to examine the appropriate forms of Maxwell's equations.

● Where does the presence of a dielectric medium enter into a discussion of electromagnetic fields?

○ The presence of a dielectric medium is embedded in the electric displacement, $\mathbf{D}$. For an LIH material, $\mathbf{D}$ is related to the electric field $\mathbf{E}$ by the relationship $\mathbf{D} = \varepsilon\varepsilon_0\mathbf{E}$, where the relative permittivity ε characterizes the dielectric properties of the medium.

For a bulk LIH medium, ε is independent of field strength, direction and position. In this chapter, we shall also assume that ε does not depend on frequency. Under these circumstances, it is reasonable to refer to ε as the dielectric *constant*, but I shall always use the term relative permittivity.

The magnetic properties of a medium are characterized by the relative permeability, μ, through $\mathbf{B} = \mu\mu_0\mathbf{H}$. Most dielectrics of interest are diamagnetic or paramagnetic and so have $\mu \simeq 1$; throughout this book we shall therefore assume $\mu = 1$.

● In addition to the fields $\mathbf{D}$, $\mathbf{B}$, $\mathbf{E}$ and $\mathbf{H}$, Maxwell's equations also include free charge and free current. Suggest what should be done about these terms in considering electromagnetic waves in bulk dielectric media.

○ The free charge density and free current density can normally both be set to zero in the bulk of a dielectric material. (Free charge could be buried in the bulk or placed on the surface of a dielectric, but there is enough to discover here without that added complication.)

If there is no free charge and no free current, then $\rho_f = 0$ and $\mathbf{J}_f = \underline{0}$, and the equations for LIH dielectric media resemble those used for free space in Chapter 1, subject to the simple replacement of ε_0 in the free space equations by $\varepsilon\varepsilon_0$. Since the changes involve simple multiplicative constants, this leads to the following simple rule.

We should also replace μ_0 by $\mu\mu_0$, but we are assuming $\mu = 1$.

> **The free space $\rightarrow$ dielectric transformation rule (version 1)**
>
> To describe electromagnetic wave propagation in a transparent LIH medium, take the results applying to free space propagation and replace ε_0 by $\varepsilon\varepsilon_0$ (and do not overlook the fact that $c = 1/\sqrt{\varepsilon_0\mu_0}$).

So, what do we find by applying this rule? Consider first the speed of plane waves. In free space they propagate with speed $c = 1/\sqrt{\varepsilon_0\mu_0}$.

● What will be the phase speed of electromagnetic waves in a transparent LIH dielectric with $\varepsilon = 2.25$ and $\mu = 1$?

○ Inside a dielectric medium, the phase speed of electromagnetic waves, v, is found by applying the free space $\rightarrow$ dielectric transformation rule to the free space speed, so

$$v = 1/\sqrt{\varepsilon\varepsilon_0\mu_0} = c/\sqrt{\varepsilon}.$$

For the given data (which correspond with typical values for ordinary glass),

$$v = c/\sqrt{\varepsilon} = 3.00 \times 10^8 \,\mathrm{m\,s^{-1}}/\sqrt{2.25} = 2.00 \times 10^8 \,\mathrm{m\,s^{-1}}.$$

An important parameter characterizing a dielectric is its **index of refraction**, or **refractive index**, n. This is defined by

$$n = c/v = \sqrt{\varepsilon} \quad \text{(when } \mu = 1\text{).} \tag{3.1}$$

To transcribe the treatment of waves in free space to waves in our model medium, it is convenient to treat the phase speed explicitly in the basic rule I introduced earlier, as follows.

> **The free space $\rightarrow$ dielectric transformation rule (version 2)**
>
> To describe electromagnetic wave propagation in a transparent LIH medium in which $\mu = 1$, take the results applying to free space propagation and replace ε_0 by $\varepsilon\varepsilon_0$, and, since $c = 1/\sqrt{\varepsilon_0\mu_0}$, replace c by c/n.

When electromagnetic waves travel across free space and arrive at the boundary of a dielectric, they do so in a succession of peaks and troughs of an orthogonal pair of electric and magnetic fields. These waves stimulate the boundary at the frequency of the wave, $f = \omega/2\pi$. This stimulation is responsible for the onward transmission of waves into the material, which therefore also takes place at frequency f. In free space the waves have a wavelength $\lambda_0 = c/f$, but in the dielectric the wavelength will be $\lambda = c/nf$.

Exercise 3.1 Complete Table 3.1 overleaf by relating expressions for a dielectric to those for free space in terms of the refractive index, n. ■

Table 3.1   Wave parameters in free space (subscript '0') and in dielectrics.

	Free space	Dielectric
frequency	$\omega/2\pi$	$\omega/2\pi$
phase speed	c	$v = c/\sqrt{\varepsilon} = c/n$
wavenumber	$k_0 = \omega/c$	$k = \omega/v = n\omega/c$
wavelength	$\lambda_0 = 2\pi/k_0$	$\lambda = 2\pi/k = \lambda_0/n$

Let us next see what happens to the expressions for the electric and magnetic fields of a linearly polarized plane wave.

Essential skill

Adapting expressions for electromagnetic waves in free space to LIH dielectrics

Worked Example 3.1

The electric field for a linearly polarized plane wave *in free space*, polarized in the x-direction, and travelling in the positive z-direction, is the real part of

$$\mathbf{E}(z,t) = E_0 \exp[\mathrm{i}(k_0 z - \omega t)]\,\mathbf{e}_x, \quad \text{where } k_0 = \omega/c.$$

Modify this so that it represents a wave in a medium with index of refraction n, and write down an expression for the associated magnetic field, $\mathbf{B}$.

Solution

To obtain the field in a dielectric, replace k_0 by k and note that $k = n\omega/c$. The electric field is therefore the real part of

$$\mathbf{E}(z,t) = E_0 \exp[\mathrm{i}(kz - \omega t)]\,\mathbf{e}_x, \quad \text{where now } k = n\omega/c. \tag{3.2}$$

In Chapter 1 the electric and magnetic fields of waves in free space were shown to be orthogonal, to have a vector product in the direction of propagation, and to have amplitudes related by $E_0 = cB_0$. The only change required by the free space $\rightarrow$ dielectric transformation rule is the replacement of c by $v = c/n$. Thus, for a plane wave travelling in the z-direction, the magnetic field is given by the real part of

$$\mathbf{B}(z,t) = \frac{n}{c} E_0 \exp[\mathrm{i}(kz - \omega t)]\,\mathbf{e}_y, \quad \text{where again } k = n\omega/c. \tag{3.3}$$

Another thing to consider about electromagnetic wave propagation through the bulk of a dielectric medium is what happens to the energy flow described by the Poynting vector.

Essential skill

Adapting expressions for electromagnetic waves in free space to LIH dielectrics

Worked Example 3.2

Calculate the time-averaged Poynting vector associated with a linearly polarized plane wave travelling in an LIH dielectric medium, polarized in the x-direction, and travelling in the *negative* z-direction.

Solution

To obtain the electric field of a wave propagating in the $-z$-direction, we simply change one of the signs in the argument of the exponential term in

Equation 3.2. The electric field is then the real part of

$$\mathbf{E}(z,t) = E_0 \exp[\mathrm{i}(-kz - \omega t)]\,\mathbf{e}_x, \quad \text{where } k = n\omega/c,$$

or the real part of a similar expression that involves the exponential term $\exp[\mathrm{i}(kz + \omega t)]$. The associated magnetic field follows from Equation 3.3 in the same way. But since $\mathbf{E} \times \mathbf{B}$ must now point along the $-z$-direction, the magnetic field of the wave associated with an electric field polarized along $\mathbf{e}_x$ must be oriented along $-\mathbf{e}_y$, as illustrated in Figure 3.3. It is the real part of

$$\mathbf{B}(z,t) = \frac{n}{c} E_0 \exp[\mathrm{i}(-kz - \omega t)]\,(-\mathbf{e}_y), \quad \text{where } k = n\omega/c.$$

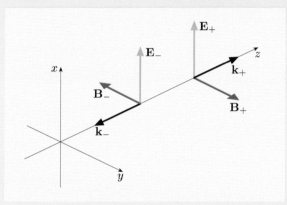

Figure 3.3 Comparison of the orientations of the electric and magnetic fields for waves propagating in the positive and negative z-directions with propagation vectors $\mathbf{k}_+$ and $\mathbf{k}_-$, respectively. Note that in each case, $\mathbf{E} \times \mathbf{B}$ is in the direction of the propagation vector.

The Poynting vector is

$$\mathbf{N} = \mathbf{E}_{\mathrm{phys}} \times \mathbf{H}_{\mathrm{phys}} = \mathbf{E}_{\mathrm{phys}} \times \mathbf{B}_{\mathrm{phys}}/\mu\mu_0,$$

but remember, we are assuming $\mu = 1$. It is especially important to use the physical fields when working with the Poynting vector, so we must explicitly take the real parts of the expressions for the fields before forming the vector product:

$$\mathbf{N}(z,t) = \frac{1}{\mu_0}\mathrm{Re}\{E_0 \exp[\mathrm{i}(-kz - \omega t)]\}\mathrm{Re}\left\{\frac{n}{c} E_0 \exp[\mathrm{i}(-kz - \omega t)]\right\}$$
$$\times (\mathbf{e}_x \times (-\mathbf{e}_y))$$
$$= -\frac{n}{c}\frac{E_0^2}{\mu_0}\cos^2(-kz - \omega t)\,(\mathbf{e}_x \times \mathbf{e}_y).$$

Because $c = 1/\sqrt{\varepsilon_0\mu_0}$, or $\mu_0 = 1/(\varepsilon_0 c^2)$, this can be simplified to

$$\mathbf{N}(z,t) = -nc\varepsilon_0 E_0^2 \cos^2(-kz - \omega t)\,\mathbf{e}_z.$$

The leading minus sign arises because the wave propagates in the $-z$-direction. The time-average of the Poynting vector — which is independent of z — is

$$\overline{\mathbf{N}} = -\tfrac{1}{2}n\varepsilon_0 E_0^2 c\,\mathbf{e}_z.$$

This result for the Poynting vector in a dielectric medium (LIH and $\mu = 1$) can be made more general as follows. Since $\varepsilon/n^2 = 1$, we can multiply by this and rearrange. The specified direction of propagation, $-\mathbf{e}_z$, can be replaced by $\widehat{\mathbf{k}}$, and we obtain a general expression for the Poynting vector:

$$\overline{\mathbf{N}} = \tfrac{1}{2}\varepsilon\varepsilon_0 E_0^2 \frac{c}{n}\,\widehat{\mathbf{k}}. \tag{3.4}$$

Exercise 3.2   Show that the time-averaged Poynting vector for electromagnetic waves travelling in an LIH dielectric in the negative z-direction can be simply obtained from the free space result given in Chapter 1,

$$\overline{\mathbf{N}} = \tfrac{1}{2}\varepsilon_0 E_0^2 c\,\widehat{\mathbf{k}}, \tag{Eqn 1.34}$$

using the second version of the free space $\rightarrow$ dielectric transformation rule.   ■

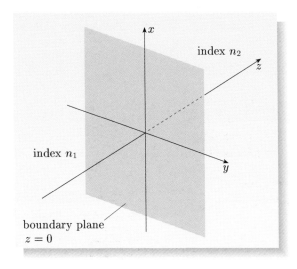

Figure 3.4   The general geometry that we shall use to study the interaction of plane electromagnetic waves with a plane boundary between dielectric materials with refractive indices n_1 and n_2.

3.2   Dielectric boundary conditions

The propagation of electromagnetic waves in an infinite LIH dielectric medium has thus far proved to be a simple extension of free space propagation. Next we are going to analyse a common physical situation in which electromagnetic waves pass from one such medium to another: for example, from glass to air, or from air to water, or from water to glass.

Figure 3.4 shows the general geometry that we shall be considering. The plane $z = 0$ locates an interface that demarcates two different dielectrics. When a plane electromagnetic wave encounters such a boundary, some energy is reflected and some is transmitted through to propagate in the second medium. We shall show this from basic principles in the next two sections, but first we need to be sure how to match electromagnetic waves at a plane boundary.

The appropriate *boundary conditions* follow directly from Maxwell's equations. We are assuming that there are no free charges and currents present within either bulk dielectric, or at their common boundary. There are, of course, *bound* charges that move and polarize under the action of the imposed fields, but this motion is accounted for by the value of ε in each medium.

You have seen the basic argument before, in Book 2, Sections 2.5 and 3.5, at least for steady electric and magnetic fields. The difference here is that the fields are time-dependent, but as you will see, the time-dependence makes no difference to the boundary conditions.

First let us look at the $\mathbf{D}$ and $\mathbf{B}$ fields. In the absence of free charges, the integral versions of Gauss's law and the no-monopole equation are

$$\int_S \mathbf{D} \cdot d\mathbf{S} = 0 \quad \text{and} \quad \int_S \mathbf{B} \cdot d\mathbf{S} = 0.$$

That is, the net flux of $\mathbf{D}(\mathbf{r}, t)$, or $\mathbf{B}(\mathbf{r}, t)$, through any *closed* surface S, is zero. In fact, without any free charge to worry about, time-dependence adds nothing here as the equations must be valid at every instant of time, so it is just like the static case. To deduce the boundary conditions, choose for S a small cylinder of vanishing length which just straddles the interface, with one end-face on each side (Figure 3.5). Since the length of the cylinder is vanishingly small, the sides contribute nothing to the surface integral of $\mathbf{D}$ (or $\mathbf{B}$), leaving only contributions from the ends. The flux through each end-face is the product of its area times the component of $\mathbf{D}$ (or $\mathbf{B}$) perpendicular to it. So we can say that at every point on the dielectric interface, the perpendicular (or 'normal') components of $\mathbf{D}$ and $\mathbf{B}$ must be continuous across it.

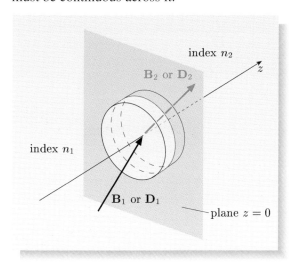

Figure 3.5 A small cylinder of infinitesimal length straddles the boundary between two insulating dielectrics, within which the magnetic fields are $\mathbf{B}_1$ and $\mathbf{B}_2$ or the electric displacements are $\mathbf{D}_1$ and $\mathbf{D}_2$.

Next, let us look at the conditions on $\mathbf{E}(\mathbf{r}, t)$ and $\mathbf{H}(\mathbf{r}, t)$ at the boundary. In the absence of free currents, the integral versions of Faraday's law and the Ampère–Maxwell law are

$$\oint_C \mathbf{E} \cdot \mathrm{d}\mathbf{l} = -\frac{\mathrm{d}}{\mathrm{d}t} \int_S \mathbf{B} \cdot \mathrm{d}\mathbf{S} \quad \text{and} \quad \oint_C \mathbf{H} \cdot \mathrm{d}\mathbf{l} = \frac{\mathrm{d}}{\mathrm{d}t} \int_S \mathbf{D} \cdot \mathrm{d}\mathbf{S},$$

where C is any closed path and S is any open surface bounded by that path. In particular, let S be a small rectangle of infinitesimal width straddling the interface, and let C be its perimeter (Figure 3.6). Then, as the width is made vanishingly small, only the long sides contribute to the path integrals. Also, the area integrals on the right-hand sides of these equations go to zero because the enclosed area goes to zero — the time derivatives therefore make no contribution, so once again the situation is equivalent to the static case. Since the longer sides of the rectangles run parallel to but straddle the interface, the parallel (or 'tangential') components of $\mathbf{E}$ and $\mathbf{H}$ must be continuous across the boundary at every point on it.

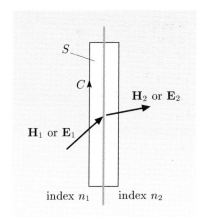

Figure 3.6 The small rectangle has infinitesimal width and straddles the boundary between two dielectrics, within which the magnetic intensities are $\mathbf{H}_1$ and $\mathbf{H}_2$, or the electric fields are $\mathbf{E}_1$ and $\mathbf{E}_2$.

Boundary conditions for a dielectric interface

For electromagnetic waves crossing a dielectric boundary, the perpendicular components of $\mathbf{D}$ and $\mathbf{B}$ and the parallel components of $\mathbf{E}$ and $\mathbf{H}$ are continuous.

We are now ready to apply these boundary conditions to the fields at a boundary as a plane electromagnetic wave crosses it. The simple case of normal incidence will be considered first. Then we shall go on to the general case of oblique incidence.

3.3 Normal incidence

3.3.1 The incident, reflected and transmitted waves

Consider a linearly polarized plane wave of angular frequency ω. The wave is directed along the z-axis, from dielectric 1 (refractive index n_1), onto an interface beyond which is dielectric 2 (refractive index n_2). The interface lies in the plane $z = 0$ and so the wave strikes the interface at right angles — see Figure 3.7. This situation is referred to as 'normal incidence', and the angle of incidence, which is measured with respect to the normal to the interface, is zero. Choosing the x-axis to be the polarization direction, the electric and magnetic fields of the incident radiation can be described as being the real parts of

Equations in this section must be considered in conjunction with Figure 3.7.

$$\mathbf{E}_i = E_{i0} \exp[i(k_1 z - \omega t)] \, \mathbf{e}_x, \tag{3.5}$$

$$\mathbf{B}_i = \frac{n_1}{c} E_{i0} \exp[i(k_1 z - \omega t)] \, \mathbf{e}_y, \tag{3.6}$$

Subscript 'i' denotes 'incident' and should not be confused with $i = \sqrt{-1}$ in the argument of the exponential.

where the wavenumber of the incident wave is $k_1 = n_1 \omega / c$. The amplitude E_{i0} is a constant whose magnitude defines the strength of the incident wave. E_{i0} is real and positive. In our analysis, we shall accept negative or complex values for the equivalent amplitudes of reflected and transmitted waves, as these would represent fixed differences of phase compared with the incident wave. For example, the simple case of a negative, real amplitude for the reflected wave corresponds to a difference of phase equivalent to π, or $180°$, compared to the incident wave.

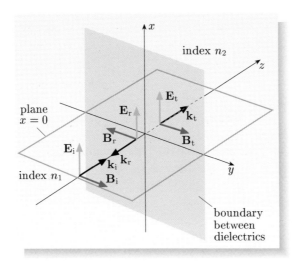

Figure 3.7 Directions of electric and magnetic fields for normally-incident, reflected and transmitted electromagnetic waves at a dielectric boundary.

The challenge is to obtain expressions for the electric and magnetic fields of the waves that are reflected and/or transmitted as a consequence of the abrupt change in dielectric properties at the interface. Their forms must of course be consistent with Maxwell's equations. We have already argued in Section 3.1 that the reflected or transmitted waves can reasonably be expected to have the same angular frequency as the incident wave. Let us set out assuming that these waves are also plane waves with the same polarization, $\mathbf{e}_x$, as the incident wave. (If we could not find a consistent solution, then we would have to revisit this assumption.)

The reflected wave moves away from the interface in the $-z$-direction, travelling in medium 1, and is described by the real parts of

$$\mathbf{E}_r = E_{r0} \exp[i(-k_1 z - \omega t)] \, \mathbf{e}_x, \tag{3.7}$$

$$\mathbf{B}_r = -\frac{n_1}{c} E_{r0} \exp[i(-k_1 z - \omega t)] \, \mathbf{e}_y. \tag{3.8}$$

Subscript 'r' denotes 'reflected'.

● Why is there a minus sign in front of the expression for $\mathbf{B}_r$?

○ This wave carries energy away from the boundary in the $-z$-direction, so the Poynting vector, $\mathbf{E}_{phys} \times \mathbf{B}_{phys}/\mu_0$, must point along $-\mathbf{e}_z$. This is consistent with what was shown in Chapter 1:

$$\mathbf{B} = \frac{1}{c} \widehat{\mathbf{k}} \times \mathbf{E}.$$

The transmitted wave moves away from the interface in the $+z$-direction, travelling in medium 2. It can be described by the real parts of

$$\mathbf{E}_t = E_{t0} \exp[i(k_2 z - \omega t)] \, \mathbf{e}_x, \tag{3.9}$$

$$\mathbf{B}_t = \frac{n_2}{c} E_{t0} \exp[i(k_2 z - \omega t)] \, \mathbf{e}_y. \tag{3.10}$$

Subscript 't' denotes 'transmitted'.

3.3.2 Applying the boundary conditions

The pairs of incident, reflected and transmitted waves must obey Maxwell's equations in their respective media. They must also satisfy the boundary conditions at $z = 0$. Since the waves strike the interface at normal incidence, they are all polarized in a direction parallel to the surface $z = 0$, so that all the components of $\mathbf{D}$, and of $\mathbf{B}$, perpendicular to the interface are automatically zero. The necessary continuity of these components is assured, but this is not particularly helpful in constraining the solution further.

However, continuity of the components of $\mathbf{H}$ and $\mathbf{E}$ parallel to the plane $z = 0$ must also hold. For $z < 0$, the net electric field is the sum of two solutions of Maxwell's equations, $\mathbf{E}_i(z, t) + \mathbf{E}_r(z, t)$. For $z > 0$, the electric field is $\mathbf{E}_t(z, t)$. In the present simple geometry, all these vector fields are actually parallel to the interface, so continuity requires that, for all times, $\mathbf{E}_i(0, t) + \mathbf{E}_r(0, t) = \mathbf{E}_t(0, t)$, or

$$E_{i0} \exp[i(-\omega t)] + E_{r0} \exp[i(-\omega t)] = E_{t0} \exp[i(-\omega t)]. \tag{3.11}$$

This justifies the assertion that incident, reflected and transmitted waves oscillate at the same frequency, as otherwise there would be no oscillatory solution of this equation that is valid at all times. So the boundary conditions require

$$E_{i0} + E_{r0} = E_{t0}. \tag{3.12}$$

Similarly, matching the parallel components of $\mathbf{H}$ at the boundary gives

$$E_{i0} - E_{r0} = \frac{n_2}{n_1} E_{t0}. \tag{3.13}$$

Exercise 3.3 Derive Equation 3.13. Remember that $\mathbf{H} = \mathbf{B}/\mu_0$ for a medium with relative permeability $\mu = 1$. ∎

Equations 3.12 and 3.13 can be combined to give two characteristic ratios. The **amplitude transmission ratio** is the ratio of the amplitudes of the transmitted and incident fields, and the **amplitude reflection ratio** is the ratio of the amplitudes of the reflected and incident fields:

$$\frac{E_{t0}}{E_{i0}} = \frac{2n_1}{n_1 + n_2} \quad \text{and} \quad \frac{E_{r0}}{E_{i0}} = \frac{n_1 - n_2}{n_1 + n_2}. \tag{3.14}$$

● In Equations 3.14, if $n_1 < n_2$, then $E_{r0}/E_{i0} < 0$. What does this imply?

○ $E_{r0}/E_{i0} < 0$ implies that for electromagnetic waves incident on a boundary where the refractive index increases, the reflected waves undergo a phase change of π, since $\exp(i\pi) = \cos\pi + i\sin\pi = -1$. This negative sign means that when $\mathbf{E}_i$ is in the $+x$-direction at the boundary, $\mathbf{E}_r$ is in the $-x$-direction.

So if $n_1 < n_2$, for example when light travels from air into glass, then the incident and reflected electric fields at the boundary are in opposite directions, so the electric field vector for the reflected wave would be in the opposite direction to that shown in Figure 3.7. The magnetic field vector for the reflected wave would also be reversed.

Exercise 3.4   Show that Equations 3.12 and 3.13 can be combined to give Equations 3.14.   ■

Thus, given E_{i0}, we now know the amplitudes of both the transmitted and reflected waves, and the problem is effectively solved.

Two quantities of physical interest are the **transmittance** T and the **reflectance** R, which are defined respectively as the proportions of power transmitted and reflected at the interface. To obtain expressions for these quantities, we begin with the general form of the time-averaged Poynting vector,

$$\overline{\mathbf{N}} = \tfrac{1}{2}\varepsilon\varepsilon_0 E_0^2 \frac{c}{n} \,\widehat{\mathbf{k}}. \tag{Eqn 3.4}$$

Remember that for the incident and transmitted waves $\widehat{\mathbf{k}}_i = \widehat{\mathbf{k}}_t = \mathbf{e}_z$, and for the reflected waves $\widehat{\mathbf{k}}_r = -\mathbf{e}_z$. Then, using the fact that $\varepsilon = n^2$, the transmittance and reflectance are

$$T = \frac{|\overline{\mathbf{N}}_t|}{|\overline{\mathbf{N}}_i|} = \frac{n_2 E_{t0}^2}{n_1 E_{i0}^2} \quad \text{and} \quad R = \frac{|\overline{\mathbf{N}}_r|}{|\overline{\mathbf{N}}_i|} = \frac{n_1 E_{r0}^2}{n_1 E_{i0}^2}. \tag{3.15}$$

Using the results in Equations 3.14 to eliminate the field amplitudes, we obtain expressions for the transmittance and reflectance in terms of the refractive indices of the two materials.

Transmittance and reflectance at normal incidence

$$T = \frac{4n_1 n_2}{(n_1 + n_2)^2}, \tag{3.16}$$

$$R = \frac{(n_1 - n_2)^2}{(n_1 + n_2)^2}. \tag{3.17}$$

Note that since energy is conserved, the incident power must equal the sum of the reflected power and the transmitted power, so

$$R + T = 1. \tag{3.18}$$

Exercise 3.5 Show that energy is conserved when a linearly polarized plane wave crosses a boundary between dielectrics at normal incidence.

Exercise 3.6 The refractive index of glass for light is about 1.5, and that of air is very nearly unity. Estimate, for normal incidence, the fraction of light energy reflected from an air–glass interface. Does this percentage depend from which side of the interface the light is incident? ∎

3.4 Oblique incidence

We now consider reflection and transmission of linearly polarized, monochromatic, plane electromagnetic waves that are *obliquely* incident upon a dielectric boundary. Figure 3.8 shows the path of a ray (that is, a line drawn perpendicular to the wavefronts of a plane wave), incident from a dielectric medium with index n_1, onto a plane boundary at $z = 0$, beyond which lies a second dielectric with index n_2. The incident wave moves in the direction given by the propagation vector $\mathbf{k}_i$, which lies at an angle θ_i to the normal to the boundary.

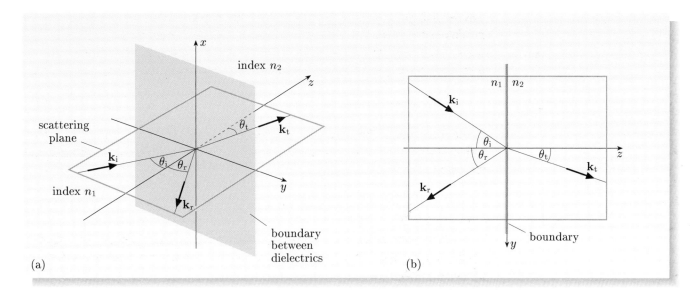

(a)   (b)

There is a reflected wave characterized by propagation vector $\mathbf{k}_r$ at angle θ_r to the normal to the boundary, and a transmitted wave with propagation vector $\mathbf{k}_t$ at angle θ_t to the normal. You should know from everyday experience that the direction of the transmitted wave is deviated by the boundary, that is, the incident wave is 'refracted'. The task here is first to determine the degree of refraction, and then, as for normal incidence, to find the amplitude transmission and reflection ratios and the transmittance and reflectance. Once again, it is the boundary conditions that determine what happens.

Figure 3.8 The transmission and reflection of a plane wave obliquely incident on an abrupt boundary: (a) 3D view; (b) the $x = 0$ (scattering) plane.

3.4.1   The geometry of reflection and refraction

The first step is to consider the general form of the expressions for incident, reflected and transmitted waves. We need to generalize Equations 3.5–3.10 that describe such waves at normal incidence to the surface. As we argued for the case of normal incidence, we shall assume that all three sets of plane waves have the same angular frequency, ω. Also, let us assume that all three waves propagate in the same plane — the $x = 0$ plane in Figure 3.8. If these assumptions lead to consistent solutions of Maxwell's equations when we apply all four boundary conditions, then they can be considered satisfactory. As a further check, we should make sure that the results are also consistent with experimental observations.

- Suggest why it is reasonable to assume that all three waves propagate in the same plane in LIH dielectric media.

○ The isotropic and homogeneous nature of LIH media would not favour any particular plane. The only factors that can impose a specific plane in which the reflected and transmitted waves might travel are a ray of the incoming wave and the normal to the boundary, which together define the plane of incidence — the $x = 0$ plane in Figure 3.8. So the normal to the boundary and the paths of the incident, reflected and transmitted rays are coplanar. This is consistent with the first law of reflection from geometric optics, which is based on observation and which states that the incident ray, the reflected ray and the normal lie in the same plane.

The plane in which $\mathbf{k}_i$, $\mathbf{k}_r$ and $\mathbf{k}_t$ all lie is generally called the **scattering plane**. Also shown in Figure 3.8 are the angles θ_i, θ_r and θ_t that the three propagation vectors make with a direction normal to the surface.

For any travelling plane wave, the fields **D**, **B**, **H** and **E** each have the general form

$$\mathbf{V}(\mathbf{r}, t) = \mathbf{V}_0 \exp[i(\mathbf{k} \cdot \mathbf{r} - \omega t)],$$

where **V** stands for any one of the vector fields **D**, **B**, **H**, or **E**; the vector $\mathbf{V}_0$ is constant, and **k** here represents any one of the incident, reflected or transmitted propagation vectors. So when we match the four boundary conditions *at the interface $z = 0$* — for example, matching the components of the electric field parallel to the boundary — we shall always obtain equations of the form

$$E_{i0\parallel} \exp[i(\mathbf{k}_i \cdot \mathbf{r} - \omega t)] + E_{r0\parallel} \exp[i(\;\mathbf{k}_r \cdot \mathbf{r} - \omega t)]$$
$$= E_{t0\parallel} \exp[i(\mathbf{k}_t \cdot \mathbf{r} - \omega t)]. \tag{3.19}$$

This is the generalization of Equation 3.11, which applies to the special case of incidence normal to the boundary. It is important to realize that this equation must hold true for all times and for all points on the plane $z = 0$. Note that this was anticipated when we chose the same frequency for all waves, as this allows us to cancel the time-dependence from both sides of Equation 3.19. But, because $\mathbf{k}_i$, $\mathbf{k}_r$ and $\mathbf{k}_t$ are *different*, the only way we can ensure that the position-dependence also cancels at *every* point on the boundary is to require that, in the plane $z = 0$,

$$\mathbf{k}_i \cdot \mathbf{r} = \mathbf{k}_r \cdot \mathbf{r} = \mathbf{k}_t \cdot \mathbf{r}, \tag{3.20}$$

for then the **r**-dependence will also cancel in Equation 3.19.

We have assumed that all three propagation vectors lie in the same plane, the scattering plane. For the choice of axes in Figure 3.8, therefore, each $\mathbf{k}$ has no x-component. On the boundary itself, $z = 0$. So (with $k_{\mathrm{i}x} = 0$ and $z = 0$) we have

$$
\begin{aligned}
\mathbf{k}_{\mathrm{i}} \cdot \mathbf{r} &= k_{\mathrm{i}x}x + k_{\mathrm{i}y}y + k_{\mathrm{i}z}z \\
&= k_{\mathrm{i}y}y \\
&= (k_{\mathrm{i}} \sin \theta_{\mathrm{i}})y \\
&= n_1 \frac{\omega}{c} y \sin \theta_{\mathrm{i}},
\end{aligned}
\tag{3.21}
$$

where in the last step, the magnitude of the propagation vector for the incident wave has been expressed in terms of the refractive index of the medium in which it travels. Similar expressions hold for $\mathbf{k}_{\mathrm{r}} \cdot \mathbf{r}$ and $\mathbf{k}_{\mathrm{t}} \cdot \mathbf{r}$, leading to

$$
n_1 \sin \theta_{\mathrm{i}} = n_1 \sin \theta_{\mathrm{r}} = n_2 \sin \theta_{\mathrm{t}}.
$$

From these follow two results that are certainly consistent with observations made in geometric optics experiments.

The second law of reflection

$$
\theta_{\mathrm{i}} = \theta_{\mathrm{r}} \quad \text{(angle of incidence equals angle of reflection)}.
\tag{3.22}
$$

Snell's law of refraction

$$
n_1 \sin \theta_{\mathrm{i}} = n_2 \sin \theta_{\mathrm{t}}.
\tag{3.23}
$$

3.4.2 Transmission and reflection: the Fresnel equations

With Equations 3.22 and 3.23 we have the basic equations of geometric optics. They determine many of the properties of mirrors and lenses, for example — obtaining them purely from consideration of Maxwell's equations is quite a triumph. The next task is to derive the equations for oblique incidence that describe amplitude transmission and reflection ratios, and the transmittance and reflectance.

Let us suppose that a wave is obliquely incident on a boundary between a dielectric medium with refractive index $n_1 = \sqrt{\varepsilon_1}$ and a second dielectric with refractive index $n_2 = \sqrt{\varepsilon_2}$.

At normal incidence, the polarization vector always lies parallel to the plane of the boundary. For oblique incidence, this is not necessarily the case and the angle between the polarization vector and the boundary plane is something we shall have to consider. Fortunately, because any polarization can be resolved into the sum of two orthogonal polarizations, we need solutions only for two 'special' cases and from these we can construct any particular solution by means of a linear combination. It is convenient to choose for these two special cases polarization in the scattering plane and polarization normal to the scattering plane. We shall treat each in turn.

Polarization in the scattering plane

To find the reflected and transmitted fields, we utilize the boundary conditions in the plane $z = 0$. The geometry for the case of polarization in the scattering plane is shown in Figure 3.9. Two boundary conditions should be sufficient to determine the relative amplitudes of reflected and transmitted radiation. We shall use the continuity requirements for the parallel component of $\mathbf{E}$ and the perpendicular component of $\mathbf{D}$. The other two conditions are, in a sense, redundant because we have already related the electric and magnetic fields through Maxwell's equations.

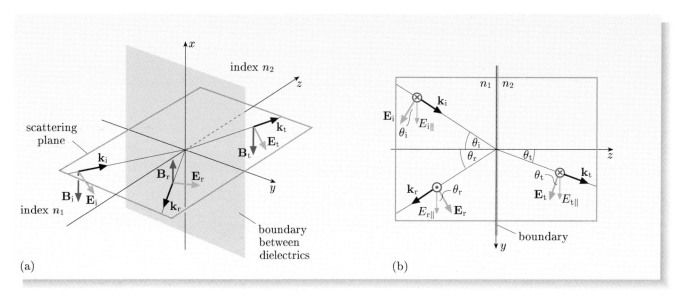

(a)   (b)

Figure 3.9   The electric field lies *in* the scattering plane: (a) 3D view; (b) the $x = 0$ (scattering) plane. This figure defines directions that are used in setting up the equations for the boundary conditions.

Figure 3.9b shows how to obtain the components of the electric fields of the three waves parallel to the plane $z = 0$. For our choice of axes, these are just the y-components. For the incident wave, the amplitude of the y-component is $E_{i0} \cos \theta_i$. The corresponding components for the amplitudes of the reflected and transmitted waves are $E_{r0} \cos \theta_i$ (since $\theta_r = \theta_i$) and $E_{t0} \cos \theta_t$. The y-components of the actual fields oscillate with position in the plane through the factor $\exp[i\mathbf{k} \cdot \mathbf{r}]$ and with time through $\exp[i\omega t]$, but these dependences match (compare Equation 3.19), leading, for example, to Snell's law. So the continuity of the parallel component of $\mathbf{E}$ gives

$$E_{i0} \cos \theta_i + E_{r0} \cos \theta_i = E_{t0} \cos \theta_t,$$

which can be rearranged to

$$E_{i0} + E_{r0} = E_{t0} \frac{\cos \theta_t}{\cos \theta_i}. \tag{3.24}$$

To apply continuity of the perpendicular component of $\mathbf{D}$, we recognize that for $z < 0$, $\mathbf{D} = \varepsilon_1 \varepsilon_0 \mathbf{E}$, but for $z > 0$, $\mathbf{D} = \varepsilon_2 \varepsilon_0 \mathbf{E}$. So equating the perpendicular components of $\mathbf{D}$ either side of the interface — that is, the z-components — gives

$$-\varepsilon_1 \varepsilon_0 E_{i0} \sin \theta_i + \varepsilon_1 \varepsilon_0 E_{r0} \sin \theta_i = -\varepsilon_2 \varepsilon_0 E_{t0} \sin \theta_t.$$

Recognizing that $\varepsilon_1 = n_1^2$ and $\varepsilon_2 = n_2^2$, we have

$$n_1^2 E_{i0} \sin\theta_i - n_1^2 E_{r0} \sin\theta_i = n_2^2 E_{t0} \sin\theta_t,$$

which can be rearranged to

$$n_1 E_{i0}(n_1 \sin\theta_i) - n_1 E_{r0}(n_1 \sin\theta_i) = n_2 E_{t0}(n_2 \sin\theta_t).$$

Then, using Snell's law (Equation 3.23), the second relation for the amplitudes is obtained:

$$E_{i0} - E_{r0} = \frac{n_2}{n_1} E_{t0}. \tag{3.25}$$

Combining Equations 3.24 and 3.25, we can obtain amplitude transmission and reflection ratios when the polarization is *in* the *scattering plane* ('isp'). Using the symbols t_{isp} and r_{isp} to denote these ratios, the results are as follows.

> **The 'isp' amplitude transmission and reflection ratios**
>
> $$t_{isp} = \left(\frac{E_{t0}}{E_{i0}}\right)_{isp} = \frac{2n_1 \cos\theta_i}{n_1 \cos\theta_t + n_2 \cos\theta_i}, \tag{3.26}$$
>
> $$r_{isp} = \left(\frac{E_{r0}}{E_{i0}}\right)_{isp} = \frac{n_1 \cos\theta_t - n_2 \cos\theta_i}{n_1 \cos\theta_t + n_2 \cos\theta_i}. \tag{3.27}$$

Note that t_{isp} and r_{isp} are *not* time and position coordinates.

These two equations relate the amplitude transmission and reflection ratios to the angle of incidence, θ_i, the angle of refraction, θ_t, and the refractive indices on either side of the boundary, n_1 and n_2.

Worked Example 3.3

Starting from the boundary conditions in Equations 3.24 and 3.25, derive the expressions in Equations 3.26 and 3.27 for the amplitude transmission and reflection ratios.

Essential skill

Applying boundary conditions to determine amplitude transmission and reflection ratios

Solution

Adding Equations 3.24 and 3.25 gives

$$2E_{i0} = E_{t0}\left(\frac{\cos\theta_t}{\cos\theta_i} + \frac{n_2}{n_1}\right).$$

This simplifies as follows:

$$\frac{E_{t0}}{E_{i0}} = 2\left(\frac{\cos\theta_t}{\cos\theta_i} + \frac{n_2}{n_1}\right)^{-1} = \frac{2n_1 \cos\theta_i}{n_1 \cos\theta_t + n_2 \cos\theta_i}.$$

This agrees with Equation 3.26.

Subtracting Equation 3.25 from $(n_2 \cos\theta_i)/(n_1 \cos\theta_t)$ times Equation 3.24 leads to

$$E_{i0}\left(\frac{n_2 \cos\theta_i}{n_1 \cos\theta_t} - 1\right) + E_{r0}\left(\frac{n_2 \cos\theta_i}{n_1 \cos\theta_t} + 1\right) = 0.$$

Then multiplying by $n_1 \cos\theta_t$ and rearranging confirms Equation 3.27:

$$\frac{E_{r0}}{E_{i0}} = \frac{n_1 \cos\theta_t - n_2 \cos\theta_i}{n_1 \cos\theta_t + n_2 \cos\theta_i}.$$

Exercise 3.7   Show that Equations 3.26 and 3.27 reduce correctly to the corresponding results for normal incidence.   ■

Finally, we can calculate the relative powers that are transmitted through, or reflected from, the boundary as we did for normal incidence, using Equation 3.4:

$$\overline{\mathbf{N}} = \tfrac{1}{2}\varepsilon\varepsilon_0 E_0^2 \frac{c}{n}\,\widehat{\mathbf{k}}, \qquad\qquad \text{(Eqn 3.4)}$$

where $\widehat{\mathbf{k}}$ is the unit vector in the direction of propagation. Since $\varepsilon = n^2$, we can equally well say

$$\overline{\mathbf{N}} = \tfrac{1}{2}n\varepsilon_0 E_0^2 c\,\widehat{\mathbf{k}}.$$

To calculate the transmittance and reflectance, that is, the relative amounts of power transmitted through, and reflected from, the boundary, we need to know the components of the incident, reflected and transmitted Poynting vectors *in the z-direction*, perpendicular to the boundary. These components are given by scalar products of the form $\overline{\mathbf{N}} \cdot \mathbf{e}_z$. The power per unit area incident on the boundary is

$$\tfrac{1}{2}n_1\varepsilon_0 E_{i0}^2 c(\widehat{\mathbf{k}}_i \cdot \mathbf{e}_z) = \tfrac{1}{2}n_1\varepsilon_0 E_{i0}^2 c \cos\theta_i.$$

Similarly, the magnitudes of the power that is transmitted through, and that is reflected from, the boundary are

$$\tfrac{1}{2}n_2\varepsilon_0 E_{t0}^2 c \cos\theta_t \quad \text{and} \quad \tfrac{1}{2}n_1\varepsilon_0 E_{r0}^2 c \cos\theta_r.$$

The transmittance and reflectance are the corresponding proportions of the incident power that are transmitted and reflected, namely

$$T_{\text{isp}} = \frac{n_2 E_{t0}^2 \cos\theta_t}{n_1 E_{i0}^2 \cos\theta_i} \quad \text{and} \quad R_{\text{isp}} = \frac{E_{r0}^2}{E_{i0}^2}.$$

Using Equations 3.26 and 3.27 to eliminate the electric field amplitudes, we obtain the following expressions.

The 'isp' transmittance and reflectance

$$T_{\text{isp}} = \frac{4n_1 n_2 \cos\theta_i \cos\theta_t}{(n_1 \cos\theta_t + n_2 \cos\theta_i)^2}, \qquad\qquad (3.28)$$

$$R_{\text{isp}} = \left(\frac{n_1 \cos\theta_t - n_2 \cos\theta_i}{n_1 \cos\theta_t + n_2 \cos\theta_i}\right)^2. \qquad\qquad (3.29)$$

As a check, conservation of energy requires $T_{\text{isp}} = 1 - R_{\text{isp}}$. For Equations 3.28 and 3.29, this is indeed the case.

Polarization normal to the scattering plane

A similar analysis of reflection and transmission at a dielectric boundary can be carried out when the incident plane waves are polarized *normal* to the *scattering plane*, which I shall label by 'nsp'. The geometry is shown in Figure 3.10. Without further ado, I shall give the results corresponding to Equations 3.26 and 3.27.

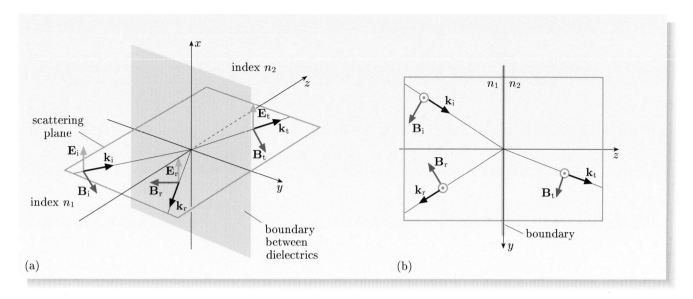

Figure 3.10 The electric field is *normal to* the scattering plane: (a) 3D view; (b) the $x = 0$ (scattering) plane. This figure defines directions that are used in setting up the equations for the boundary conditions.

The 'nsp' amplitude transmission and reflection ratios

$$t_{\text{nsp}} = \left(\frac{E_{t0}}{E_{i0}}\right)_{\text{nsp}} = \frac{2n_1 \cos\theta_i}{n_1 \cos\theta_i + n_2 \cos\theta_t}, \tag{3.30}$$

$$r_{\text{nsp}} = \left(\frac{E_{r0}}{E_{i0}}\right)_{\text{nsp}} = \frac{n_1 \cos\theta_i - n_2 \cos\theta_t}{n_1 \cos\theta_i + n_2 \cos\theta_t}. \tag{3.31}$$

Equations 3.26, 3.27, 3.30 and 3.31 are known as the **Fresnel equations**. In the next section we shall use the Fresnel equations with Snell's law, Equation 3.23, to eliminate θ_t and so link the transmission and reflection ratios to a single angle (θ_i) and the refractive indices on each side of the interface.

The reflectance and transmittance in the 'nsp' case are as follows.

The 'nsp' transmittance and reflectance

$$T_{\text{nsp}} = \frac{4n_1 n_2 \cos\theta_i \cos\theta_t}{(n_1 \cos\theta_i + n_2 \cos\theta_t)^2}, \tag{3.32}$$

$$R_{\text{nsp}} = \left(\frac{n_1 \cos\theta_i - n_2 \cos\theta_t}{n_1 \cos\theta_i + n_2 \cos\theta_t}\right)^2. \tag{3.33}$$

3.4.3 Total transmission and total reflection

The analysis we have done so far has been very productive. We have obtained laws for geometric optics and we have been able to deduce the polarization-dependent reflectance and transmittance of a boundary between two LIH dielectrics. There is still a little more insight to be gained by looking more closely at the general equations for the reflection ratios (two of the Fresnel equations) together with Snell's law. Figure 3.11a shows graphs of the ratios r_{isp}

and r_{nsp} for an air–glass interface, assuming $n_1 = 1$ for air and $n_2 = 1.5$ for glass. Figure 3.11b shows the same quantities but for a wave passing from glass to air, for which we should write $n_1 = 1.5$ and $n_2 = 1$.

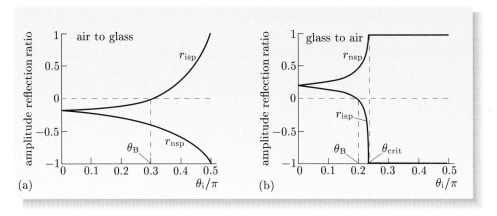

Figure 3.11   Amplitude reflection ratios versus angle of incidence, found by solving the Fresnel equations simultaneously with Snell's law (a) for an air–glass interface and (b) for a glass–air interface.

There are several things to note about Figure 3.11a, which shows the amplitude reflection ratios for light passing from air to glass.

- Under some conditions the reflection ratio is positive, and under others it is negative. As noted for normal incidence, a negative ratio implies that a phase change of π occurs on reflection — the boundary conditions cannot be met without it.

- At large angles of incidence, both states of polarization are reflected almost completely ($|r| \to 1$).

- The amplitude reflection ratio for polarization in the scattering plane, r_{isp}, vanishes at some angle of incidence between 0 and $\pi/2$, marked θ_{B} in the figure. At this angle, light polarized in the scattering plane must be completely transmitted.

  ● According to Figure 3.11a, what is the angle in radians at which there is no reflection of light with polarization in the scattering plane?

  ○ Reading from the figure, the angle is about 0.3π.

Things to note about Figure 3.11b, which shows the amplitude reflection ratios for light passing from glass to air, are as follows.

- Depending on the angle of incidence, the reflection ratio can be positive or negative, the latter again implying a phase change of π on reflection.

- At angles larger than that marked θ_{crit}, both states of polarization are wholly reflected ($|r_{\mathrm{isp}}| = |r_{\mathrm{nsp}}| = 1$) — this is total internal reflection, with which you are probably familiar.

- The reflection ratio r_{isp} vanishes at some angle of incidence between 0 and $\pi/2$, again marked θ_{B} in the figure.

Light from most ordinary sources like candles, light bulbs or the Sun, is randomly polarized. It consists of a mixture of waves with a random, or nearly random, spread of polarizations. But the polarization of each component can always be expressed as a linear combination of two different linear polarizations. So we would expect that in most cases the incident light would contain polarization components both in, and normal to, the scattering plane. The strengths of the reflected waves for these two polarizations are given by Equations 3.27 and 3.31. We now know that after reflection the relative amounts of the polarization components will be different — at certain angles, remarkably so, as can be seen from Figure 3.11.

The Brewster angle

To define θ_B for the 'isp' case, notice that when $\theta_i = \theta_B$, then Snell's law and $r_{isp} = 0$ simultaneously require

$$n_1 \sin \theta_B = n_2 \sin \theta_t \quad \text{and} \quad n_1 \cos \theta_t = n_2 \cos \theta_B.$$

To solve these, first square both equations:

$$n_1^2 \sin^2 \theta_B = n_2^2 \sin^2 \theta_t \quad \text{and} \quad n_1^2 \cos^2 \theta_t = n_2^2 \cos^2 \theta_B.$$

[handwritten annotation] $\sin^2\theta_t = \frac{n_1^2}{n_2^2}\sin^2\theta_B \quad \cos^2\theta_t = \frac{n_2^2}{n_1^2}\cos^2\theta_B$

Then, using the identity $\sin^2 \theta + \cos^2 \theta = 1$, we can eliminate θ_t to give

[handwritten annotation] $1 = \frac{n_1^2}{n_2^2}\sin^2\theta_B + \frac{n_2^2}{n_1^2}\cos^2\theta_B$

$$n_1^2 \left(1 - \frac{n_1^2}{n_2^2} \sin^2 \theta_B \right) = n_2^2 \cos^2 \theta_B. \quad \longleftarrow$$

[handwritten annotation] $n_1^2 = \frac{n_1^4}{n_2^2}\sin^2\theta_B + n_2^2\cos^2\theta_B$

Dividing by $\cos^2 \theta_B$ and using the identity $1/\cos^2 \theta = 1 + \tan^2 \theta$, we obtain

$$n_1^2 \left(1 + \tan^2 \theta_B - \frac{n_1^2}{n_2^2} \tan^2 \theta_B \right) = n_2^2.$$

[handwritten annotation] NOTE! $\frac{1}{\cos^2\theta_B} = \sec^2\theta_B = 1 + \tan^2\theta_B$

Finally, rearranging this equation gives

$$\tan^2 \theta_B = \frac{n_2^2/n_1^2 - 1}{1 - n_1^2/n_2^2} = \frac{n_2^2}{n_1^2},$$

so

$$\theta_B = \tan^{-1} \left(\frac{n_2}{n_1} \right).$$

This special angle of incidence is called the **Brewster angle**. For light incident at the Brewster angle, there is no reflection of components with polarization in the scattering plane; thus light with this polarization is totally transmitted. At the Brewster angle, the reflected light is therefore polarized in the direction normal to the scattering plane.

Exercise 3.8 Calculate θ_B for air–glass and glass–air boundaries, assuming values of 1.0 and 1.5 for the refractive indices of air and glass, respectively.

Exercise 3.9 At what angle should a beam of unpolarized light be directed at a glass window (in air) if the goal is to ensure that the maximum amount of light is transmitted through the window? Give supporting qualitative evidence based on Figure 3.11. ■

The critical angle

The **critical angle** θ_{crit} is the maximum angle of incidence for which there is a transmitted beam when light is incident from one medium onto the boundary of another medium that has a lower refractive index. Snell's law alone is sufficient to define θ_{crit}. Since we are assuming $n_1 > n_2$, Snell's law gives $\theta_t = \sin^{-1}(n_1 \sin\theta_i / n_2)$. This has real solutions only if $n_1 \sin\theta_i / n_2 \leq 1$. So θ_{crit} corresponds with the threshold value: $n_1 \sin\theta_{crit} / n_2 = 1$. There are no real-valued solutions for θ_t at larger angles of incidence, so transmission ceases and all energy is reflected.

Exercise 3.10   Calculate θ_{crit} for a water–air boundary, assuming values of 1.3 and 1.0 for the refractive indices of water and air, respectively.   ∎

3.4.4   Polarization by reflection

The intensity of light depends on the square of the electric field. We have established that the amplitude of the electric field in a reflected wave depends on the angle of incidence and the polarization (Figure 3.11). For polarization in the scattering plane, the amplitude of the reflected wave passes through zero at the Brewster angle. So, for randomly polarized light, after reflection at a dielectric surface, over a range of angles close to the Brewster angle, the reflected light is predominantly made up of light that is polarized normal to the scattering plane.

If you have a pair of Polaroid sunglasses, you can see this for yourself. Observe the light reflected from various objects through one of the Polaroid lenses held a little way in front of your eye. Note the extent to which the brightness of an object varies as you rotate the lens. If the brightness does not vary as you rotate the Polaroid lens, the object must be reflecting light in an unpolarized fashion (or else emitting unpolarized light). If, however, the brightness does vary, from maximum to minimum twice per revolution, then the light is to some degree polarized, and this is what you would expect to see when looking at reflection from dielectric surfaces.

You will observe that reflection from bare metals appears to be unpolarized.

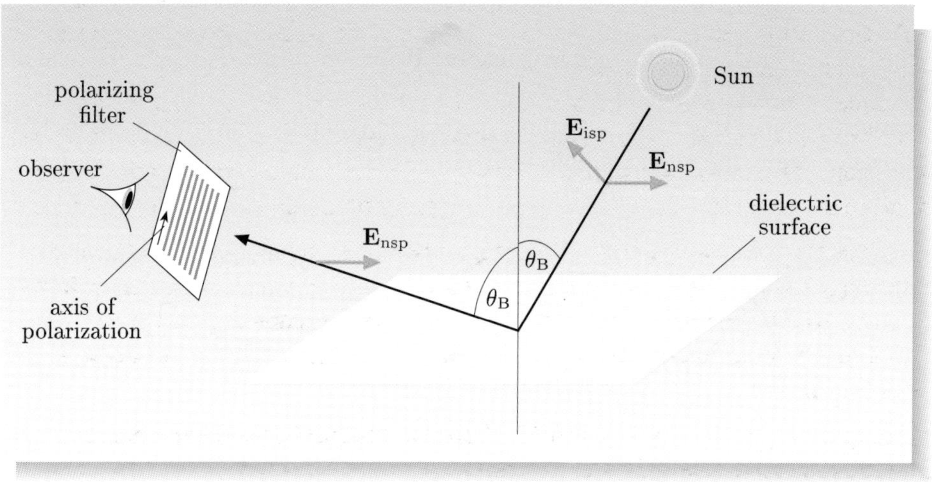

Figure 3.12   Observing polarization produced by reflection. Direct light from the Sun is a mix of linear polarizations and the vectors on the incident ray represent the electric field direction for polarization in the scattering plane and normal to the scattering plane. Light reflected from a horizontal dielectric surface at the Brewster angle is linearly polarized in the horizontal direction, normal to the scattering plane.

Polaroid lenses include a polarization filter. The filter has an **axis of polarization**, which is a specific direction in the plane of the polarizer. Linearly polarized light with the electric field vector parallel to the axis of polarization is allowed to pass with little absorption. By contrast, light polarized normal to the axis is strongly attenuated. In effect, the Polaroid lens passes only the component of light that is polarized in the direction of the axis of polarization.

Exercise 3.11   With reference to Figure 3.12, explain why Polaroid sunglasses, with the axis of polarization of the lenses in the vertical direction, are effective in reducing the glare from sunlight reflected directly off horizontal surfaces of glass and water. ∎

3.4.5   Fibre optics

Total internal reflection can occur at a boundary where there is a step down in the value of the refractive index. This basic observation gives a clue as to how dielectric sheets and rods can be used to guide electromagnetic radiation. Figure 3.13 illustrates a ray of light striking one boundary of a sheet of dielectric at an angle greater than θ_{crit} and, as a consequence of total internal reflection, being reflected across the sheet to strike the opposite boundary, and again experiencing total internal reflection. The ray is trapped in the sheet until it strikes the boundary at an angle less than θ_{crit}, either on reaching the end or else on encountering a sharp bend in the sheet.

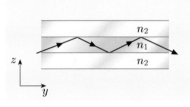

Figure 3.13   A ray is reflected back and forth between the boundaries of a sheet of dielectric with refractive index n_1 that is sandwiched between sheets of material with lower refractive index n_2. The angle of incidence at the boundaries is greater than the critical angle for total internal reflection.

This simple picture is not entirely correct, however. A ray indicates a direction perpendicular to wavefronts, which for true plane waves would extend out to infinity on each side of the ray. However, we must be careful not to overlook the effect of one or more reflections. The total reflection at the dielectric boundary will fold the wavefronts back in on themselves, so we should allow for interference between waves moving towards and away from the boundary. You can imagine that constructive interference will arise for rays that cross the sheet and return if their phase difference is an exact multiple of 2π — and that difference includes the phase change from two reflections and the propagation across the sheet and back. The situation is made more complicated by the fact that at angles of incidence greater than θ_{crit}, Snell's law suggests that $\sin\theta_t > 1$, so that $\cos\theta_t = \sqrt{1 - \sin^2\theta_t}$ must make a purely imaginary contribution to the reflection ratios (Equations 3.27 and 3.31). This effectively introduces a phase change on reflection that varies with the angle of incidence. Summing over all plane waves that strike the boundary at angles which lead to constructive interference sounds like hard work. Fortunately, there is a simpler way to describe what happens, based on inspired guesswork. The inspiration comes from looking in more detail at the transmission ratio for angles of incidence greater than θ_{crit}.

For $\theta_i > \theta_{\mathrm{crit}}$, the value of $\cos\theta_t$ is imaginary, and so the amplitude reflection ratios r_{isp} and r_{nsp} are complex. But it turns out that they each have a magnitude of unity, so total internal reflection occurs and is accompanied by a phase change. However, the amplitude transmission ratios t_{isp} and t_{nsp} are *not* zero. So what does this mean?

Writing the equivalent of Equation 3.21 for the general transmitted wave, but looking beyond the boundary at $z = 0$,

$$\mathbf{k}_t \cdot \mathbf{r} = k_{tx}x + k_{ty}y + k_{tz}z$$
$$= (k_t \sin\theta_t)y + (k_t \cos\theta_t)z,$$

where $k_t = n_2 \omega / c$. Allowing for the imaginary nature of $\cos \theta_t$ when $\theta_i > \theta_{crit}$, we can write

$$\mathbf{k_t} \cdot \mathbf{r} = k_t y \sin \theta_t + iz/\delta.$$

So for $z > 0$, there is a transmitted wave that has the form

$$E_{t0} \exp[i(k_t y \sin \theta_t + iz/\delta - \omega t)] = E_{t0} \exp(-z/\delta) \exp[i(k_t y \sin \theta_t - \omega t)],$$

where $\sin \theta_t = (n_1/n_2) \sin \theta_i > 1$. This looks like a wave that travels in the y-direction, but which decays in amplitude beyond the boundary ($z > 0$); see Figure 3.14. It does not propagate in the z-direction. The field in medium 2 is said to be **evanescent** in the z-direction. An important point is that although energy does not propagate *away* from the boundary into medium 2, some energy is stored in the evanescent fields and is transported *along* the boundary, in the y-direction. In considering the reflectance, we were interested in energy that was transported *away* from the boundary by the associated pair of reflected electric and magnetic waves. The reflected fields in region 1 also transport energy *parallel* to the boundary. So with dielectric 1 sandwiched between layers of dielectric 2, energy is effectively propagated in the y-direction both within dielectric 1 *and* in a thin boundary layer in dielectric 2.

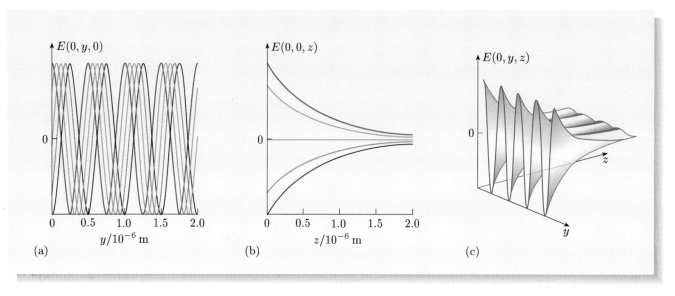

(a)

(b)

(c)

Figure 3.14   The electric field in dielectric 2 ($z > 0$) close to the boundary in the plane $z = 0$ with dielectric 1, which has a higher refractive index.
(a) The travelling-wave field $E(0, y, 0)$ along the y-axis at five successive instants.
(b) The evanescent field $E(0, 0, z)$ along the z-axis at five successive instants.
(c) The instantaneous field $E(0, y, z)$ on the $x = 0$ plane.

This is how optical fibres guide energy, though optical fibres must be modelled as cylinders, not infinite 'sandwiches'. Furthermore, the diameter of fibres used in telecommunications is comparable with the wavelength of the light used. Solutions of Maxwell's equations under these circumstances are best found by looking for so-called guided wave (or *waveguide*) modes that propagate energy parallel to the dielectric boundaries.

The idea that energy is propagated *between and along* the boundaries in the y-direction is the inspiration for seeking waveguide solutions. Trying to take account simultaneously of all the possible angles of incidence that give rise to constructive interference of multiply reflected waves is too complicated. It is simpler to try to find a solution that from the outset has the key features identified above. Then, in the case of the dielectric sheet, we can look for solutions of Maxwell's equations of the form

$$E(y, z, t) = E_0(z) \exp[i(k_y y - \omega t)],$$

that match the appropriate boundary conditions. We shall not go further into this solution here, but optical fibres are discussed further in the next chapter, and metallic waveguides are discussed in Chapter 5.

Exercise 3.12   Explain why the cladding of optical fibres usually has a refractive index that is lower than that of the core, and why the difference in refractive index is generally just a few per cent.   ■

3.5   Challenging the LIH assumption

The results of the analysis of reflection and refraction at the interface between transparent dielectric materials are certainly consistent with geometric optics and observations of the behaviour of polarized light. Central to the analysis is the assumption that the materials involved are linear, isotropic and homogeneous in their dielectric response. As a consequence, in Maxwell's equations, the divergence and curl operations pass over ε, which acts as a constant scalar multiplier of ε_0. This leads, in particular, to a speed of propagation that is given by the simple expression $v = c/\sqrt{\varepsilon}$. There are many exceptions to this LIH behaviour, and they have some striking consequences, for example as shown in Figure 3.15.

Linearity

In physics we often begin by supposing that if one thing depends on another, it does so linearly. By definition, small disturbances are those for which this is the case. However, focusing a beam of light raises its intensity to a point where linearity is by no means to be expected. When a linear model fails to provide an adequate description, we have to accept the added complexity of non-linearity. In the case of light interacting with dielectric matter, that means we have to consider what happens when ε depends on the intensity of the light. It is not that uncommon, and one sign that something curious is happening is that the frequency of radiation emerging from a material is a multiple of the incident frequency — my colleagues who use lasers regularly exploit this to generate green, blue and even ultraviolet radiation from a red laser.

Isotropy

Crystalline materials are inherently anisotropic at the atomic scale because the atoms are arranged on a regular lattice. If the crystallinity extends over scales that are larger than the wavelength, and the atomic arrangements do not have simple cubic symmetry, then electromagnetic radiation is sensitive to this crystalline anisotropy. Dimensions of the individual crystals within a material depend on many factors, and sizes range from nm to mm in naturally occurring minerals and manufactured materials. We should not be surprised if the LIH model cannot account for the properties of all crystalline materials.

● From a structural point of view, suggest why glass and water are well modelled by the theory outlined in this chapter.

○ Glass and water have no long-range order, so the isotropic assumption is valid.

Figure 3.15   Iceland spar, a transparent form of calcite, $CaCO_3$, is birefringent. One consequence is the double refraction shown in this figure.

The double image in Figure 3.15 is one consequence of crystalline anisotropy. The material is a large crystal of calcite. Its crystal structure gives it two refractive indices — and hence two different phase speeds — dependent upon the orientation of polarization with respect to the crystal axes. There are therefore two angles of refraction, so that unpolarized light, resolved into orthogonal components, gives rise to a double image when objects are viewed obliquely through the crystal, as in the figure. The property of having polarization-dependent refractive indices is called **birefringence**.

Homogeneity

Panes of very old glass found in some ancient buildings are somewhat inhomogeneous. We are not concerned here with any thickness variations that tend to distort the image of what lies beyond. Light gets through a pane of inhomogeneous glass without significant absorption, but scenes are blurred — we can describe the material as translucent but not transparent. The reason for the loss of transparency is non-uniformity in the composition of the glass which translates directly into non-uniformity in ε and hence n. Light waves are refracted by each small change in refractive index, leading to the breaking up and smearing of images.

Summary of Chapter 3

Section 3.1   Expressions for electromagnetic wave propagation in LIH dielectrics (with $\mu = 1$) can be obtained from those for free space by replacing ε_0 with $\varepsilon\varepsilon_0$ and replacing c with c/n, where the refractive index, $n = \sqrt{\varepsilon}$, is the ratio of the speed of propagation in free space to that in the dielectric. In particular, the wavenumber and angular frequency are linked by

$$k = n\omega/c,$$

and the time-averaged energy flux per unit area is

$$\overline{\mathbf{N}} = \tfrac{1}{2}\varepsilon\varepsilon_0 E_0^2 \frac{c}{n}\,\widehat{\mathbf{k}}.$$

Section 3.2   In the absence of free charges and currents in the bulk or at surfaces, the boundary conditions on the time-dependent fields $\mathbf{E}$, $\mathbf{D}$, $\mathbf{B}$ and $\mathbf{H}$ at the interface between two different dielectric media are the same as for static fields, namely that the parallel components of $\mathbf{E}$ and $\mathbf{H}$, and the perpendicular components of $\mathbf{D}$ and $\mathbf{B}$, are continuous at the boundary.

Section 3.3   Transmission and reflection of electromagnetic waves at an interface between two different dielectric media can be quantified in terms of the amplitude transmission and reflection ratios, which are defined as the ratios of the amplitudes of the transmitted and reflected fields to the amplitude of the incident field, or by the transmittance and reflectance, which are defined as the ratios of the transmitted and reflected powers to the incident power. Expressions for these quantities can be determined by applying the boundary conditions at the interface.

Section 3.4   The laws of reflection and Snell's law can be derived from a consideration of travelling wave solutions of Maxwell's equations at a dielectric boundary.

The behaviour of an electromagnetic wave incident at any angle onto an interface between two different dielectric media can be built up from a linear combination of two special cases: one in which the wave is polarized in the scattering plane, and one in which it is polarized normal to the scattering plane. Applying the standard boundary conditions to these two cases leads to the Fresnel equations for the amplitude transmission and reflection ratios. For light incident at the Brewster angle, $\theta_{\mathrm{B}} = \tan^{-1}(n_2/n_1)$, the component of the wave that is polarized in the scattering plane is completely transmitted, so the reflected wave is wholly polarized normal to the scattering plane.

If light passes from one dielectric to another of lower refractive index (e.g. from glass to air), then for incidence at the so-called critical angle, $\theta_{\mathrm{crit}} = \sin^{-1}(n_2/n_1)$, the transmitted wave emerges parallel to the interface, i.e. $\theta_{\mathrm{t}} = \pi/2$. When the angle of incidence is greater than the critical angle, there is no real solution for the angle of refraction, and the wave is said to undergo total internal reflection.

The propagation of electromagnetic energy in a slab, rod or fibre of dielectric, immersed in a second dielectric with lower refractive index, can result in energy being guided along the high index material and along the boundaries. This is the basis of optical fibre telecommunications.

Section 3.5   Results derived for LIH media are appropriate for the study of optics in simple transparent dielectrics such as glass and water. Materials that are non-linear, anisotropic or inhomogeneous have different properties.

Achievements from Chapter 3

After studying this chapter you should be able to do the following.

3.1   Explain the meanings of the newly defined (emboldened) terms and symbols, and use them appropriately.

3.2   Justify the use of the free space $\rightarrow$ dielectric transformation rule.

3.3   Use Maxwell's equations to show that for time-dependent fields at the boundary between two dielectrics, the normal components of **D** and **B**, and the parallel components of **E** and **H**, are continuous.

3.4   Demonstrate that electromagnetic waves incident on a boundary between two dielectrics obey Snell's law and the laws of reflection, and use these laws to solve problems.

3.5   Use the boundary conditions to derive the Fresnel equations for amplitude transmission and reflection ratios at the interface between two LIH dielectrics (with $\mu = 1$), and derive expressions for transmittance and reflectance, and use these results to solve problems.

3.6   Explain the significance of the Brewster angle and the critical angle, and solve problems related to these angles.

3.7   Describe how optical fibres confine light between dielectric boundaries.

3.8   Discuss some of the limitations of the LIH dielectric model.

Chapter 4   Dielectrics: dispersion and absorption

This chapter continues the study of the interaction of electromagnetic waves with dielectric media. The aim is to describe the dielectric properties of materials and their effects on the propagation of electromagnetic radiation.

In Chapter 2, to account for the scattering of sunlight by the atmosphere, we looked at how induced molecular dipoles act as Hertzian dipole radiators that scatter energy from the path of an electromagnetic wave. In the low-density gas of the atmosphere, such scattering events occur at the random positions of the molecules, so there is no coherence between the radiation from the dipoles that are induced by the passing wave. In the present chapter we are going to consider electromagnetic waves in a solid or liquid dielectric within which the density of induced dipoles is thousands of times greater than that of molecules in the atmosphere. That means that millions of oscillating dipoles are induced, simultaneously and locally, so that there is a high degree of coherence in the dipole radiation. As a result, you can imagine that radiation from these induced sources locally interferes, cancelling side-scattered waves and reinforcing only in the forward direction. In effect, this is the manner in which the wave is propagated forwards. Separating the mechanism into dipole-induction, re-radiation and interference slightly oversimplifies the situation. These processes actually occur simultaneously, and the net effect is that the propagation of electromagnetic disturbances through matter is slower than it is through free space.

The interaction of electromagnetic waves with dielectrics is an important topic, with far-reaching consequences in optics. In optical instruments, dielectrics are used for lenses, mirrors and filters. Structural shapes and angles of incidence are especially important in determining what happens to electromagnetic radiation in these cases. In these situations, light travels through no more than a few millimetres of dense dielectric material. In contrast, in optical telecommunications, light travels through many kilometres of dielectric material, and phenomena in the bulk are more important than what happens at the interfaces.

4.1   Losing signals in optical fibres

Figure 4.1 shows the fate of a short pulse of radiation, from an infrared *light-emitting diode* (LED), after it is launched into a long optical fibre. Beyond about ten kilometres, the signal has almost completely disappeared.

● Examine Figure 4.1 and identify two distinct ways in which the pulse deteriorates as it travels along the fibre.

○ The pulse gets *broader* and also its amplitude gets *smaller*.

In earlier chapters we encountered two mechanisms that might account for the lost signal. The first is the partial reflection that occurs when electromagnetic waves cross a dielectric boundary. However, this cannot account for the progressive decay of the pulse. The second is the sideways scattering of energy discussed in Chapter 2: localized impurities and inhomogeneities thinly spread throughout the fibre give rise to incoherent scattering. This could account for a gradual reduction of energy in the pulse, but not for the broadening of the pulse.

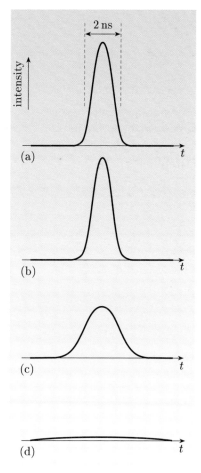

Figure 4.1   A pulse of 660 nm (red) light at different distances along an optical fibre. (a) Initial pulse shape; (b) after travelling 0.1 km; (c) after 1 km; (d) after 10 km.

What happens to electromagnetic waves as they travel through a dielectric medium is the main subject of this chapter. Starting from a simple model of the interaction of electromagnetic waves with dielectric media, we shall show that the relative permittivity is a complex quantity, and its real and imaginary parts depend in a systematic manner on the frequency of an electromagnetic wave. The refractive index also emerges as a frequency-dependent, complex quantity. Two consequences are investigated in subsequent sections. The first is that waves with different frequencies may travel at appreciably different speeds in a dielectric medium, and this leads to pulses of light broadening as they travel, and also to spectral splitting of light as it passes between different dielectrics. This process is called *dispersion*. The second is that a dielectric medium may absorb energy from an electromagnetic wave that passes through it. Whereas scattering from impurities just redirects the electromagnetic energy, *dielectric absorption* transforms electromagnetic energy into thermal energy. At the end of the chapter, the simple model is used to gain physical insight into the dielectric properties of two common media: water and glass (silica).

4.2   A simple model of dielectric behaviour

The principal interaction of electromagnetic waves with a dielectric medium arises from the oscillations of bound electrons that are induced by the electric component of the wave. As a consequence of this interaction, as we shall see, the relative permittivity is inevitably a frequency-dependent quantity, $\varepsilon(\omega)$, which in this chapter in particular, I shall refer to as the **dielectric function**.

A full theoretical explanation of the dielectric properties of materials is, properly, quantum mechanical, and continues to be a topic of research. There is, however, a simple model based on classical physics which does show qualitatively several of the important features of the dielectric function. In this model we consider electrons to be bound to their host atoms by spring-like forces — that is, any displacement from an equilibrium position is resisted by a force that is proportional to the magnitude of the displacement (Figure 4.2). This is actually not a bad approximation for small displacements from equilibrium of a particle bound by a smooth potential energy function. Let us build up the model starting with a single, bound electron moving in response to an electromagnetic field. Then the response of a dense dielectric medium, in which there is a large number of polarizable atoms or molecules 'per cubic wavelength', will be the combined effects of the total number of electrons that are free to respond in this way. The goal is to obtain an expression for the dielectric function in terms that are related to the dynamics of the bound electrons.

The displacements of ions and permanent dipoles also contribute to relative permittivity.

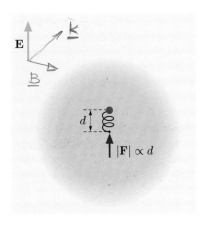

Figure 4.2   When an external electric field **E** is applied, the centre of an electron cloud is displaced from the nucleus by distance d and it experiences a spring-like restoring force **F** with magnitude proportional to d.

The response of a single bound electron

Denoting the effective spring constant as a, the restoring force for a displaced electron is $-a\,\mathbf{r}(t)$, where $\mathbf{r}(t)$ is the displacement from equilibrium. A simple loss mechanism can be represented in this kind of dynamical model by a friction force $-b\,\mathbf{v}(t) = -b\,\mathrm{d}\mathbf{r}(t)/\mathrm{d}t$, which adds a viscous drag proportional to the instantaneous speed. Here, the bound particle is an electron, with charge $-e$, so it is subject to a force $-e\,\mathbf{E}(\mathbf{r}(t), t)$ in response to the electric field of a passing electromagnetic wave. Note that this field is evaluated at the position of the electron, $\mathbf{r}(t)$. For electromagnetic waves in free space, $|\mathbf{B}| = |\mathbf{E}|/c$, so the magnetic contribution to the Lorentz force $(-e\,\mathbf{v} \times \mathbf{B})$ will be v/c times the electric force and may therefore be safely neglected.

We shall also suppose that the host nucleus is fixed: at relatively high frequencies this is a good approximation since nuclei have a relatively large inertia, being thousands of times more massive than electrons.

Bringing all these factors together, the equation of motion for a bound electron (charge $-e$ and mass m) is then

$$m \frac{\mathrm{d}^2\mathbf{r}(t)}{\mathrm{d}t^2} = -a\,\mathbf{r}(t) - b\,\frac{\mathrm{d}\mathbf{r}(t)}{\mathrm{d}t} - e\,\mathbf{E}(\mathbf{r}(t), t). \qquad (4.1)$$

To solve this equation analytically with the full spatial-dependence of $\mathbf{E}(\mathbf{r}(t), t)$ would be a major distraction. But remember that $\mathbf{r}(t)$ is the displacement from equilibrium, and we are here interested in displacements that are a small fraction of the size of a single atom, so $r(t) \ll 1\,\mathrm{nm}$. If the driving field is due to electromagnetic waves, then $\lambda \gg 1\,\mathrm{nm}$ for all except the harder X-rays and gamma rays (see Figure 4 in the Introduction to this book), and we may safely replace $\mathbf{E}(\mathbf{r}, t)$ by $\mathbf{E}(\mathbf{0}, t)$ because the field will be very nearly constant over the region in which the electron moves. We shall use the complex exponential notation for the field of an electromagnetic wave, $\mathbf{E}_0 \exp[\mathrm{i}(\mathbf{k} \cdot \mathbf{r} - \omega t)]$, to calculate the response of the electron, so $\mathbf{E}(\mathbf{0}, t) = \mathbf{E}_0 \exp[-\mathrm{i}\omega t]$ is the driving field. The equation of motion then simplifies to

$$m \frac{\mathrm{d}^2\mathbf{r}(t)}{\mathrm{d}t^2} + a\,\mathbf{r}(t) + b\,\frac{\mathrm{d}\mathbf{r}(t)}{\mathrm{d}t} = -e\,\mathbf{E}_0 \exp[-\mathrm{i}\omega t].$$

Steady-state solutions of this forced-oscillator equation are of the form $\mathbf{r}(t) = \mathbf{r}_0 \exp[-\mathrm{i}\omega t]$, with $\mathbf{r}_0$ representing the amplitude of the oscillatory displacement. Substituting this solution, collecting terms, and cancelling $\exp[-\mathrm{i}\omega t]$ from both sides, gives

$$[-m\omega^2 + a - \mathrm{i}\omega b]\mathbf{r}_0 = -e\,\mathbf{E}_0.$$

This relationship describes the amplitude of the displacement of a single electron in the model system in a time-dependent electric field. We can simplify the notation by defining a characteristic frequency $\omega_\mathrm{n} = \sqrt{a/m}$ and a friction parameter $\gamma = b/m$. The amplitude of the displacement, $\mathbf{r}_0$, of a bound electron in response to an electric field of amplitude $\mathbf{E}_0$ and angular frequency ω is then given by

$$\mathbf{r}_0 = -\frac{e\mathbf{E}_0}{m}\frac{1}{(\omega_\mathrm{n}^2 - \omega^2) - \mathrm{i}\omega\gamma}. \qquad (4.2)$$

ω_n is the *natural* frequency of a mass m on a spring with spring constant a, and γ is a parameter that characterizes the friction force.

This expression for the displacement is a complex quantity. To split a fraction with a complex denominator into the sum of separate real and imaginary parts, you multiply top and bottom by the complex conjugate of the denominator:

$$\frac{1}{x - \mathrm{i}y} = \frac{(x + \mathrm{i}y)}{(x - \mathrm{i}y)(x + \mathrm{i}y)} = \frac{(x + \mathrm{i}y)}{x^2 + y^2} = \frac{1}{x^2 + y^2}(x + \mathrm{i}y). \qquad (4.3)$$

Complex numbers are used here because the displacement and the driving field are generally not in phase.

The magnitude (or modulus) of a complex number $|(x \pm \mathrm{i}y)|$ is $\sqrt{x^2 + y^2}$. The magnitude of $1/(x - \mathrm{i}y)$ is therefore

$$\frac{1}{x^2 + y^2}|(x + \mathrm{i}y)| = \frac{1}{x^2 + y^2}\sqrt{x^2 + y^2} = \frac{1}{\sqrt{x^2 + y^2}}.$$

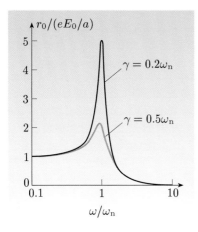

Figure 4.3   The magnitude of the amplitude of the oscillations of a bound electron in response to an oscillatory electric field, for two values of the frictional parameter γ. Note that the horizontal axis has a logarithmic scale.

n is also used in this chapter to represent the refractive index — it pays to check the context in which a symbol is being used before jumping to conclusions about what it represents.

Thus, the magnitude of the amplitude of the oscillations of a single bound electron in response to an oscillating electric field is

$$r_0 = \frac{eE_0}{m} \frac{1}{\sqrt{(\omega_n^2 - \omega^2)^2 + (\omega\gamma)^2}}.$$

The general form of this relationship is shown in Figure 4.3. At low frequencies, $\omega \ll \omega_n$, the displacement has a steady value of $eE_0/m\omega_n^2 = eE_0/a$, equivalent to that in a steady field. At high frequencies, $\omega \gg \omega_n$, the displacement tends to zero, as the inertia of the electron prevents it from keeping up with the oscillating field. Between these two extremes, when $\omega \sim \omega_n$, there is a resonant response, with the displacement building up to several times the low-frequency limit, provided that the damping is not too strong.

● From Figure 4.3, identify the effect of the frictional term, γ, on the resonance.

○ The height of the resonance peak is decreased, and its width is broadened relative to its height, when the strength of the frictional term increases. (One common definition of width uses the full width of the peak at half its maximum height.)

The aggregate response of a solid dielectric

A dielectric medium can be thought of as an assembly of bound electrons. So we next take the displacement of a single bound electron, Equation 4.2, and use it to construct the aggregate response of a system comprising many similarly-bound electrons. The electric field produces an induced polarization $\mathbf{P}(t)$ — an induced dipole moment per unit volume — due to the displacement of a uniform distribution of bound electrons with number density n_e:

$$\begin{aligned}
\mathbf{P}(t) &= n_e(-e)\,\mathbf{r}(t) \\
&= -n_e e \mathbf{r}_0 \exp[-\mathrm{i}\omega t] \\
&= \frac{n_e e^2}{m} \frac{1}{(\omega_n^2 - \omega^2) - \mathrm{i}\omega\gamma} \mathbf{E}_0 \exp[-\mathrm{i}\omega t] \\
&= \omega_p^2 \frac{1}{(\omega_n^2 - \omega^2) - \mathrm{i}\omega\gamma} \varepsilon_0 \mathbf{E}_0 \exp[-\mathrm{i}\omega t].
\end{aligned} \tag{4.4}$$

To keep things tidy, I have embodied the number density of bound electrons, n_e, in another characteristic frequency,

$$\omega_p = \sqrt{n_e e^2/m\varepsilon_0}. \tag{4.5}$$

For reasons that will become clear in Chapter 6, I shall call ω_p the *plasma frequency*.

In your studies of electrostatics, you will have related induced polarization to the relative permittivity, ε, via the electric susceptibility, χ_E, as follows:

$$\mathbf{P} = \chi_E\,\varepsilon_0\mathbf{E}, \quad \text{where } \chi_E = \varepsilon - 1. \tag{4.6}$$

The difference here is that the relative permittivity must be replaced by the more general dielectric function, $\varepsilon(\omega)$, and $\mathbf{E}$ is an oscillating electric field, $\mathbf{E}_0 \exp[-\mathrm{i}\omega t]$. Combining Equations 4.4 and 4.6, we obtain

$$\varepsilon(\omega) = 1 + \omega_p^2 \frac{1}{(\omega_n^2 - \omega^2) - \mathrm{i}\omega\gamma}. \tag{4.7}$$

As anticipated in Section 4.1, the dielectric function is frequency-dependent and complex. Equation 4.3 will separate it into its real and imaginary parts.

The complex dielectric function, $\varepsilon(\omega) = \varepsilon_{\text{real}}(\omega) + i\varepsilon_{\text{imag}}(\omega)$

$$\varepsilon_{\text{real}}(\omega) = 1 + \omega_{\text{p}}^2 \frac{(\omega_{\text{n}}^2 - \omega^2)}{(\omega_{\text{n}}^2 - \omega^2)^2 + \omega^2\gamma^2}, \tag{4.8}$$

$$\varepsilon_{\text{imag}}(\omega) = \omega_{\text{p}}^2 \frac{\omega\gamma}{(\omega_{\text{n}}^2 - \omega^2)^2 + \omega^2\gamma^2}. \tag{4.9}$$

Figure 4.4 shows the general shapes of both $\varepsilon_{\text{real}}$ and $\varepsilon_{\text{imag}}$. They are plotted for parameters that roughly correspond to the properties of glass at optical frequencies. Note that if $\omega = \omega_{\text{n}}$, then $\varepsilon_{\text{real}}$ is exactly 1, and $\varepsilon_{\text{imag}}$ has its maximum very near to $\omega = \omega_{\text{n}}$.

● Use Equation 4.8 to determine the low and high frequency limits of $\varepsilon_{\text{real}}$, and confirm that these are in agreement with Figure 4.4.

○ Setting $\omega \ll \omega_{\text{n}}$ in Equation 4.8 gives $\varepsilon_{\text{real}}(\omega \to 0) = 1 + \omega_{\text{p}}^2/\omega_{\text{n}}^2$. For Figure 4.4, $\omega_{\text{p}} = 1.12\omega_{\text{n}}$, and this corresponds with $\varepsilon_{\text{real}}(\omega \to 0) = 2.25$. Setting $\omega \gg \omega_{\text{n}}$ in Equation 4.8 gives $\varepsilon_{\text{real}}(\omega \to \infty) = 1$. Both these limits are apparent in Figure 4.4.

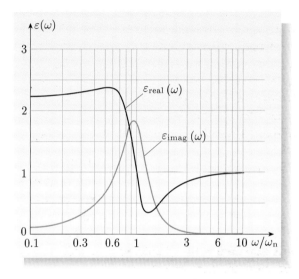

Figure 4.4   The real and imaginary parts of $\varepsilon(\omega)$. For the case shown here, $\omega_{\text{p}} = 1.12\omega_{\text{n}}$ and $\gamma = 0.70\omega_{\text{n}}$.

Exercise 4.1   In Figure 4.4, $\omega_{\text{p}} = 1.12\omega_{\text{n}}$. What is the number density of bound electrons according to the simple model if $\omega_{\text{n}} = 8.8 \times 10^{15}\,\text{s}^{-1}$?   ■

In practice, even the simplest dielectrics are more complicated than we have considered here. For example, the simple model assumes that the polarization is due solely to the displacement of a number of identically bound ('representative') electrons. In reality, there are often contributions to polarization from two or more classes of differently bound electrons, especially for substances comprised of more than one type of atom. Furthermore, the model has overlooked ionic bonds and permanent dipoles, which both also contribute to polarization. On the basis of this simple model, we can anticipate that equivalent resonances will also arise from these other contributions to polarization, but at lower frequencies, due to the greater inertia of ions and permanent dipoles. The dielectric function for a material will therefore be the sum of many contributions like that shown in Figure 4.4, each with a different natural frequency, different friction parameter and different plasma frequency.

In Section 4.5 we shall look at the details of the dielectric functions of water and silica to see if Figure 4.4 is consistent with what is observed in practice. Before that, we must follow up the general consequences of having a dielectric function that is both frequency-dependent and complex. The frequency-dependence will be shown in Section 4.3 to account for dispersion, while the complex nature of the dielectric function will be shown in Section 4.4 to account for absorption. First, though, there is one last task to complete this model of dielectric behaviour: we need to see what becomes of the refractive index n when the dielectric function has real and imaginary components.

Refractive index

The properties of materials are conveniently modelled in terms of the dielectric function, $\varepsilon(\omega)$, since that is directly related to induced polarization. However, it is the refractive index n and the wavenumber k that appear in expressions relating to the propagation of waves. In Chapter 3 it was said that the speed of propagation of electromagnetic waves in a dielectric is slower by a factor given by the refractive index, $n = \sqrt{\varepsilon}$. Similarly, the wavenumber in a dielectric was found to be given by $k = n\omega/c$. The model of dielectric behaviour developed in this section has resulted in a complex, frequency-dependent dielectric function, so what happens to n and k?

Note that n is now being used to refer to refractive index rather than number density.

Since $\varepsilon(\omega)$ is a complex quantity, we expect to find a complex refractive index, so let us write it as

$$n(\omega) = n_{\text{real}}(\omega) + \mathrm{i}\, n_{\text{imag}}(\omega). \tag{4.10}$$

Throughout this chapter we shall continue to assume that μ is unity, which is a good approximation for materials like air, water and glass, so

$$n^2(\omega) = \varepsilon(\omega)\mu = \varepsilon(\omega).$$

The corresponding complex wavenumber can similarly be expressed as

$$k(\omega) = \frac{n(\omega)\,\omega}{c} = k_{\text{real}}(\omega) + \mathrm{i}\, k_{\text{imag}}(\omega). \tag{4.11}$$

To keep the algebra tidy, I am no longer going to show the functional dependence on frequency. However, don't forget that n_{real}, n_{imag}, k_{real} and k_{imag} are all real, frequency-dependent quantities.

Expressions for n_{real} and n_{imag} in terms of $\varepsilon_{\text{real}}$ and $\varepsilon_{\text{imag}}$ are obtained as follows. First, we set the square of the refractive index, as given by Equation 4.10, equal to the complex dielectric function:

$$n_{\text{real}}^2 + 2\mathrm{i}\, n_{\text{real}} n_{\text{imag}} - n_{\text{imag}}^2 = \varepsilon_{\text{real}} + \mathrm{i}\, \varepsilon_{\text{imag}}.$$

Then, separately equating real and imaginary parts,

$$n_{\text{real}}^2 - n_{\text{imag}}^2 = \varepsilon_{\text{real}} \quad \text{and} \quad 2 n_{\text{real}} n_{\text{imag}} = \varepsilon_{\text{imag}}.$$

Substituting from the second of these expressions into the first to eliminate n_{imag} gives

$$n_{\text{real}}^4 - \varepsilon_{\text{real}} n_{\text{real}}^2 - \frac{\varepsilon_{\text{imag}}^2}{4} = 0,$$

which is quadratic in n_{real}^2. A similar equation emerges for n_{imag}^2 if instead n_{real} is eliminated. The solutions are therefore as follows.

The complex refractive index

$$n_{\text{real}}^2 = \frac{\varepsilon_{\text{real}} + \sqrt{\varepsilon_{\text{real}}^2 + \varepsilon_{\text{imag}}^2}}{2}, \tag{4.12}$$

$$n_{\text{imag}}^2 = \frac{-\varepsilon_{\text{real}} + \sqrt{\varepsilon_{\text{real}}^2 + \varepsilon_{\text{imag}}^2}}{2}. \tag{4.13}$$

Note that the positive roots should be taken, because otherwise the left-hand sides, which are supposed to be squares of real numbers, would be equal to negative numbers. Notice that if $\varepsilon_{\text{imag}} \to 0$, then $n_{\text{real}}^2 \to \varepsilon_{\text{real}}$ and $n_{\text{imag}}^2 \to 0$.

We obtain the complex wavenumber by combining Equations 4.10 and 4.11:

$$k_{\text{real}} = n_{\text{real}} \frac{\omega}{c} \quad \text{and} \quad k_{\text{imag}} = n_{\text{imag}} \frac{\omega}{c}, \tag{4.14}$$

where n_{real} and n_{imag} are given by Equations 4.12 and 4.13.

It is the complex values of ε and n that must be used in the free space $\to$ dielectric transformation rule that was introduced in Section 3.1, in which ε_0 is replaced by $\varepsilon\varepsilon_0$ and c is replaced by c/n. However, the phase speed of a wave is a physical quantity, and this is given by

$$v = \omega/k_{\text{real}} = c/n_{\text{real}}. \tag{4.15}$$

I shall confirm this result in Section 4.4, where the significance of k_{imag} will also be discussed.

Exercise 4.2   Show that $n_{\text{real}} \simeq \sqrt{\varepsilon_{\text{real}}}$ and $n_{\text{imag}} \simeq \varepsilon_{\text{imag}}/2\sqrt{\varepsilon_{\text{real}}}$ when $\varepsilon_{\text{imag}} \ll \varepsilon_{\text{real}}$.

Exercise 4.3   Figure 4.5 shows part of the model dielectric function from Figure 4.4. Use data from these two figures to estimate the phase speed of blue light ($\omega_{\text{blue}}/\omega_{\text{n}} = 0.54$) and that of red light ($\omega_{\text{red}}/\omega_{\text{n}} = 0.29$). ■

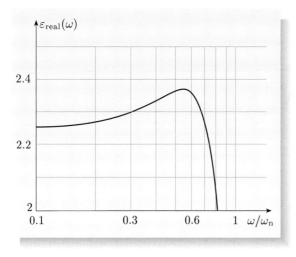

Figure 4.5   Detail of the real part of $\varepsilon(\omega)$ from Figure 4.4.

4.3   Dispersion

The frequency-dependence of the speed of propagation of electromagnetic radiation has emerged from the model of dielectric behaviour, in terms of the frequency-dependence of the real part of the dielectric function. If $\omega \ll \omega_{\mathrm{n}}$, then as Figure 4.4 shows, $\varepsilon_{\mathrm{imag}} \ll \varepsilon_{\mathrm{real}}$, and $n_{\mathrm{real}} \simeq \sqrt{\varepsilon_{\mathrm{real}}}$ changes only slightly with frequency. In this section we look at the consequences of this small frequency-dependence for electromagnetic radiation — particularly for light — as it crosses dielectric boundaries and also as it travels large distances through dielectrics.

Throughout this section, it is assumed that $\varepsilon_{\mathrm{imag}} \ll \varepsilon_{\mathrm{real}}$.

For an electromagnetic wave with angular frequency ω, travelling in the positive z-direction and polarized in the x-direction, the electric and magnetic fields are the real parts of

$$\mathbf{E}(z,t) = E_0 \exp[\mathrm{i}(kz - \omega t)]\, \mathbf{e}_x \tag{4.16}$$

and

$$\mathbf{B}(z,t) = \frac{n(\omega)}{c}\, E_0 \exp[\mathrm{i}(kz - \omega t)]\, \mathbf{e}_y, \tag{4.17}$$

where $k = n\omega/c$. If $\varepsilon_{\mathrm{imag}} \ll \varepsilon_{\mathrm{real}}$, then $n \to n_{\mathrm{real}}$ and $k \to k_{\mathrm{real}}$, so the electric and magnetic fields can be rewritten as the real parts of

$$\mathbf{E}(z,t) = E_0 \exp[\mathrm{i}(k_{\mathrm{real}} z - \omega t)]\, \mathbf{e}_x \tag{4.18}$$

and

$$\mathbf{B}(z,t) = \frac{n_{\mathrm{real}}}{c}\, E_0 \exp[\mathrm{i}(k_{\mathrm{real}} z - \omega t)]\, \mathbf{e}_y, \tag{4.19}$$

where $k_{\mathrm{real}} = n_{\mathrm{real}}\, \omega/c$. Note that the speed at which this wave propagates, $v = \omega/k_{\mathrm{real}} = c/n_{\mathrm{real}}$, will depend on its frequency through n_{real}. This is illustrated schematically in Figure 4.6, which shows a **dispersion diagram** — a graph showing the relationship between ω and k — for a material in which the speed decreases with increasing frequency, compared with the diagram for a material in which the speed is independent of frequency. The next two subsections will demonstrate that a frequency-dependent phase speed leads to the spreading out, or **dispersion**, of electromagnetic waves in space and time.

4.3.1   Dispersion at interfaces

Have a look at Figure 4.7, which shows what happens to sunlight when it is refracted by the air–water interfaces of a distribution of water droplets. At a certain angle, rain seen against a dark sky, and spray around waterfalls seen against dark rock, both clearly display the effect of **angular dispersion**, the splitting of electromagnetic radiation into its spectral components at an interface between dielectric materials.

Figure 4.8 shows a second example of angular dispersion, this time associated with the air–glass interfaces of a prism. As with the raindrops, angular dispersion occurs at each crossing of an interface, with the second crossing reinforcing the spread initiated by the first. For given materials on either side of the interface, the extent of the angular dispersion depends on the angle of incidence and the spectral range of the light. You can see this from Snell's law (see Equation 3.23),

$$n_1 \sin \theta_{\mathrm{i}} = n_2 \sin \theta_{\mathrm{t}}, \tag{4.20}$$

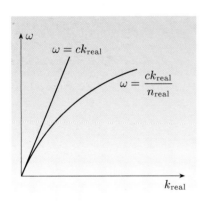

Figure 4.6   A schematic dispersion diagram. A non-dispersive medium has a linear relationship between ω and k, whereas for a medium in which higher frequencies propagate more slowly than lower frequencies, the ω versus k relationship drops progressively lower than the linear relationship.

which relates the angle of refraction of the transmitted wave (θ_t) to the angle of incidence (θ_i) and the refractive indices each side of an interface. Either one or both of the refractive indices may be frequency-dependent and complex, but since refraction comes about because of differences in phase speed, Snell's law involves only the real parts of the refractive indices.

Figure 4.7 A rainbow produced in water spray over the Iguassu Falls, at the border between Brazil and Argentina.

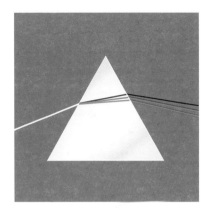

Figure 4.8 Light is dispersed by a prism into its different component colours.

Rainbows

Outside the laboratory, we don't normally notice angular dispersion because the images of everyday life are generally a complicated mixture of colours. Just occasionally, as with the rainbow in Figure 4.7, under steady, high-contrast conditions a clear demonstration of angular dispersion does arise.

Figure 4.9 reveals the origin of rainbows. Consider rays of sunlight arriving horizontally at a spherical drop of water. For angles of incidence up to about 0.4π radians (about $70°$), most of the light is transmitted across the interface, and is refracted according to Snell's law. The angles of incidence and refraction of a horizontal ray depend on where it impinges on the drop's surface. Denoting the vertical distance of the point of impact of a horizontal ray from the horizontal axis of the drop as y, and the radius of the drop as a, with $0 < y < a$, it is a simple matter of geometry to show that $\sin \theta_i = y/a$.

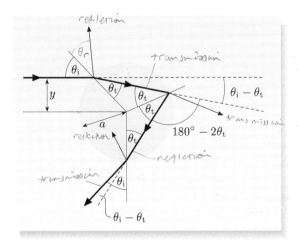

Figure 4.9 Deviation of light by transmission, reflection and transmission on encountering a sphere of water, with refraction occurring at each transmission.

The real refractive index of air is, to a good approximation, unity; I shall denote the refractive index of water simply by n, representing a real, frequency-dependent quantity. Using Snell's law then gives $\theta_t = \sin^{-1}(y/na)$.

On entering a drop, the refracted ray is deviated from its horizontal path through an angle $\theta_i - \theta_t$ (see Figure 4.9). After crossing the drop to the back surface, the ray strikes the interface at θ_t to the normal, where again partial reflection and partial transmission take place. This time we are interested in the reflected component, which has been deviated through a further angle of $180° - 2\theta_t$. The ray crosses the drop again, and encounters the water–air interface for a second time, where again refraction and reflection occur. The transmitted light emerges at angle θ_i, with the refraction adding a further deviation of $\theta_i - \theta_t$. This ray has been transmitted, reflected and transmitted, as a result of which it has been deviated by

$$D = (\theta_i - \theta_t) + (180° - 2\theta_t) + (\theta_i - \theta_t) = 180° + 2\theta_i - 4\theta_t, \qquad (4.21)$$

where $\theta_t = \sin^{-1}(y/na)$ and $\theta_i = \sin^{-1}(y/a)$.

Figure 4.10 shows how the angle of deviation is related to the relative height of the point of impact, y/a. The incident light is distributed over values of y/a in the range $0 < y/a < 1$. However, notice that around the angle of minimum deviation D_{min}, a considerable fraction of the incident light is deviated through almost the same angle. Therefore, an observer on the ground looking up at an angle given by

$$180° - D_{min} = 4\theta_t - 2\theta_i$$

will see a somewhat concentrated reflection of sunlight from the back surfaces of drops along the line of sight — markedly stronger than at other angles. The angle D_{min} depends on n, and it turns out that blue light, which has a slightly higher index of refraction, is reflected to the observer most strongly, at a slightly different angle from that at which red light is most strongly reflected — see the inset in Figure 4.10. So, different colours are seen to come from slightly different regions of sky. The bow shape follows from the rotational symmetry of the raindrops.

Note that the angle D_{min} is defined with respect to the direction of rays of sunlight that strike airborne raindrops.

arc

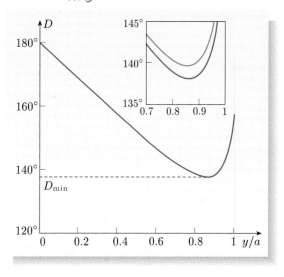

Figure 4.10   The variation of angle of deviation D with relative impact height y/a for $n = 1.334$ (red light); the inset shows detail around the minimum also for $n = 1.345$ (blue light).

Exercise 4.4   Given $D_{\min}(\text{blue}) = 140°$ and $D_{\min}(\text{red}) = 138°$, calculate the angle subtended by a rainbow, and state which colour appears closer to the ground. ∎

Optical components

Another situation where white light crosses dielectric interfaces is in the formation of images by lenses in telescopes and microscopes. Here degradation of the images caused by different colours of light being refracted through different angles by the lenses is regarded as a nuisance, and is called **chromatic aberration**. It has long been known how to reduce chromatic aberration.

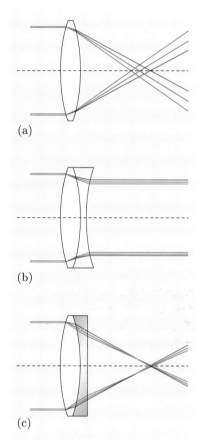

(a)

(b)

(c)

● Identify three factors that contribute to angular dispersion, and propose three means by which chromatic aberration might therefore be reduced in a microscope.

○ Chromatic aberration is due to (i) the range of frequencies in white light, together with (ii) the frequency-dependence of the refractive index, and (iii) the angles of incidence. So chromatic aberration in a microscope would be markedly reduced by using monochromatic illumination — for example, you could use yellow light. A second strategy, which preserves colour-contrast, is to restrict angles of incidence at the lens surfaces to near normal by reducing the effective diameters of lenses with irises. Under these circumstances, there is less refraction, and so less angular dispersion, but brighter illumination is needed. A third strategy is to use relatively non-dispersive materials, or to use combinations of materials for which the effects of chromatic aberration can be compensated.

In the manufacture of high quality lenses for optical instruments, chromatic aberration is minimized by using **compound lenses**. These are made by combining a number of separate lenses made from different types of glass. The fundamental process of image formation by lenses relies on refraction to deviate light from its path in accordance with the distance from the axis where the light crosses the plane of the lens. Without going into the geometric optics of lenses, Figure 4.11 illustrates the principle behind compound structures. In part (a), a ray of light undergoes angular dispersion as it passes through a lens. The angular dispersion can be arrested, as in part (b), by adding a second lens of the same material but with the curvatures of the surfaces opposite to those of the first lens. However, since the outer surfaces are now effectively parallel, there is no focusing effect. But with a careful choice of materials for the two lenses, as in part (c), with appropriate refractive indices and dispersions, the angular dispersion can be cancelled while preserving some focusing effect.

Figure 4.11   (a) Angular dispersion of white light by a lens leads to chromatic aberration. (b) Passing the light through a second lens of the same material, which has surfaces of the opposite curvature, results in no net angular deviation, but no focusing effect either. (c) By using two lenses of different refractive indices, and different tendencies to disperse, different colours can be focused at about the same point. Note that the horizontal scale in (a) is different from that in (c); the focal length in (c) is significantly longer than in (a).

Exercise 4.5   White light is composed of a continuous spread of frequencies between about 4.0 and 7.5×10^{14} Hz, corresponding with free space wavelengths ranging from about 750 nm (for deep red) to about 400 nm (for violet). Account for the effect displayed in Figure 4.8 in terms of the frequency-dependence of the index of refraction of glass, n_{real}. ∎

4.3.2   Dispersion in the bulk

Once across the boundary of a dielectric, propagation proceeds at a speed set by the real part of the refractive index of the medium. That would be the end of the story if one were only ever interested in the behaviour of waves of a single frequency. But this is rarely the case — even laser radiation, which is often described as being the most monochromatic light, comprises a narrow band of frequencies distributed around a central value. Furthermore, if a wave is to carry information, it must be modulated in some way, and this necessarily involves more than a single frequency. It is important to investigate how the weak frequency-dependence of the refractive index might affect the propagation of light *through* dielectric media.

Throughout this section, $\varepsilon_{\text{imag}} \ll \varepsilon_{\text{real}}$, so the frequency-dependence of the refractive index is 'weak'.

Dispersion and d'Alembert solutions

Owing to the linearity of Maxwell's equations, we can construct solutions of them that are linear combinations of other solutions. Since plane waves are valid solutions of Maxwell's equations, any linear combination of these plane waves must also be a valid solution. In free space, or in a material for which the phase speed is independent of frequency, a combination of plane waves travelling in the same direction can be described by a d'Alembert solution of the form

$$\mathbf{E}(z, t) = g(z - vt)\,\mathbf{e}_x, \tag{4.22}$$

which represents a fixed shape travelling at speed v in the positive z-direction. But this cannot be a solution of the wave equation in a dispersive medium, where the propagation speed depends on frequency, and consequently the component sinusoidal waves travel at different speeds. So what happens to the shapes of non-monochromatic waves?

When there is dispersion, any linear combination of plane waves is still a valid solution of each of Maxwell's equations, even though the propagation speeds of individual component waves depend on their frequencies. Let us check that this is so.

For instance, for polarization in the x-direction and propagation in the positive z-direction, the plane wave pair $\{\mathbf{E}, \mathbf{B}\}$ of Equations 4.18 and 4.19 provide a solution of Maxwell's equations for any chosen angular frequency ω. Let us suppose that we have two such solution pairs, $\{\mathbf{E}_1, \mathbf{B}_1\}$ and $\{\mathbf{E}_2, \mathbf{B}_2\}$, corresponding to *different* frequencies, ω_1 and ω_2. Then a linear combination of these would be $\mathbf{E}_{\text{sum}} = a_1\mathbf{E}_1 + a_2\mathbf{E}_2$ and $\mathbf{B}_{\text{sum}} = a_1\mathbf{B}_1 + a_2\mathbf{B}_2$, where a_1 and a_2 are arbitrary constants.

Essential skill

Testing solutions of Maxwell's equations

Worked Example 4.1

Show that $\mathbf{E}_{\text{sum}}$ and $\mathbf{B}_{\text{sum}}$ obey Faraday's law.

Solution

Start with the electric field terms:

$$\text{curl}\,\mathbf{E}_{\text{sum}} = \text{curl}(a_1\mathbf{E}_1 + a_2\mathbf{E}_2) = a_1\,\text{curl}\,\mathbf{E}_1 + a_2\,\text{curl}\,\mathbf{E}_2. \tag{4.23}$$

Then compare this with the magnetic field terms:

$$-\frac{\partial \mathbf{B}_{\text{sum}}}{\partial t} = -a_1\frac{\partial \mathbf{B}_1}{\partial t} - a_2\frac{\partial \mathbf{B}_2}{\partial t}.$$

We know that curl $\mathbf{E}_1 = -\partial \mathbf{B}_1/\partial t$ and curl $\mathbf{E}_2 = -\partial \mathbf{B}_2/\partial t$, since each of the pairs $(\mathbf{E}_1, \mathbf{B}_1)$ and $(\mathbf{E}_2, \mathbf{B}_2)$ satisfies Faraday's law separately. Thus curl $\mathbf{E}_{\text{sum}} = -\partial \mathbf{B}_{\text{sum}}/\partial t$, and so $\mathbf{E}_{\text{sum}}$ and $\mathbf{B}_{\text{sum}}$ obey Faraday's law.

Similar arguments show that $\mathbf{E}_{\text{sum}}$ and $\mathbf{B}_{\text{sum}}$ also obey the other three of Maxwell's equations. However, they do *not* generally obey a wave equation, as we shall now demonstrate.

Consider the plane waves represented by the expressions

$$\mathbf{E}_1(z, t) = E_1 \exp[\mathrm{i}(k_1 z - \omega_1 t)] \, \mathbf{e}_x, \quad \text{where } k_1 = n(\omega_1)\frac{\omega_1}{c},$$

and

$$\mathbf{E}_2(z, t) = E_2 \exp[\mathrm{i}(k_2 z - \omega_2 t)] \, \mathbf{e}_x, \quad \text{where } k_2 = n(\omega_2)\frac{\omega_2}{c}.$$

The first expression obeys the wave equation

$$\frac{\partial^2 \mathbf{E}_1}{\partial z^2} = \frac{1}{v_1^2} \frac{\partial^2 \mathbf{E}_1}{\partial t^2},$$

where $v_1 = c/n(\omega_1)$; we can identify v_1 as the phase speed, since in this section we are assuming n is real. The second expression obeys the wave equation,

$$\frac{\partial^2 \mathbf{E}_2}{\partial z^2} = \frac{1}{v_2^2} \frac{\partial^2 \mathbf{E}_2}{\partial t^2},$$

but with a different phase speed, $v_2 = c/n(\omega_2)$.

However, $\mathbf{E}_{\text{sum}}$ is *not* a solution of the wave equation, because

$$\frac{\partial^2 \mathbf{E}_{\text{sum}}}{\partial z^2} = \frac{a_1}{v_1^2} \frac{\partial^2 \mathbf{E}_1}{\partial t^2} + \frac{a_2}{v_2^2} \frac{\partial^2 \mathbf{E}_2}{\partial t^2},$$

and when there is dispersion we must suppose that $v_1 \neq v_2$, so

$$\frac{\partial^2 \mathbf{E}_{\text{sum}}}{\partial z^2} \neq \frac{1}{v^2} \frac{\partial^2 \mathbf{E}_{\text{sum}}}{\partial t^2}.$$

Clearly, the linear combination $\mathbf{E}_{\text{sum}}$ is not a simple function that propagates unchanged in shape like a d'Alembert solution. The point here is that $\mathbf{E}_{\text{sum}}$ comprises two plane waves moving at *different* speeds, so they shift relative to one another in time; that is, they *disperse*.

In a dispersive medium, where n depends on frequency:

- any linear combination of plane wave solutions of Maxwell's four equations — even for different frequencies — is itself a solution of Maxwell's equations;

- linear combinations of plane waves with different frequencies do not propagate as fixed shapes, that is, d'Alembert solutions are *not* solutions of the wave equation except in the special case where the contributing plane waves all travel with the same speed.

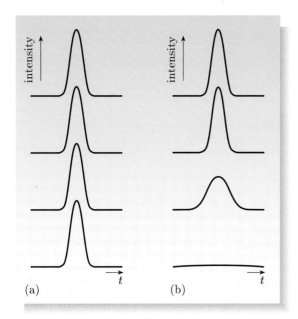

(a)

(b)

Figure 4.12 (a) The intensity profile of a pulse propagating in a non-dispersive medium, measured at four successive positions along the direction of propagation. (b) A pulse with a similar initial intensity profile but propagating in a dispersive medium; the pulse becomes wider and consequently its amplitude decreases.

We can take this process further by constructing arbitrary linear combinations of any number of plane waves. These are solutions of Maxwell's equations. In fact, travelling signals of finite extent, such as short pulses, can be constructed by adding together a *continuum* of plane wave solutions. These objects, sometimes called *wave packets*, are also proper solutions of Maxwell's equations. When there is no dispersion, they are in effect d'Alembert solutions. However, in a dispersive medium, wave packets change shape as they propagate, tending to spread out as the various different components drift apart due to their different speeds of propagation.

Figure 4.12 compares the shapes of pulses propagating in non-dispersive and dispersive media. You can see that the d'Alembert solution is valid in the former case. In a dispersive medium, pulse shapes slowly evolve, generally becoming broader.

Group speed

You cannot send effective messages with a continuous wave. A wave needs to be tailored in some way for it to carry information, for instance, by varying its amplitude. Amplitude modulation (AM) of a high-frequency carrier wave by a lower-frequency 'message' signal is widely used in radio communication. The simple signalling of Morse code by radio transmissions or flash lamps, with short and long pulses signifying dots and dashes, is a simple form of amplitude modulation. So too is the communication of digital data (as sequential pulses of electromagnetic energy) through free space or along transmission lines (pairs of wires or conducting strips, co-axial cables, waveguides and optical fibres). Information can also be encoded in a wave train as a modulation of the frequency of a carrier wave — hence frequency modulation (or FM). The modulation of a monochromatic sinusoidal wave inevitably introduces sinusoidal waves at other frequencies. When the transmission medium is dispersive, so that different frequency components propagate at different phase speeds, it is important to consider what determines the speed at which a modulated waveform travels.

Let us look at a simple situation in which a pair of sinusoidal waves with equal amplitude, polarized in the same direction, with frequencies ω_1 and ω_2 and wavenumbers k_1 and k_2, propagates in the positive z-direction. At any point z and time t, the magnitude of the electric field will be

$$E(z,t) = E_0[\sin(k_1 z - \omega_1 t) + \sin(k_2 z - \omega_2 t)]. \tag{4.24}$$

I want to work backwards to see what sort of amplitude modulation would give rise to this simple result.

Using the standard trigonometric relationship

$$\sin A + \sin B = 2 \sin\left(\frac{A+B}{2}\right) \cos\left(\frac{A-B}{2}\right),$$

the dual-sinusoid waveform of Equation 4.24 can be re-expressed as

$$E(z,t) = 2E_0 \sin\left(\frac{(k_1+k_2)z - (\omega_1+\omega_2)t}{2}\right) \cos\left(\frac{(k_1-k_2)z - (\omega_1-\omega_2)t}{2}\right),$$

which looks like a sine wave modulated by a cosine wave, or vice versa. Let us concentrate on the situation when the angular frequencies of the two waves are quite close, so that $\omega_1 = \omega_0 + \Delta\omega$ and $\omega_2 = \omega_0 - \Delta\omega$. We can then also expect that the wavenumbers will be close, so that $k_1 = k_0 + \Delta k$ and $k_2 = k_0 - \Delta k$. Then the equation for $E(z,t)$ becomes

$$E(z,t) = 2E_0 \sin(k_0 z - \omega_0 t) \cos(\Delta k\, z - \Delta\omega\, t). \quad (4.25)$$

Figure 4.13a shows a snapshot of this modulated waveform at $t = 0$; one of the peaks is marked with a red blob. The waveform is a sine wave modulated by a cosine wave with a longer wavelength. Part (b) shows the waveform some moments later in a dielectric medium for which the relationship between ω and k is like that shown in part (c). Note that since in (b) the rapidly-oscillating structure has advanced a little more than the overall envelope, two of the peaks have squeezed through the neck at the minimum and have appeared on the other side.

Having chosen $\Delta\omega$, the dispersive property of the medium, as expressed by the relationship between ω and k, gives $\Delta k \simeq (\mathrm{d}k/\mathrm{d}\omega)\,\Delta\omega$.

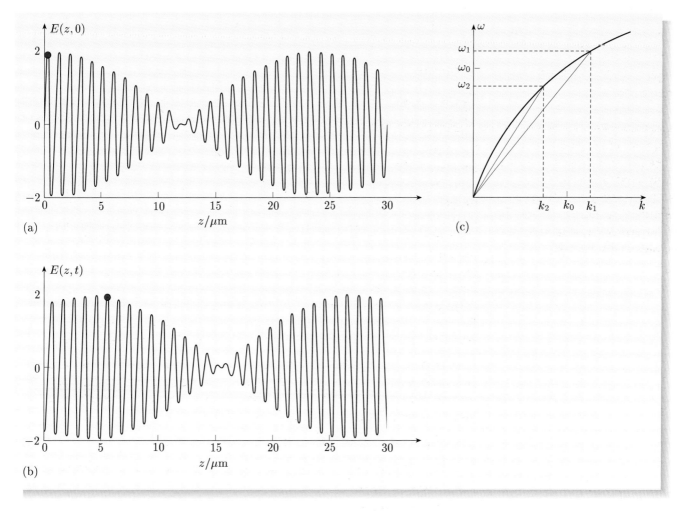

(a)

(b)

(c)

Figure 4.13 (a) A snapshot of a dual-sinusoid wave ($\omega_1 = 1.29 \times 10^{15}\,\mathrm{s}^{-1}$ and $\omega_2 = 1.26 \times 10^{15}\,\mathrm{s}^{-1}$) reveals that it is a modulated sine wave. (b) The same wave some moments later in a dispersive medium with $n(\omega_1) = 1.52$ and $n(\omega_2) = 1.50$; the first narrow peak in (a) reaches $z = 5\,\mu\mathrm{m}$ in the time it takes the first broad minimum to travel from 12 to 15 μm. (c) The dispersion diagram that links ω and k in the medium.

● Try to identify four propagation speeds that are associated with $E(z,t)$ through Equations 4.24 and 4.25.

○ Equation 4.24 involves ω_1/k_1 and ω_2/k_2; Equation 4.25 and Figure 4.12 involve ω_0/k_0 and $\Delta\omega/\Delta k$.

So, is any one of these speeds equivalent to the speed at which the modulated waveform, $E(z,t)$, travels? The answer is that, on the basis of Equation 4.25, since the envelope structure is determined by $\cos(\Delta k\, z - \Delta\omega\, t)$, it is $\Delta\omega/\Delta k$ that sets the speed of propagation of the modulated waveform.

We can extend this result by thinking about what would happen if we were to add more waves with frequencies close to ω_0. If you do this, what you find is that as more waves are added, the shape of the envelope changes, but it still propagates at speed $\Delta\omega/\Delta k$. In general, therefore, any group of waves that is closely spaced in frequency ($\Delta\omega \ll \omega_0$) will add together to constitute a disturbance that propagates at the so-called **group speed**,

$$v_{\text{group}} = \frac{\mathrm{d}\omega}{\mathrm{d}k}. \tag{4.26}$$

This is also commonly referred to as the **group velocity**, though strictly, for vectorial status, the direction of propagation must also be specified. Notice that in a non-dispersive medium ($\omega = kc$), the magnitude of the group speed and the phase speed are identical. Since any information-carrying wave is modulated, it is reasonable to conjecture that information travels through a medium with the modulation, that is, at the group speed.

Group speed and refractive index

Remember that we are assuming that $n(\omega)$ and k are real in this section.

We know that, in general, $k = n(\omega)\omega/c$. Then

$$\frac{\mathrm{d}k}{\mathrm{d}\omega} = \frac{\omega\, n'(\omega) + n(\omega)}{c},$$

where $n' \equiv \mathrm{d}n/\mathrm{d}\omega$. Inverting this gives $\mathrm{d}\omega/\mathrm{d}k$. So if ω_0 is the central frequency of a wave packet, corresponding to a wavenumber $k_0 = n(\omega_0)\omega_0/c$, then the wave packet moves at the group speed v_{group}, where

$$v_{\text{group}} = \frac{c}{\omega_0\, n'(\omega_0) + n(\omega_0)}. \tag{4.27}$$

Exercise 4.6   With reference to Figure 4.4, and subject to the constraint $\varepsilon_{\text{imag}} \ll \varepsilon_{\text{real}}$, identify regions where you would expect the group speed to be different from the phase speed.   ■

The discussion in this section has carefully avoided the vicinity of the resonance in Figure 4.4. Here not only is the real part of the refractive index changing rapidly with frequency, but also the imaginary part is now significant; the next section looks at what that means.

4.4 Absorption

4.4.1 Attenuation of field strength

In general, the dielectric function is frequency-dependent and complex. In the previous section we looked at the consequences of having a *real* frequency-dependent dielectric function. Now we must consider the consequences of the imaginary part, $\varepsilon_{imag}(\omega)$.

The electric field of a plane monochromatic electromagnetic wave in a dielectric, which is polarized in the x-direction and moving in the positive z-direction, can be written as the real part of

$$\mathbf{E}(z,t) = E_0 \exp[\mathrm{i}(kz - \omega t)]\,\mathbf{e}_x, \quad \text{where } k = n(\omega)\frac{\omega}{c}. \qquad \text{(Eqn 4.16)}$$

The companion magnetic field is given by the real part of

$$\mathbf{B}(z,t) = \frac{n(\omega)}{c}\,E_0 \exp[\mathrm{i}(kz - \omega t)]\,\mathbf{e}_y. \qquad \text{(Eqn 4.17)}$$

If k were a real number, then the plane waves represented by Equations 4.16 and 4.17 would have constant amplitude. This might be a satisfactory model in some situations, but it is somewhat naïve, for it does not allow for **absorption** — the transformation of electromagnetic energy transported by the wave into other forms of energy, particularly thermal energy — as the wave travels through the medium. We expect a degree of energy loss from the wave as it propagates through a dielectric. Frictional losses are already built into the simple classical model that was used in Section 4.2 to derive the complex dielectric function, namely

$$\varepsilon(\omega) = \varepsilon_{\mathrm{real}}(\omega) + \mathrm{i}\,\varepsilon_{\mathrm{imag}}(\omega), \qquad (4.28)$$

where $\varepsilon_{\mathrm{real}}(\omega)$ and $\varepsilon_{\mathrm{imag}}(\omega)$ are real-valued functions. The knock-on effects of the complex dielectric function are that the index of refraction, $n(\omega) = \sqrt{\varepsilon(\omega)}$, and the propagation vector, $k = n(\omega)\omega/c$, are also complex quantities. We need in particular to examine Equations 4.16 and 4.17 when the wavenumber has real and imaginary components,

$$k(\omega) = k_{\mathrm{real}}(\omega) + \mathrm{i}\,k_{\mathrm{imag}}(\omega), \qquad (4.29)$$

where k_{real} and k_{imag} are real quantities. Using this complex wavenumber in Equation 4.16, the electric field is the real part of

$$\begin{aligned} \mathbf{E}(z,t) &= E_0 \exp[\mathrm{i}(kz - \omega t)]\,\mathbf{e}_x \\ &= E_0 \exp[\mathrm{i}(\{k_{\mathrm{real}} + \mathrm{i}\,k_{\mathrm{imag}}\}z - \omega t)]\,\mathbf{e}_x. \end{aligned}$$

This can be simplified to

$$\mathbf{E}(z,t) = E_0 \exp[-k_{\mathrm{imag}}z] \exp[\mathrm{i}(k_{\mathrm{real}}z - \omega t)]\,\mathbf{e}_x. \qquad (4.30)$$

Taking the real part then gives the physical electric field as

$$\mathbf{E}_{\mathrm{phys}}(z,t) = E_0 \exp[-k_{\mathrm{imag}}z] \cos(k_{\mathrm{real}}z - \omega t)\,\mathbf{e}_x. \qquad (4.31)$$

Provided that k_{imag} is positive, this is a travelling plane wave that is *damped* along the direction of travel by the factor $\exp(-k_{\mathrm{imag}}z)$. Figure 4.14 shows the physical electric field as a function of space at three successive instants.

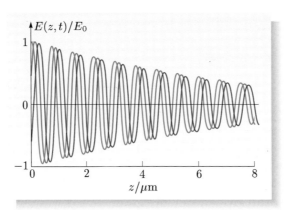

Figure 4.14 The electric field propagating through a dielectric that has a complex refractive index, shown at three instants (blue curve earliest, then green, then red). The case shown corresponds with strong absorption of light.

The imaginary part of the wavenumber is associated with a decrease in the amplitude of the wave, and this is caused by frictional damping of the driven oscillations of bound electrons. Note that there is no absorption if k_{imag} is zero. The distance over which the amplitude is reduced by a factor of $\exp(-1) = 0.37$ is $1/k_{\text{imag}}$, and this is known as the **absorption length**.

Essential skill

Finding the physical fields from complex expressions

Worked Example 4.2

Obtain an expression for the physical magnetic field that accompanies the electric field represented by Equation 4.31.

Solution

Starting from Equation 4.17, and substituting $n(\omega)/c = k/\omega = (k_{\text{real}} + \mathrm{i}\,k_{\text{imag}})/\omega$, the magnetic field is the real part of

$$\mathbf{B}(z,t) = \frac{(k_{\text{real}} + \mathrm{i}\,k_{\text{imag}})}{\omega} E_0 \exp[-k_{\text{imag}}z] \exp[\mathrm{i}(k_{\text{real}}z - \omega t)]\,\mathbf{e}_y.$$

Taking the real part then gives the physical magnetic field as

$$\mathbf{B}_{\text{phys}}(z,t) = \frac{E_0}{\omega} \exp[-k_{\text{imag}}z]$$
$$\times \left(k_{\text{real}} \cos(k_{\text{real}}z - \omega t) - k_{\text{imag}} \sin(k_{\text{real}}z - \omega t) \right)\mathbf{e}_y.$$

(4.32)

There is an important point to note about the phase relationship between the electric and magnetic fields of electromagnetic waves in a dielectric. In free space, and when $k_{\text{imag}} = 0$, the fields are exactly in phase. However, comparing Equations 4.31 and 4.32, it is apparent that when $k_{\text{imag}} \neq 0$, the magnetic field is no longer exactly in phase with its companion electric field, but there is a fixed phase difference between the two. This is the hallmark of an electromagnetic wave that is damped as it propagates. The stronger the damping, the closer the phase difference is to $\pi/2$.

Equation 4.32 can be rewritten to show the phase difference explicitly:

$$\mathbf{B}_{\text{phys}}(z,t) = \frac{E_0}{\omega} \exp[-k_{\text{imag}}z]\, \alpha \cos(k_{\text{real}}z - \omega t + \beta)\,\mathbf{e}_y,$$

$A\cos\theta - B\sin\theta$
$= \sqrt{A^2 + B^2} \cos(\theta + \beta),$
where $\beta = \tan^{-1}(B/A).$

where $\alpha = \sqrt{k_{\text{real}}^2 + k_{\text{imag}}^2}$ and $\beta = \tan^{-1}(k_{\text{imag}}/k_{\text{real}})$. Comparing this with

Equation 4.31, we see that there is a phase difference β between the electric and magnetic components of the wave.

In principle, we should now go back and see how the boundary conditions cope with the sudden phase shift between electric and magnetic fields that must arise as the wave passes into the dielectric, say from free space. We shall not go into the details here. What happens is that the electric and magnetic fields of the reflected wave are in phase with each other, but both are shifted in phase with respect to the incident wave.

Calculating the absorption length

Since $k = n(\omega)\omega/c$, we can write expressions for the real and imaginary parts of the wavenumber using Equations 4.12 and 4.13. Many dielectric materials only weakly absorb electromagnetic waves across a wide range of frequencies. For such dielectrics, except near specific 'absorption frequencies', $\varepsilon_{\text{imag}} \ll \varepsilon_{\text{real}}$. When this is the case, $n_{\text{real}} \simeq \sqrt{\varepsilon_{\text{real}}}$, so

$$k_{\text{real}} \simeq \sqrt{\varepsilon_{\text{real}}(\omega)}\,\frac{\omega}{c}, \tag{4.33}$$

— see Ex 4.2.

and $n_{\text{imag}} \simeq \varepsilon_{\text{imag}}(\omega)/2\sqrt{\varepsilon_{\text{real}}(\omega)}$, so

$$k_{\text{imag}} = \frac{1}{\text{absorption length}} = n_{\text{imag}}\frac{\omega}{c} \simeq \frac{\varepsilon_{\text{imag}}(\omega)}{2\sqrt{\varepsilon_{\text{real}}(\omega)}}\frac{\omega}{c}. \tag{4.34}$$

Exercise 4.7   Calculate the absorption length for light with a free space wavelength, λ_0, of $600\,\text{nm}$, when it travels through a glass material for which $\varepsilon(\omega) = 1.50 + i(2.00 \times 10^{-5})$.

Exercise 4.8   Pure quartz has a complex relative permittivity at $30\,\text{MHz}$ given by $\varepsilon_{\text{real}} = 4.3$ and $\varepsilon_{\text{imag}} = 8.6 \times 10^{-4}$. Confirm that the degree to which the amplitude of the electric component of a $30\,\text{MHz}$ electromagnetic wave is attenuated on passing through a $10\,\text{mm}$ thick quartz window is a little over one part per million. (Ignore reflections at the surfaces.)   ∎

4.4.2   Attenuation of energy flux density

In earlier chapters, the energy flux density — the energy per unit time crossing unit area perpendicular to the direction of propagation — has been identified with the Poynting vector, $\mathbf{N}(z,t) = \mathbf{E}_{\text{phys}} \times \mathbf{H}_{\text{phys}}$. Before looking at the detail, see if you can predict how the energy flux density is attenuated by a medium with a complex dielectric function.

- An electromagnetic wave travels through a distance z in a dielectric medium for which the complex wavenumber is $k_{\text{real}} + i\,k_{\text{imag}}$. Suggest the factor by which the energy flux density is reduced.

○ Both $\mathbf{E}_{\text{phys}}$ and $\mathbf{H}_{\text{phys}}$ fields are attenuated by the factor $\exp(-k_{\text{imag}}z)$, so their product is expected to be attenuated by $\exp(-2k_{\text{imag}}z)$.

To confirm this expectation, we can substitute expressions for the physical electric and magnetic fields from Equations 4.31 and 4.32 into the standard expression for the Poynting vector, $\mathbf{N}(z, t)$. This will lead to an expression for the time-averaged energy flux density, $\overline{\mathbf{N}}(z)$.

Essential skill

Calculating the energy flux density for electromagnetic waves in dielectric media

Worked Example 4.3

Calculate the time-averaged Poynting vector associated with an electromagnetic wave that is travelling through a dielectric in the positive z-direction and is polarized in the x-direction.

Solution

Taking $\mu = 1$, the Poynting vector takes the form

$$\mathbf{N}(z, t) = \mathbf{E}_{\text{phys}}(z, t) \times \frac{\mathbf{B}_{\text{phys}}(z, t)}{\mu_0}.$$

The fields $\mathbf{E}$ and $\mathbf{B}$ are given by Equations 4.31 and 4.32. Using $\mathbf{e}_x \times \mathbf{e}_y = \mathbf{e}_z$ and simplifying the algebra leads to

$$\mathbf{N}(z, t) = \frac{E_0^2}{\mu_0 \omega} \exp(-2k_{\text{imag}} z)$$
$$\times \left[k_{\text{real}} \cos^2(k_{\text{real}} z - \omega t) \right.$$
$$\left. - k_{\text{imag}} \cos(k_{\text{real}} z - \omega t) \sin(k_{\text{real}} z - \omega t) \right] \mathbf{e}_z.$$

Recognizing that $\sin \theta \cos \theta = \frac{1}{2} \sin(2\theta)$, we can rewrite this as

$$\mathbf{N}(z, t) = \frac{E_0^2}{\mu_0 \omega} \exp(-2k_{\text{imag}} z)$$
$$\times \left[k_{\text{real}} \cos^2(k_{\text{real}} z - \omega t) - \frac{1}{2} k_{\text{imag}} \sin(2k_{\text{real}} z - 2\omega t) \right] \mathbf{e}_z.$$

Now, $\cos^2(k_{\text{real}} z - \omega t)$ has a time-average of $\frac{1}{2}$, and the second term in the square brackets has a time-average of 0, so

$$\overline{\mathbf{N}}(z) = \frac{E_0^2}{2\mu_0 \omega} k_{\text{real}} \exp(-2k_{\text{imag}} z) \, \mathbf{e}_z. \tag{4.35}$$

As anticipated, the energy flux density in the electromagnetic wave is progressively reduced by a factor of $\exp(-2k_{\text{imag}} z)$ as the wave propagates.

4.5   Dielectric characteristics of water and glass

In this section we shall examine experimental data for two common dielectrics. The aim is to see that the classical model of a dielectric offers a qualitative understanding.

4.5.1   Water

The electrons associated with the H_2O molecules in a drop of water interact with each other and their parent nuclei in many complicated ways. This complexity is imprinted into the dielectric properties of water. In particular, consider Figure 4.15, which shows measured values of the real and imaginary parts of the refractive index, n_{real} and n_{imag}, for a wide range of values of λ_0, the free space wavelength.

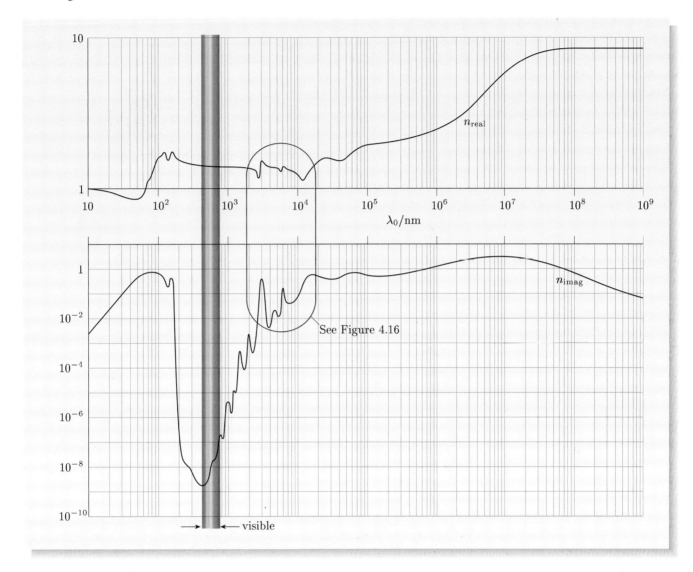

Figure 4.15 Measured real and imaginary parts, n_{real} and n_{imag}, of the refractive index of pure water, over a wide range of values of the free space wavelength λ_0. The scales are logarithmic. The scale for n_{real} is expanded about six times compared with the scale for n_{imag}. The visible part of the spectrum is from about 400 nm to 750 nm.

I especially draw your attention to the fact that the imaginary part of water's refractive index varies over many powers of ten. According to Equation 4.35, the absorption of a wave's energy is governed by the imaginary part of the wavenumber, $k_{\mathrm{imag}} = n_{\mathrm{imag}}\omega/c$. It is remarkable that over the visible spectrum (approximately 400 nm to 750 nm), light passes through pure water with virtually no absorption, yet in the ultraviolet region below about 200 nm, radiation is strongly absorbed. Life would be very different if this were not the case, particularly since ultraviolet radiation can be very damaging to organic tissue. The absorption length for ultraviolet radiation is less than a millimetre, so clouds comprising tiny droplets of water attenuate ultraviolet radiation very effectively.

Exercise 4.9 Estimate the absorption length in water for electromagnetic radiation with free space wavelengths of 100 nm (near ultraviolet), 500 nm (visible) and 1000 nm (near infrared). ∎

Figure 4.16 shows detail of the *dielectric function* of water, $\varepsilon(\omega) = n^2$, that corresponds to the data for its *refractive index* in the infrared region ringed in Figure 4.15. Note that in Figure 4.16 the vertical axis is linear and the primary horizontal axis is angular frequency, whereas in Figure 4.15 it is wavelength. Notice in particular the two narrow peaks in the imaginary part of the dielectric function in Figure 4.16. These peaks occur where the corresponding real part of the dielectric function changes relatively rapidly: as the frequency increases, $\varepsilon_{\text{real}}$ first rises, then steps down before climbing back a little. Qualitatively, each peak in $\varepsilon_{\text{imag}}$, and the associated step in $\varepsilon_{\text{real}}$, resembles the resonant behaviour we found with the simple classical model in Section 4.2 (compare with Figure 4.4). However, the simple model had only a single resonant frequency, and for the example quoted in Exercise 4.1, that was in the ultraviolet region.

In developing the model, we explicitly followed the motion of electrons and did not include the slower reorientation of the permanent molecular dipole moments, which are expected to occur at lower frequencies. It is reasonable to suggest that the infrared resonances shown in Figure 4.16 are associated with the excitation of the molecular motions. Indeed, this interpretation is broadly correct. If you now go back to inspect Figure 4.15 you will see that every peak in n_{imag} corresponds with a step in n_{real}. Each peak corresponds with a particular resonance in the charge distribution associated with clusters of water molecules, or with individual molecules, or with electrons bound to the constituent oxygen and hydrogen atoms.

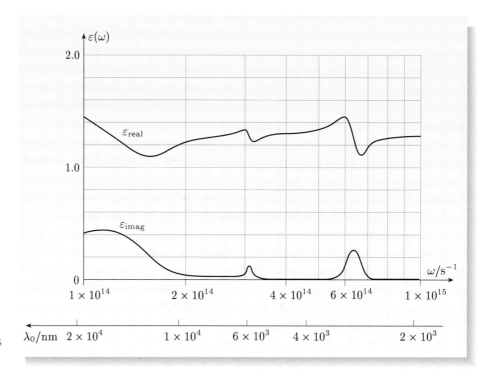

Figure 4.16 $\varepsilon_{\text{real}}$ and $\varepsilon_{\text{imag}}$ for pure water as functions of ω over the part of the infrared region of the spectrum ringed in Figure 4.15. The vertical scale is linear.

- Describe how the shapes of the steps in n_{real} shown in Figure 4.15 correlate with the shapes of the corresponding peaks in n_{imag}.

○ Broad peaks in n_{imag} accompany slow changes in n_{real}. Sharper peaks in n_{imag} correspond with more abrupt changes in n_{real}. The heights of peaks in n_{imag} correlate with the sizes of steps in n_{real}.

4.5.2 Silica

Most optical fibre used for telecommunications is based on amorphous silica (i.e. silicon dioxide, SiO_2). Figure 4.17 shows the measured values of the real and imaginary parts of the *refractive index*, n_{real} and n_{imag}, of optical-fibre-grade silica, for a range of wavelengths.

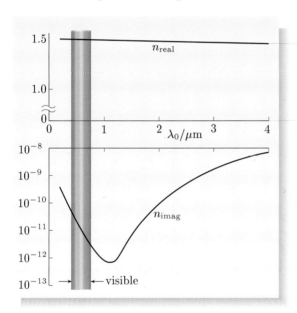

Figure 4.17 Measured real and imaginary parts of the refractive index of amorphous silica, over a range of values of λ_0, the free space wavelength.

Figure 4.18 indicates schematically the structure of the *dielectric function* over a much wider spectral range, plotted here against angular frequency; the low frequency (long wavelength) limit, which includes the dynamical response of all bound charges, ionic and electronic, is also shown. The dielectric function of silica is evidently much less complicated than water. There seem to be two major absorption zones. The higher frequency, shorter wavelength zone is associated with electrons; the lower frequency, longer wavelength feature can be attributed to impurity ions.

We can estimate the extent to which pulses of light become dispersed and lose energy through absorption as they pass through optical fibres by applying the results of Sections 4.3 and 4.4. As an example, we shall consider the dispersion of a 40 ns pulse of light from a 'white' LED after transmission down 1 km of silica-based fibre. A white-light diode typically

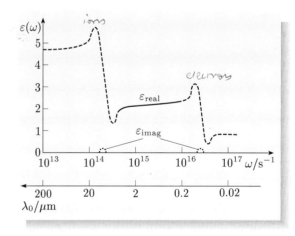

Figure 4.18 A sketch of the general form of the dielectric function for amorphous silica as a function of frequency. The solid line corresponds with the data in Figure 4.17.

comprises three separate diodes, emitting light in narrow bands of wavelengths centred on 480, 585 and 630 nm.

First let us consider the temporal separation between signal components at the three centre wavelengths. We need to know the group speeds for each band of wavelengths, and these can be determined from Equation 4.27, using data about $n_{\text{real}}(\omega)$ which could, with a little patience, be extracted from Figure 4.17. The results have been recorded in Table 4.1, along with the time taken for pulses with the three wavelengths to travel down the fibre ($t(1\,\text{km}) = 10^3\,\text{m}/v_{\text{group}}$).

Table 4.1 Group speeds and transit times.

λ_0/nm	$v_{\text{group}}/10^8\,\text{m s}^{-1}$	$t(1\,\text{km})/\mu\text{s}$
480	2.00	5.00
585	2.01	4.98
630	2.02	4.95

The data indicate that the red component of the original pulse arrives 50 ns before the blue component. This temporal dispersion of the pulse is due to the 150 nm range of wavelengths in the pulse. For a single-colour diode, the range of wavelengths emitted is only about $\frac{1}{3}$ of that for a white-light diode, so the spreading of the pulse would be about $\frac{50}{3}$ ns. A laser diode emits a much narrower range of wavelengths, about 3 nm around a central frequency, and the spreading of the pulse is reduced proportionately to about 1 ns per km.

In the following exercise, you can compare the intensities of the three colour components emitted by a white-light diode after they have travelled through a silica fibre.

Exercise 4.10 A white LED typically emits simultaneously in three narrow bands centred around wavelengths of 480, 585 and 630 nm. The values of n_{imag} for silica at these wavelengths are shown in Table 4.2.

(a) Check that the values in the table are roughly consistent with the data in Figure 4.17.

(b) Assuming that the three colour components from this diode initially have the same amplitudes, determine their relative intensities (proportional to the squares of the amplitudes) after transmission down 1 km of silica-based fibre, and hence complete the table. ◼

Table 4.2 Imaginary part of the refractive index and relative intensity after travelling 1 km through amorphous silica for light of three wavelengths.

λ_0/nm	$n_{\text{imag}}/10^{-11}$	Relative intensity
480	3	
585	1	
630	0.6	

4.5.3 Losing signals in optical fibres: reprise

You have seen that the model for dielectric response outlined at the start of this chapter is consistent with data for two common dielectrics. The model provides a qualitative description of the dielectric response in terms of damped resonances. In this final section, I want to restore your faith in optical-fibre telecommunications, which may have been shaken at the start of the chapter and by the example and exercise in the previous subsection.

Dispersion is a consequence of a frequency-dependent dielectric function, which spreads electromagnetic energy through time and space, smearing the sharp edges of pulses. The complex nature of the dielectric function leads to absorption, which transfers electromagnetic energy into heat. But the absorption mechanisms that we have discussed so far are not the only challenges facing optical telecommunications. Figure 4.19 shows the signal attenuation encountered in practical optical fibres, in terms of decibels per kilometre — the engineering unit for attenuation. In addition to the absorption associated with the oscillations of electrons and ions, there are two additional attenuation mechanisms whose effects are included here. In Chapter 2 we noted that the process of Rayleigh scattering can transfer energy out of a beam of electromagnetic radiation. Although in this process the energy remains electromagnetic, the information content of signals in optical fibres is degraded by Rayleigh scattering from impurities and inhomogeneities, and this plays a major part in the attenuation of the signals. There is also additional dielectric absorption arising from hydroxyl groups (OH), which are extremely difficult to keep out of silica, and which give rise to the peaks at $1.2\,\mu$m and $1.4\,\mu$m in the total attenuation shown in Figure 4.19. The technology has literally worked around the problems caused by these peaks by concentrating on transmission of signals within the low-loss windows at $1.3\,\mu$m and $1.55\,\mu$m.

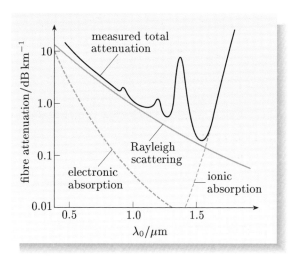

Figure 4.19 Signal loss in optical fibre, expressed in $\mathrm{dB\,km^{-1}} \equiv 2.0 \times 10^4 \times k_{\mathrm{imag}} \times \log_{10}(\mathrm{e})$.

Two other challenges have had to be overcome for long-distance optical-fibre telecommunications — amplification to offset the effects of absorption, and compensation for the effects of dispersion. The first requires a medium for which k_{imag} is negative — that is one way of thinking about a laser and, in practice, sections of fibre-lasers are used to boost signals. There is plenty of scope also, through tailoring the composition and structure of fibres, to construct sections of dispersion-compensating fibre that undo the effects of dispersion, rather like the way compound lenses reduce the chromatic aberration of individual lenses. It also pays to use sources with narrow spectral widths; diode lasers, with wavelength spreads of 3 nm, are clearly preferable to white-light sources for minimizing the effects of dispersion.

Transatlantic communications have relied on optical fibre systems for several decades, and the latest generation has the capacity to transfer several gigabits of data per second down a single fibre. As you should now be able to appreciate, the technology owes much to a proper understanding of electromagnetic wave propagation in dielectrics.

Summary of Chapter 4

Section 4.1   Dispersion and absorption degrade light pulses as they travel along optical fibres. This establishes the need for a model that accounts for these processes.

Section 4.2   The classical model of a dielectric is based on a dynamical description of electrons bound to atoms. The model leads to a dielectric function that expresses the relative permittivity as a complex, frequency-dependent quantity, $\varepsilon_{\text{real}}(\omega) + \mathrm{i}\,\varepsilon_{\text{imag}}(\omega)$. The real part of the dielectric function is almost constant except in the neighbourhood of characteristic resonant frequencies, where it changes rapidly. In the same frequency band, the imaginary part of the dielectric function rises from virtually zero to a peak. The refractive index is similarly a complex function of frequency.

Section 4.3   The frequency-dependence of the real part of the dielectric function leads to dispersion of waves of different frequencies owing to their different speeds of propagation. Angular dispersion arises when electromagnetic radiation is refracted as it crosses an interface between two dielectric materials. Dispersion also spreads radiation energy as it propagates through the bulk of a dielectric. Linear combinations of plane waves with different frequencies do not propagate as a fixed shape in a dispersive medium; that is, the wave equation does *not* have solutions of the d'Alembert form except in the special case where the contributing plane waves all travel with the same speed. Information is transmitted by modulated waves and wave packets rather than continuous sinusoidal waves. Energy and information propagate at the group speed $\mathrm{d}\omega/\mathrm{d}k$, whereas the component waves travel at the phase speed ω/k.

Section 4.4   The imaginary part of the dielectric function is associated with the loss of energy from an electromagnetic wave as it traverses a dielectric medium. The amplitude of the fields decreases exponentially with distance as $\exp(-k_{\text{imag}}z)$, and the energy as $\exp(-2k_{\text{imag}}z)$.

Section 4.5   Measurements of refractive index yield dielectric data for water and for silica. In both cases there are features that can be recognized from the simple model of Section 4.2. The overall picture is complicated by the presence of a variety of absorption pathways. The attenuation of the signal in a dielectric is also in part due to scattering from impurities and inhomogeneities.

Achievements from Chapter 4

After studying this chapter you should be able to do the following.

4.1 Explain the meanings of the newly defined (emboldened) terms and symbols, and use them appropriately.

4.2 Describe the phenomena of dispersion and absorption in dielectrics with reference to propagation of light pulses in optical fibres.

4.3 Use a dynamical model of dielectric behaviour to relate the harmonic response of electrons to the electric field and changes in the complex, frequency-dependent dielectric function.

4.4 Show that monochromatic waves individually satisfy Maxwell's equations even when there is dispersion.

4.5 Show that wave packets are analogous to d'Alembert solutions in the absence of dispersion.

4.6 Explain what is meant by the group speed of an electromagnetic signal, and determine the group speed from the dispersion relation between ω and k.

4.7 Show that the imaginary part of the dielectric function gives rise to absorption of energy by dielectric material and thereby attenuates the energy flux density of the electromagnetic wave.

4.8 Make quantitative estimates of dispersion and absorption given data (graphical or otherwise) for the dielectric function or refractive index of a material.

Chapter 5 Conductors: absorption and reflection

The management of air traffic by means of radar (Figure 5.1) is one of the more obvious technological exploitations of reflections of electromagnetic waves from conductors. Radar systems use electromagnetic radiation at microwave frequencies. Electrical circuitry converts pulses of electrical oscillations (around $1\,\mu s$ duration at 1 GHz frequency) into electromagnetic waves with the same pulse duration and frequency, and these waves are guided along a hollow rectangular metal tube, a few centimetres across, to the focal spot F of a parabolic antenna. Outgoing radiation is directed from here onto the antenna and is reflected to form a beam, which sweeps around as the entire antenna rotates. Pulses are reflected back to the antenna from aircraft and other conducting objects in their path, and the antenna reflects the incoming waves onto the focal spot from where the electromagnetic waves are guided back along the metal tube to detection circuitry where they are interchanged with electrical oscillations. The time delay between transmission of a pulse and the detection of a reflection (or echo) from an object in the beam is proportional to the distance to the object (about $7\,\mu s\,km^{-1}$). The pulsed electromagnetic waves are literally piped along a hollow metal tube 'waveguide' between the ground-based electronics and the focus F of the parabolic reflector, and are reflected from the metallic antenna. For these applications we must understand how electromagnetic waves interact with conductors.

Figure 5.1   The antenna of an air traffic control radar (*ra*dio *d*etection *a*nd *r*anging) system. Microwave pulses are piped along a metal-tube waveguide to the focus F of the parabolic metallic antenna, and reflected from the rotating antenna to produce a rotating pulsed microwave beam.

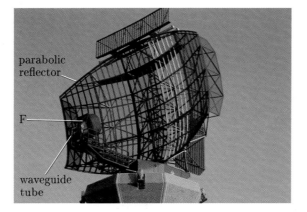

This chapter is primarily concerned with the reflection of electromagnetic waves from conductors, and we shall discuss the limited extent to which such waves penetrate into conductors. The goals are to establish under what conditions a given conducting material will be an effective reflector, and how hollow tubes of conducting material can be used as a way of linking circuits to antennas.

We start by adapting the model we introduced in Chapter 4 to describe the response of dielectric materials to electromagnetic waves so that it describes the response of conductors. We then use Maxwell's equations to derive the equation obeyed by an electromagnetic wave inside a conductor. We shall consider the boundary conditions that must be satisfied at a conductor's surface, and apply them to some simple cases to quantify the reflection from the surface. Chapter 5 ends with a brief description of rectangular waveguides, which do for microwaves what optical fibres do for light.

5.1   Absorption of electromagnetic waves by conductors

When an electromagnetic wave enters a conductor, its electric field causes currents to flow, leading to a loss of energy from the wave through Joule heating. The aim of this section is to model the propagation of monochromatic plane waves in a conducting medium so that this loss process can be quantified.

Our starting point is the Ampère–Maxwell law,

$$\operatorname{curl}\mathbf{H} = \mathbf{J}_\mathrm{f} + \frac{\partial \mathbf{D}}{\partial t}, \tag{5.1}$$

where $\mathbf{J}_\mathrm{f}$ is the free current given by Ohm's law,

$$\mathbf{J}_\mathrm{f} = \sigma\mathbf{E}, \tag{5.2}$$

and σ is the conductivity.

For LIH materials, the second term on the right in the Ampère–Maxwell law can also be expressed in terms of the electric field using $\mathbf{D} = \varepsilon\varepsilon_0\mathbf{E}$:

$$\operatorname{curl}\mathbf{H} = \sigma\mathbf{E} + \varepsilon\varepsilon_0\frac{\partial\mathbf{E}}{\partial t}.$$

As usual, we shall study solutions with a time-dependence of the form $\exp[-\mathrm{i}\omega t]$, for which this equation becomes

$$\operatorname{curl}\mathbf{H} = \sigma\mathbf{E} - \mathrm{i}\omega\varepsilon\varepsilon_0\mathbf{E}. \tag{5.3}$$

But what is ε for a conductor? To define a relative permittivity for a conductor, we use the same sort of approach as used in Chapter 4, for which a further regrouping of the terms in Equation 5.3 is useful. We combine conductivity and permittivity into an effective relative permittivity function, $\varepsilon_\mathrm{eff}(\omega)$:

$$\operatorname{curl}\mathbf{H} = -\mathrm{i}\omega\,\varepsilon_\mathrm{eff}(\omega)\,\varepsilon_0\mathbf{E}, \tag{5.4}$$

where $\varepsilon_\mathrm{eff}(\omega) = \varepsilon - \sigma/\mathrm{i}\omega\varepsilon_0$. The goal of the next section is to determine $\varepsilon_\mathrm{eff}(\omega)$, which is analogous to the dielectric function of Chapter 4, by building a model of the response of a conducting material to an electromagnetic wave.

5.1.1   A simple classical model of a conductor

In Chapter 4 we developed a classical model of dielectric behaviour based on the aggregate response of bound electrons that are displaced by the electric field of an electromagnetic wave. In that model it is supposed that the displacement of an electron from its equilibrium position is much less than the wavelength of the radiation. This means that the spatial variation of the electric field can be ignored when calculating the response of a single electron. Provided that this condition is met, the same approach can be used as the basis of an equivalent model for conductors. For dielectrics, the conclusion was that the dielectric function, which accounts for the presence of material through $\mathbf{D} = \varepsilon(\omega)\varepsilon_0\mathbf{E}$, is given by

$$\varepsilon(\omega) = 1 + \omega_\mathrm{p}^2 \frac{1}{(\omega_\mathrm{n}^2 - \omega^2) - \mathrm{i}\omega\gamma}, \tag{5.5}$$

where $\omega_\mathrm{p}^2 = n_\mathrm{e}e^2/m\varepsilon_0$ scales the response in proportion to the number density of electrons involved.

Note that n_e here is the number density of free electrons, not a refractive index.

● What do ω_n and γ represent?

○ First, ω_n represents the natural frequency of the spring-like bonds that bind electrons to their parent atoms within a material. Second, γ represents a friction parameter associated with the loss of energy by damping of the oscillatory motion of electrons.

The complex relative permittivity function for a conductor

To adapt the dielectric model so that it applies to a conductor, we start again with the equation of motion for a single electron, which was introduced in Section 4.2:

$$m \frac{\mathrm{d}^2 \mathbf{r}(t)}{\mathrm{d}t^2} = -a\,\mathbf{r}(t) - b\,\frac{\mathrm{d}\mathbf{r}(t)}{\mathrm{d}t} - e\,\mathbf{E}(\mathbf{r}(t), t). \tag{5.6}$$

In a conductor there is a significant population of free electrons, which are not bound to any particular parent atoms. For these virtually unbound electrons, there is no restoring force opposing displacement, so $a = 0$. However, the motion of these unbound electrons is damped by collisions with the lattice, and these collisions dissipate energy. This is what gives rise to the finite electrical conductivity, σ, of a real conductor that appears in Ohm's law (Equation 5.2).

Electrical conductivity is a readily measurable quantity and we can use it to quantify the damping that accompanies collisions between electrons and the lattice. It is simplest to look at the average drift motion of an electron in a steady electric field, during which the electrical force, $-e\mathbf{E}$, in Equation 5.6 is balanced only by the friction term, $-b\,\mathrm{d}\mathbf{r}/\mathrm{d}t$, which effectively gives the rate at which collisions transfer momentum from electron drift into random thermal motion. If the mean time between collisions of an electron with the lattice is τ_c (so that $1/\tau_c$ is the frequency of collisions between an electron and the lattice), then we can replace the friction parameter b with m/τ_c, so the steady drift, $\mathbf{v}_{\mathrm{drift}}$, is given by

$$\mathbf{0} = -\frac{m\mathbf{v}_{\mathrm{drift}}}{\tau_c} - e\,\mathbf{E} \quad \text{or} \quad \mathbf{v}_{\mathrm{drift}} = -\frac{e\tau_c}{m}\mathbf{E}. \tag{5.7}$$

The current density associated with the free electrons, which have number density n_e and travel at the drift velocity $\mathbf{v}_{\mathrm{drift}}$, is

$$\mathbf{J}_f = n_e(-e)\mathbf{v}_{\mathrm{drift}} = \frac{n_e e^2 \tau_c}{m}\mathbf{E}.$$

Comparing this with Ohm's law, $\mathbf{J}_f = \sigma\mathbf{E}$, we see that the conductivity is given by

$$\sigma = \frac{n_e e^2 \tau_c}{m}. \tag{5.8}$$

This defines τ_c in terms of the dc electrical conductivity, and we can use τ_c in the general model of electron dynamics. Thus, Equation 5.5 can be adapted to give a complex relative permittivity function for a conductor by setting ω_n to zero (since $a \to 0$) and replacing γ with $1/\tau_c$ (since $\gamma = b/m$):

$$\varepsilon_{\mathrm{eff}}(\omega) = 1 - \omega_p^2 \frac{1}{\omega^2 + \mathrm{i}\omega/\tau_c}. \tag{5.9}$$

We will examine the consequences of this form of the equation for $\varepsilon_{\mathrm{eff}}(\omega)$ at high, intermediate and low frequencies.

Effective permittivity at high and intermediate frequencies

In Equation 5.9, when $\omega \gg 1/\tau_c$, the effective permittivity is purely real. The effect of the material on electromagnetic radiation then depends only on the relative size of ω and ω_p. For metallic conductors, $1/\tau_c \sim 10^{13}\,\text{s}^{-1}$, which corresponds with the frequency of far infrared radiation, whereas $\omega_p \sim 10^{16}\,\text{s}^{-1}$ corresponds with ultraviolet radiation.

At sufficiently high frequency, when $\omega \gg \omega_p$, the free electrons in a conductor cannot respond quickly enough to have any appreciable effect on electromagnetic waves, and $\varepsilon_{\text{eff}}(\omega) \to 1$ as $\omega_p/\omega \to 0$. This is consistent with the partial transparency of metals to X-rays, though our model is only classical, and absorption of energy via quantum mechanical processes must be included in a complete description. We return to this high-frequency regime in connection with plasmas in Chapter 6.

At intermediate frequencies, when $1/\tau_c \ll \omega < \omega_p$, the relative permittivity is real and negative, $\varepsilon_{\text{eff}}(\omega) < 0$. For metals, this range corresponds with visible and near infrared frequencies. When the relative permittivity is real and negative, the wavenumber, k, is purely imaginary:

$$k = n\omega/c = \sqrt{\varepsilon_{\text{eff}}(\omega)}\,\frac{\omega}{c} = \mathrm{i}\sqrt{|\varepsilon_{\text{eff}}(\omega)|}\,\frac{\omega}{c} = \mathrm{i}k_{\text{imag}}.$$

If the wavenumber is imaginary, disturbances of the form $E = E_0 \exp[\mathrm{i}(kz - \omega t)]$ do not propagate but simply evanesce, as shown in Figure 5.2 (compare with Subsection 3.4.5). Without propagation, there is no transport of electromagnetic energy beyond the surface layer of the conductor. In this intermediate frequency regime, where $1/\tau_c \ll \omega < \omega_p$, the classical model indicates that there must be total reflection of radiation that is incident on a conductor. That is consistent with the high reflectivity of metals in the visible and near infrared frequency ranges.

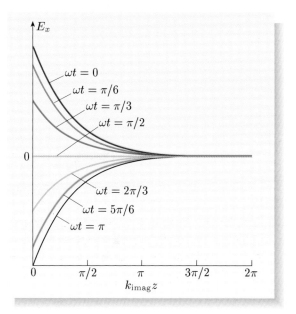

Figure 5.2 A wave in the region $z < 0$ becomes an evanescent disturbance when it crosses the boundary (in the $z = 0$ plane) of a conductor, which occupies the space $z > 0$. The electric field is shown for successive instants separated by time intervals of $\pi/6\omega$.

The classical model that we have developed for conductors offers nothing to account for why gold and silver have different colours when viewed in white light. This is because the simple classical model considers only the role of unbound electrons. However, there are also bound electrons around the atom cores in a conductor, and these bound electrons behave much like those considered for dielectrics. We could try to add them into the model, but a quantum mechanical analysis is required to deal properly with the subtleties of absorption that lead to the characteristic colours of particular metals, and that is beyond the scope of this course.

Effective permittivity at low frequency

The low-frequency limit of Equation 5.9 is reached when $\omega \ll 1/\tau_c$. According to Equation 5.8, $\tau_c = m\sigma/n_e e^2$, so in this limit

$$\varepsilon_{\text{eff}}(\omega) = 1 - \frac{\omega_{\text{p}}^2}{\mathrm{i}\omega/\tau_c} = 1 - \frac{n_e e^2}{m\varepsilon_0} \frac{\tau_c}{\mathrm{i}\omega}$$

$$= 1 - \frac{\sigma}{\mathrm{i}\omega\varepsilon_0}, \qquad \text{for } \omega \ll n_e e^2/m\sigma. \tag{5.10}$$

$\omega_{\text{p}}^2 = n_e e^2/m\varepsilon_0$

In metals, this frequency range corresponds with $\omega \ll 10^{13}\,\mathrm{s}^{-1}$ — less than for the infrared and visible bands but encompassing all of the microwave and radio communication frequencies. In this low-frequency limit, the regrouped form of the Ampère–Maxwell law (Equation 5.4) becomes

$$\operatorname{curl}\mathbf{H} = -\mathrm{i}\omega\left(1 - \frac{\sigma}{\mathrm{i}\omega\varepsilon_0}\right)\varepsilon_0\mathbf{E} = (\sigma - \mathrm{i}\omega\varepsilon_0)\,\mathbf{E}, \tag{5.11}$$

which is just Equation 5.3 with $\varepsilon = 1$. We have made progress, since at the outset we did not know what value to use for ε in a conductor. In the low-frequency limit, the model suggests that the presence of a conductor simply adds free current (carried by free electrons in the conductor) to the $-\mathrm{i}\omega\varepsilon_0\mathbf{E}$ term for free space. We shall explore this regime in the remaining parts of this chapter.

In metals, the ratio of the magnitudes of the two terms on the right-hand side of Equation 5.11 is

$$\frac{\sigma}{\omega\varepsilon_0} = \frac{n_e e^2 \tau_c}{m\varepsilon_0\omega} = \frac{\omega_{\text{p}}^2 \tau_c}{\omega} = \frac{\omega_{\text{p}}}{\omega}\frac{\omega_{\text{p}}}{1/\tau_c}.$$

In the low-frequency range, $\omega \ll \omega_{\text{p}}$, and for metals $1/\tau_c \ll \omega_{\text{p}}$, so the ratio $\sigma/\omega\varepsilon_0 \gg 1$. The second term on the right-hand side of Equation 5.11 is therefore negligible compared with the first term. Figure 5.3 shows how readily this inequality is satisfied when light, or a wave with lower frequency, interacts with good conductors; it also summarizes the results of the modelling in this subsection.

Table 5.1   Conductivities of various materials at 25 °C.

Conductor	$\sigma/\Omega^{-1}\,\mathrm{m}^{-1}$
silver	6.1×10^7
copper	5.8×10^7
graphite	$\sim 1 \times 10^5$
seawater	~ 5
distilled water	$\sim 2 \times 10^{-2}$

Exercise 5.1   Conductivities for various materials are given in Table 5.1.

(a) Estimate the angular frequencies at which the two terms on the right-hand side of Equation 5.11 would be equal in magnitude for (i) copper and (ii) seawater.

(b) Estimate the ratio of the magnitudes of the two terms on the right-hand side of Equation 5.11 for graphite at microwave frequencies ($\omega \sim 10^{10}\,\mathrm{s}^{-1}$). ∎

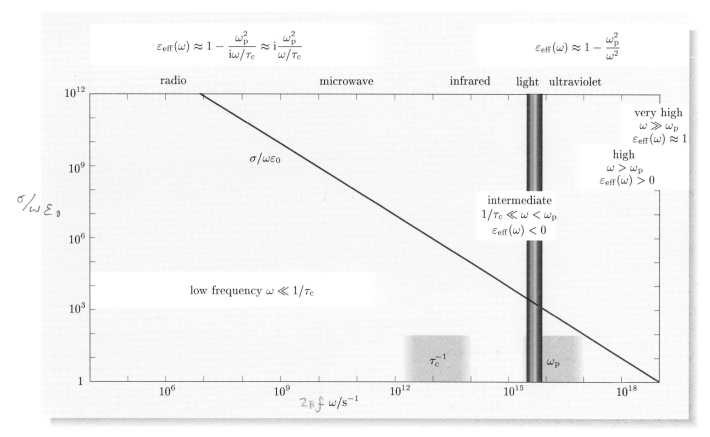

$$\varepsilon_{\text{eff}}(\omega) \approx 1 - \frac{\omega_{\text{p}}^2}{\mathrm{i}\omega/\tau_{\text{c}}} \approx \mathrm{i}\,\frac{\omega_{\text{p}}^2}{\omega/\tau_{\text{c}}} \qquad\qquad \varepsilon_{\text{eff}}(\omega) \approx 1 - \frac{\omega_{\text{p}}^2}{\omega^2}$$

Figure 5.3 The variation of the magnitude of the ratio of the two terms on the right-hand side of Equation 5.11, $\sigma/\omega\varepsilon_0$, with frequency for a good metallic conductor. The regions shaded grey indicate the ranges of typical values of $1/\tau_{\text{c}}$ and ω_{p} for metals. The different frequency regimes discussed in this subsection are indicated by the white bands.

5.1.2 Differential equation for low-frequency radiation in conductors

From now onwards in this chapter we shall consider only the low-frequency regime, where $\omega \ll 1/\tau_{\text{c}}$ and $\omega \ll \sigma/\varepsilon_0$. As we have shown in the previous subsection, in a conducting medium, the Ampère–Maxwell law is then given to a good approximation by

$$\operatorname{curl}\mathbf{H} = \sigma\mathbf{E}. \tag{5.12}$$

As usual let us assume that the conducting medium is linear, isotropic and homogeneous, and that the relative permeability, μ, is unity, so that $\mathbf{B} = \mu_0\mathbf{H}$. (Throughout this chapter, it is assumed that $\mu = 1$.) Then Equation 5.12 becomes

$$\operatorname{curl}\mathbf{B} = \mu_0\sigma\mathbf{E}. \tag{5.13}$$

To derive an equation for $\mathbf{B}$ alone, we start by taking the curl of Equation 5.13:

$$\operatorname{curl}(\operatorname{curl}\mathbf{B}) = \mu_0\sigma\operatorname{curl}\mathbf{E}.$$

We use an identity from inside the back cover to simplify the $\operatorname{curl}(\operatorname{curl}\mathbf{B})$ term (just as we did in Chapter 1 when deriving the wave equation for free space):

$$\operatorname{curl}(\operatorname{curl}\mathbf{B}) = \operatorname{grad}(\operatorname{div}\mathbf{B}) - \nabla^2\mathbf{B}.$$

Since div $\mathbf{B} = 0$ (no-monopole law), this reduces to $\text{curl}(\text{curl}\,\mathbf{B}) = -\nabla^2\mathbf{B}$, and using Faraday's law to eliminate $\text{curl}\,\mathbf{E}$, we obtain

$$\nabla^2\mathbf{B} = \mu_0\sigma\frac{\partial\mathbf{B}}{\partial t}. \tag{5.14}$$

● What assumptions were made when deriving Equation 5.14?

○ We assumed that: (a) we are dealing with the low-frequency regime, which requires that $\omega \ll 1/\tau_c$; (b) the conduction current dominates the $\varepsilon\varepsilon_0\,\partial\mathbf{E}/\partial t$ term in the Ampère–Maxwell law, which requires that $\omega \ll \sigma/\varepsilon_0$; (c) the conductor has an LIH, vacuum-like response to magnetic fields, which sets $\mu = 1$.

● What common metal has been excluded by setting $\mu = 1$?

○ Iron (and other ferromagnetic conductors).

Free charge disperses rapidly within a conductor, ensuring that div $\mathbf{D} = 0$, and since we are considering only LIH materials, div $\mathbf{E} = 0$. This means that an equation that is similar to Equation 5.14 can be derived for the electric field:

$$\nabla^2\mathbf{E} = \mu_0\sigma\frac{\partial\mathbf{E}}{\partial t}. \tag{5.15}$$

The form of Equations 5.14 and 5.15 generally describes diffusion, although we have come across it here in the search for an equation that describes electromagnetic waves in conductors.

To solve Equation 5.15 for a plane wave travelling in the z-direction, let us see if there are solutions of the form $\mathbf{E}(z, t) = \mathbf{E}_0 \exp[i(kz - \omega t)]$, where $\mathbf{E}_0$ is a constant vector perpendicular to the z-axis. Substituting this expression into Equation 5.15 gives

$$-k^2 = -i\omega\mu_0\sigma.$$

If k^2 is an imaginary number, then k itself is a complex number. To find k, we first write

$$k = k_{\text{real}} + ik_{\text{imag}},$$

so that

$$k^2 = (k_{\text{real}}^2 - k_{\text{imag}}^2) + 2ik_{\text{real}}k_{\text{imag}}.$$

Then, since k^2 is purely imaginary, it must be that $k_{\text{real}}^2 = k_{\text{imag}}^2$, and it follows that

$$k_{\text{real}} = k_{\text{imag}} = \sqrt{\frac{\mu_0\sigma\omega}{2}}. \tag{5.16}$$

We discussed waves with complex wavenumbers in Section 4.4. This situation is revisited in the next subsection.

5.1.3   Skin depth

The physical electric field of an electromagnetic wave, polarized in the x-direction and travelling in the z-direction through a conducting medium where $\omega \ll 1/\tau_c$

and $\omega \ll \sigma/\varepsilon_0$, takes the form

$$\mathbf{E}_{\mathrm{phys}} = \mathrm{Re}\{\mathbf{E}_0 \exp[\mathrm{i}(kz - \omega t)]\}$$
$$= E_0 \exp[-k_{\mathrm{imag}}z] \cos(k_{\mathrm{real}}z - \omega t)\,\mathbf{e}_x, \qquad (5.17)$$

where k_{real} and k_{imag} are given by Equation 5.16. The amplitude of the electric field is proportional to $\exp[-k_{\mathrm{imag}}z]$, so after a distance $\delta = 1/k_{\mathrm{imag}}$, it has fallen by the factor $1/\mathrm{e} \simeq 0.37$. This characteristic penetration distance δ is known as the **skin depth**, and is given by

$$\delta = \frac{1}{k_{\mathrm{imag}}} = \sqrt{\frac{2}{\mu_0 \sigma \omega}}. \qquad (5.18)$$

The amplitude of the magnetic field has the same exponential decay. The attenuation is very rapid, as can be seen by comparing the skin depth with the free space wavelength λ_0:

$$\frac{\delta}{\lambda_0} = \delta\,\frac{\omega}{2\pi c} = \sqrt{\frac{2}{\mu_0 \sigma \omega}}\,\frac{\omega}{2\pi}\sqrt{\varepsilon_0 \mu_0} = \frac{1}{\sqrt{2}\,\pi}\sqrt{\frac{\omega \varepsilon_0}{\sigma}}.$$

Since we are assuming that $\omega \ll \sigma/\varepsilon_0$, the ratio $\delta/\lambda_0 \ll 1$, so the distance that the fields penetrate into a metal is very much less than the free space wavelength. Figure 5.4 compares the electric field at several instants during half a cycle of a wave propagating into a conductor, with the field for a wave with the same frequency propagating in free space. Because $\delta \ll \lambda_0$, the physical scale in part (a) of Figure 5.4 is much shorter than that in part (b).

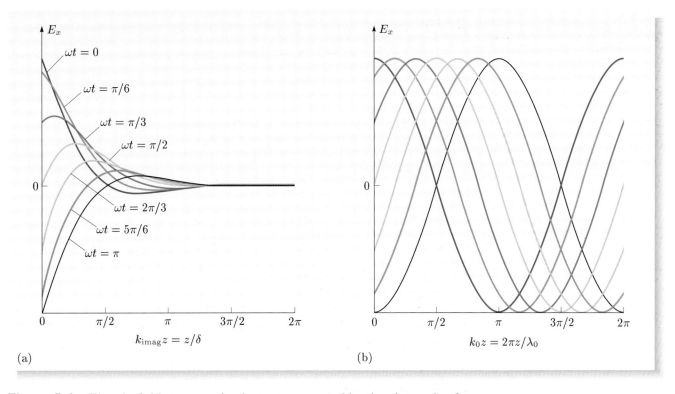

(a)   (b)

Figure 5.4 Electric field at successive instants, separated by time intervals of $\pi/6\omega$, over a half cycle of a wave (a) just below the surface (at $z = 0$) of a conductor and (b) in free space.

Exercise 5.2   (a) Use data from Table 5.1 to calculate the skin depth of copper at 50 Hz, 50 MHz and 50 THz, and compare the results with the free space wavelengths at these frequencies.

(b) Calculate the skin depth of seawater for (low and very low frequency) radio waves with free space wavelengths 3000 m and 3000 km. ■

The skin effect in good conductors

Since the skin depth is proportional to $\omega^{-1/2}$, high-frequency currents are largely carried in a thin outer layer of a conductor. This is known as the **skin effect**. To drive oscillating currents deeper requires an electric field to penetrate more deeply and, as we have just seen, there is severe attenuation of an oscillating electric field below the surface of a conductor. Consequently, the effective resistance of a wire increases with frequency since only a small proportion of its cross-sectional area is actually carrying the current. There is no point in using solid wires with a radius much larger than the skin depth of the highest frequency being used — that is why fine-strand, braided cables are commonly used in radio-frequency applications to increase the surface area available to carry current.

5.2   Conditions at a conducting boundary

I now want to consider the reflection and transmission of electromagnetic waves that are incident from a non-conducting medium onto a conducting surface. Just as in Chapter 3, where we modelled the interaction of waves with a dielectric interface, we shall need to match various parallel and perpendicular components of the electromagnetic fields at the surface.

When matching boundary conditions at a dielectric interface in Section 3.2, we assumed that $\mathbf{J}_f$ was zero exactly on the interface. That is also a reasonable assumption for ordinary conductors because any current will be carried in a layer that extends about one skin depth beyond the interface. But in the limiting case of a **perfect conductor**, for which the conductivity is $\sigma = \infty$, the skin depth is $\delta = 0$, so that any current induced by changing magnetic fields is confined exactly to the surface. So when high-conductivity material is modelled as a perfect conductor, which will be done in the next section, the possible presence of such surface currents must be acknowledged in the boundary conditions.

In stating the boundary conditions for the fields at the surface of a conductor, we will label fields in the non-conducting material with the subscript 1 and fields within the conductor with the subscript 2. Positive perpendicular components are directed into the conductor. The magnetic field, as always, obeys the no-monopole law, and this requires that $\int_S \mathbf{B}(\mathbf{r}, t) \cdot d\mathbf{S} = 0$, where S is any closed surface. Just as in Section 3.2 this leads to the boundary condition that the component of $\mathbf{B}$ *perpendicular* to the surface of a conductor must be continuous.

At the surface of a conductor, $B_{1\perp} = B_{2\perp}$.   (5.19)

Although it is reasonable to propose that the interior of a good conductor is effectively free of charge accumulations, we must consider that there may be time-dependent *surface* charges. Indeed, you should already know that surface charges do build up on conducting surfaces in response to externally applied *static* electric fields. The electric displacement, $\mathbf{D}(\mathbf{r}, t)$, obeys Gauss's law:

$$\int_S \mathbf{D} \cdot \mathrm{d}\mathbf{S} = Q_\mathrm{f}(t),$$

where $Q_\mathrm{f}(t)$ is the free charge contained at time t within the closed surface S. We can apply this law to a small cylinder of vanishing height straddling the interface. If there is a surface charge density $\sigma_\mathrm{f}(\mathbf{r}, t)$ at a point $\mathbf{r}$ on the surface, then the charge within the small cylinder is $\Delta A \, \sigma_\mathrm{f}$, where ΔA is the area of the cylinder's ends. Gauss's law requires that $\Delta A \, (D_{2\perp} - D_{1\perp}) = \Delta A \, \sigma_\mathrm{f}$. This leads to the condition that at any point on the surface, the discontinuity in the perpendicular component of $\mathbf{D}$ is equal to the free surface charge density there.

Note that σ_f here is a surface charge density, not conductivity. Surface charge density σ_f has the unit $\mathrm{C\ m^{-2}}$.

> At the surface of a conductor, $\quad D_{2\perp} - D_{1\perp} = \sigma_\mathrm{f}.$ (5.20)

Faraday's law is unchanged in form by the presence of a conductor. Just as in Section 3.2 this leads to the condition that the parallel component of $\mathbf{E}$ is continuous across the boundary.

> At the surface of a conductor, $\quad E_{1\parallel} = E_{2\parallel}.$ (5.21)

The integral version of the Ampère–Maxwell law is

$$\oint_C \mathbf{H} \cdot \mathrm{d}\mathbf{l} = \int_S \left(\mathbf{J}_\mathrm{f} + \frac{\partial \mathbf{D}}{\partial t} \right) \cdot \mathrm{d}\mathbf{S}.$$

In a conductor, unlike in the dielectric of Chapter 3, we can have a free current density, $\mathbf{J}_\mathrm{f}$. If (by analogy with the surface charge density above) we allow for the possibility of a *surface* current $\mathbf{i}_\mathrm{s}$ per unit length, then when we apply the Ampère–Maxwell law to a small rectangle of infinitesimal width straddling the interface (compare Figure 3.6), we find that the discontinuity in the parallel component of the magnetic field $\mathbf{H}$ across the boundary is equal to the surface current per unit length.

> At the surface of a conductor, $\quad H_{2\parallel} - H_{1\parallel} = i_\mathrm{s}.$ (5.22)

Now that we have stated the boundary conditions that must be satisfied by electromagnetic fields on the surface of a conductor, we shall follow the pattern of Chapter 3 and look at what happens when a plane wave encounters a boundary, first at normal incidence and then obliquely.

The surface current flows in a direction perpendicular to $H_\parallel$. Surface current per unit length i_s has the unit $\mathrm{A\ m^{-1}}$.

5.3 Normal incidence

We now examine a plane polarized electromagnetic wave arriving from air at normal incidence onto the boundary of a good conductor. The relative permittivity of air is about 1.0005, so we can regard air as being equivalent to free space, and we shall assume that the wavelength and wavenumber of an electromagnetic wave in air have the same values as in free space. There are two cases to consider. In the first we shall treat an ordinary good conductor so that we can quantify the absorption of the small fraction of energy that penetrates below the surface. In the second case, we shall model the good conductor as being virtually perfect, so that a surface current is induced by the incident wave, preventing penetration of any electromagnetic energy.

5.3.1   Boundary with an ordinary conductor

Suppose that a conductor occupies the half-space $z \geq 0$, with air in the half-space $z < 0$. As illustrated in Figure 5.5, an incident plane wave, which is travelling in the z-direction and polarized in the x-direction, is reflected from and, to some extent, transmitted through the interface at $z = 0$. The wavenumber in air is the same as the free space value, $k_0 = \omega/c$. According to Subsection 5.1.2, the wavenumber in the conductor is complex, and from Equation 5.16, $k = k_{\mathrm{real}} + \mathrm{i}k_{\mathrm{imag}} = (1 + \mathrm{i})/\delta$, where the skin depth is $\delta = \sqrt{2/\mu_0 \sigma \omega}$.

We solved a problem like this in detail in Section 3.3: we write down the appropriate general form of plane wave solutions of Maxwell's equations for incident, reflected and transmitted waves, and then adjust their amplitudes to satisfy the boundary conditions. For a plane wave polarized in the x-direction, the incident, reflected and transmitted fields have the same form as those in Equations 3.5–3.10. When discussing these equations, we showed that the incident, reflected and transmitted waves must have the same frequency if the boundary conditions are to be matched at all times, and that is true at the surface of a conductor too.

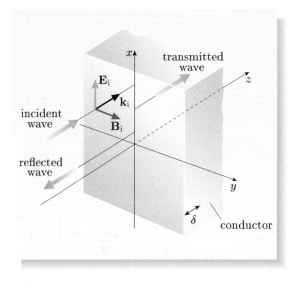

Figure 5.5 A boundary between air and a conductor at which an electromagnetic wave arrives and is reflected, at normal incidence. The transmitted wave is absorbed over a distance characterized by the skin depth δ.

What boundary conditions must be satisfied here by the electric and magnetic fields? Since we are considering a plane polarized wave at normal incidence, there are no perpendicular components of the fields to worry about. The conductivity, σ, is finite, so the fields penetrate the surface and are continuous across the boundary. There is no current exactly at the surface, so in this case i_s in Equation 5.22 vanishes. So the parallel components of $\mathbf{E}$ and $\mathbf{H}$ must be continuous, just as in Section 3.2. These two boundary conditions are sufficient to determine the amplitude reflection ratio and the amplitude transmission ratio, exactly as they did in Chapter 3.

Figure 5.5 shows the orientation of the electric and magnetic fields of the incident wave. The incident electric field is the real part of

$$\mathbf{E}_i(z, t) = E_{i0} \exp[\mathrm{i}(k_0 z - \omega t)]\, \mathbf{e}_x. \tag{5.23}$$

Within the conductor, $k = (1 + \mathrm{i})/\delta$, so the transmitted wave is the real part of

$$\mathbf{E}_t(z, t) = E_{t0} \exp[-z/\delta] \exp[\mathrm{i}(z/\delta - \omega t)]\, \mathbf{e}_x. \tag{5.24}$$

The boundary conditions at $z = 0$ are just the same as those used in Chapter 3, so the results in Equations 3.14 apply here too, namely

$$\frac{E_{t0}}{E_{i0}} = \frac{2n_1}{n_1 + n_2} \quad \text{and} \quad \frac{E_{r0}}{E_{i0}} = \frac{n_1 - n_2}{n_1 + n_2}. \tag{5.25}$$

However, here $n_1 = 1$ (in air) and $n_2 = kc/\omega = (1 + i)c/\omega\delta$ (in the conductor). We can simplify the second expression as follows:

$$\begin{aligned} n_2 &= (1 + i)\frac{c}{\omega\delta} = \frac{c}{\omega}\sqrt{\frac{\mu_0\sigma\omega}{2}}(1 + i) \\ &= \frac{1}{\omega\sqrt{\varepsilon_0\mu_0}}\sqrt{\frac{\mu_0\sigma\omega}{2}}\sqrt{2}\exp[i\pi/4] \\ &= \sqrt{\frac{\sigma}{\varepsilon_0\omega}}\exp[i\pi/4]. \end{aligned}$$

In the low-frequency limit under consideration, $\sigma/\varepsilon_0\omega \gg 1$. If we further constrain the frequency such that $\sqrt{\sigma/\varepsilon_0\omega} \gg 1$, then $|n_2| \gg 1$, and E_{t0} is given by

$$\begin{aligned} E_{t0} &= E_{i0}\frac{2n_1}{n_1 + n_2} \\ &\simeq \frac{2E_{i0}}{n_2} \\ &\simeq 2E_{i0}\sqrt{\frac{\varepsilon_0\omega}{\sigma}}\exp[-i\pi/4]. \end{aligned} \tag{5.26}$$

The factor of $\exp[-i\pi/4]$ indicates a constant phase difference between the electric field of the incident wave and the field transmitted into the conductor. Since $\sqrt{\sigma/\varepsilon_0\omega} \gg 1$, the magnitude E_{t0} of the transmitted field just inside the conductor (at $z = 0$) is a tiny fraction of the incident field.

A little caution is called for in taking results from Chapter 3, where absorption of energy was not included, and applying them to the present case, where absorption is inevitable. This becomes apparent when investigating the transmitted and reflected power. Within the conductor there is a phase difference between the electric field and its companion magnetic field — this arises because k is complex. We also found a phase difference between electric fields and magnetic fields in dielectrics when absorption was included in Section 4.4.

Worked Example 5.1

Consider the general damped 'wave' inside a conductor, as given by Equation 5.24.

(a) What is the magnitude of the time-averaged Poynting vector at the surface ($z = 0$) for this wave? (This is the (average) power flow per unit area into the conductor.)

(b) The field induces a current density $\mathbf{J}_f = \sigma\mathbf{E}$. Calculate the time-averaged power dissipated inside the conductor by Joule heating per square metre of its surface. Compare this with the result of part (a).

Essential skill

Accounting for the power associated with electromagnetic waves

Solution

(a)   The Poynting vector associated with this sort of damped wave is discussed in Section 4.4. In particular, Equation 4.35 gives an expression for the time-averaged Poynting vector. Writing δ^{-1} for k_{real} and for k_{imag} in that equation, we obtain

$$\overline{\mathbf{N}}_{\mathrm{t}}(z) = \frac{E_{\mathrm{t0}}^2}{2\mu_0\omega}\,\frac{1}{\delta}\,\exp\left[-\frac{2z}{\delta}\right]\mathbf{e}_z,$$

so at the surface

$$\overline{N}_{\mathrm{t}}(0) = \frac{E_{\mathrm{t0}}^2}{2\mu_0\omega\delta}.$$

(b)   The power dissipated per square metre of surface of the conductor is $\int_0^\infty \overline{\mathbf{J}_{\mathrm{phys}}\cdot\mathbf{E}_{\mathrm{phys}}}\,\mathrm{d}z$. The bar over the top implies a time-average, and the integral adds all the local contributions along the path of the damped wave. $\mathbf{E}_{\mathrm{phys}}$ is given by the real part of Equation 5.24, and $\mathbf{J}_{\mathrm{phys}} = \sigma\mathbf{E}_{\mathrm{phys}}$, so

$$\overline{\mathbf{J}_{\mathrm{phys}}\cdot\mathbf{E}_{\mathrm{phys}}} = \sigma E_{\mathrm{t0}}^2\exp\left[-\frac{2z}{\delta}\right]\overline{\cos^2\left(\frac{z}{\delta}-\omega t\right)} = \frac{1}{2}\sigma E_{\mathrm{t0}}^2\exp\left[-\frac{2z}{\delta}\right].$$

Then

$$\int_0^\infty \overline{\mathbf{J}_{\mathrm{phys}}\cdot\mathbf{E}_{\mathrm{phys}}}\,\mathrm{d}z = \frac{1}{2}\sigma E_{\mathrm{t0}}^2\int_0^\infty \exp\left[-\frac{2z}{\delta}\right]\mathrm{d}z = \frac{1}{4}\sigma E_{\mathrm{t0}}^2\,\delta.$$

The power per unit area entering the conductor must equal the dissipation per unit surface area of the conductor, so we expect $\int_0^\infty \overline{\mathbf{J}_{\mathrm{phys}}\cdot\mathbf{E}_{\mathrm{phys}}}\,\mathrm{d}z$ to equal $\overline{N}_{\mathrm{t}}(0)$. We can check whether this is the case by evaluating the ratio of the results obtained in part (a) and here:

$$\frac{E_{\mathrm{t0}}^2}{2\mu_0\omega\delta}\times\frac{4}{\sigma E_{\mathrm{t0}}^2\delta} = \frac{2}{\mu_0\omega\sigma}\frac{1}{\delta^2} = \frac{2}{\mu_0\omega\sigma}\frac{\mu_0\sigma\omega}{2} = 1.$$

So the magnitude of the time-averaged Poynting vector at the surface of the conductor is indeed equal to the power dissipated per unit area of surface.

Transmittance and reflectance

Consider a plane wave in air that strikes the surface of a conductor at normal incidence. From Equation 1.34 we can see that the magnitude of the time-averaged Poynting vector for the incident wave is $\overline{N}_{\mathrm{i}} = \varepsilon_0 E_{\mathrm{i0}}^2 c/2$. From part (a) of Worked Example 5.1, the magnitude of the time-averaged Poynting vector of the transmitted wave at $z = 0$ is $\overline{N}_{\mathrm{t}} = E_{\mathrm{t0}}^2/2\mu_0\omega\delta$. The transmittance of the boundary is therefore

The transmittance T of a boundary is the fraction of the incident power that is transmitted across it.

$$T = \frac{\overline{N}_{\mathrm{t}}}{\overline{N}_{\mathrm{i}}} = \frac{1}{2\mu_0\omega\delta}\frac{2}{\varepsilon_0 c}\frac{E_{\mathrm{t0}}^2}{E_{\mathrm{i0}}^2}. \qquad (5.27)$$

From Equation 5.26,

$$\left|\frac{E_{\mathrm{t0}}}{E_{\mathrm{i0}}}\right| = 2\sqrt{\frac{\varepsilon_0\omega}{\sigma}},$$

and substituting this into Equation 5.27, together with $\delta = \sqrt{2/\mu_0 \sigma \omega}$ and $c = 1/\sqrt{\varepsilon_0 \mu_0}$, we obtain

$$T = \frac{\overline{N_t}}{\overline{N_i}} = 2\sqrt{\frac{2\varepsilon_0 \omega}{\sigma}}. \qquad (5.28)$$

Since $\omega \ll \sigma/\varepsilon_0$ in the low-frequency limit, T is small.

This is the fraction of incident power that is not reflected. It is dissipated by Joule heating in the conductor.

- ● What is the reflectance of this conductor?

- ○ The incident power that is not transmitted into the conductor must be reflected, so $R = 1 - T$.

Exercise 5.3   A plane electromagnetic wave, with a free space wavelength of 3 m, is incident normally onto a flat copper surface. Evaluate the characteristic depth to which this radiation penetrates the conductor, and the transmittance of the boundary.

Exercise 5.4   The reflectance of a conducting surface, for normal incidence of electromagnetic radiation in the low-frequency limit, is

$$R = 1 - T = 1 - 2\sqrt{\frac{2\varepsilon_0 \omega}{\sigma}}.$$

Which of the materials listed in Table 5.1, in sheet form, would be the most effective reflector of radio waves? What is the reflectance of a boundary with this material for microwaves with a frequency of 1.4 GHz, incident from air?   ■

5.3.2   Boundaries with a perfect conductor

Good conductors are very nearly perfect reflectors of electromagnetic waves at radio and microwave frequencies; in this range the thin skin depth is typically less than one-hundredth of a millimetre (see Exercise 5.3). Currents are constrained to flow very close to the surface; in fact, if the conductivity were to become infinitely large, the skin depth would become zero. It therefore greatly simplifies the modelling of the reflection of electromagnetic waves by conductors if we step back from the detail of what happens within the skin depth, and simply treat good conductors as if they were indeed perfect. This is what we shall do for the remainder of this chapter.

The boundary conditions for normal conductors and perfect conductors are significantly different. For normal conductors, electric and magnetic fields penetrate the skin of the conductor, and $D_\perp$, $B_\perp$, $E_\parallel$ and $H_\parallel$ are all continuous across the boundary. By contrast, since the skin depth for a perfect conductor is zero, electric and magnetic fields cannot penetrate below the surface. So $E_\parallel$ and $B_\perp$ are zero just inside the surface, which means that $E_\parallel$ and $B_\perp$ must also be zero just outside the surface. However, $E_{1\perp}$ need not vanish since $D_{1\perp}$ can terminate on surface charge, and $B_{1\parallel}$ need not vanish since $H_{1\parallel}$ is equal to the free surface current per unit length.

> **Boundary conditions at the surface of a perfect conductor**
> $$E_\parallel = 0, \quad B_\perp = 0.$$

Now we are ready to look at what happens when a plane wave is directed at normal incidence onto the interface between air and a perfectly conducting surface. Suppose, as before, that the boundary coincides with the plane $z = 0$, as shown in Figure 5.6.

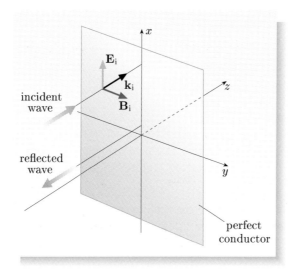

Figure 5.6   Plane wave normally incident on the boundary of a perfect conductor.

In the region $z \geq 0$, both **E** and **B** are zero because the skin depth is zero. This means that a very thin sheet of a perfect conductor will have the same effect on the incident wave as a thick block, and this is why the perfect conductor is shown as a thin sheet in Figure 5.6.

For $z \leq 0$, we are interested in plane wave solutions of Maxwell's equations, so choosing the electric fields to be parallel to the x-axis, the incident and reflected electric fields are given by the real parts of

$$\mathbf{E}_i(z, t) = E_{i0} \exp[\mathrm{i}(k_0 z - \omega t)] \, \mathbf{e}_x$$

and

$$\mathbf{E}_r(z, t) = E_{r0} \exp[\mathrm{i}(-k_0 z - \omega t)] \, \mathbf{e}_x,$$

where

$$k_0 = \omega/c = \omega \sqrt{\varepsilon_0 \mu_0}.$$

Since we are considering normal incidence and reflection, the waves have no electric field components perpendicular to the boundary, that is, $E_\perp = 0$. One of the boundary conditions for a perfect conductor is that $E_\parallel = 0$; the parallel component of the electric field at the surface must always be zero. So at the boundary $\mathbf{E}_i(0, t) + \mathbf{E}_r(0, t) = \mathbf{0}$.

The only way for this condition to be satisfied is to have $E_{i0} = -E_{r0}$, which indicates that a phase change of π occurs for the electric field reflected at a perfectly conducting boundary. Using this result, the net electric field for $z \leq 0$ is the real part of

$$
\begin{aligned}
\mathbf{E}(z, t) &= \mathbf{E}_i(z, t) + \mathbf{E}_r(z, t) \\
&= E_{i0} \left(\exp[\mathrm{i}(k_0 z - \omega t)] - \exp[\mathrm{i}(-k_0 z - \omega t)] \right) \mathbf{e}_x \\
&= E_{i0} \left(\exp[\mathrm{i}k_0 z] - \exp[-\mathrm{i}k_0 z] \right) \exp[-\mathrm{i}\omega t] \mathbf{e}_x \\
&= 2\mathrm{i}\, E_{i0} \sin(k_0 z) \exp[-\mathrm{i}\omega t] \, \mathbf{e}_x.
\end{aligned}
\tag{5.29}
$$

$\exp[\mathrm{i}\theta] - \exp[-\mathrm{i}\theta] = 2\mathrm{i} \sin\theta$

The total magnetic field for $z \leq 0$ is given by the real part of $\mathbf{B} = \mathbf{B}_i + \mathbf{B}_r$, where the real parts of $\mathbf{B}_i$ and $\mathbf{B}_r$ are the magnetic fields for the incident and reflected waves. Since we are assuming incidence at a perfect conductor, there *can* be currents exactly at the surface, so we cannot use the boundary condition $H_\parallel = 0$ to relate the two magnetic fields.

Moreover, the $B_\perp$ condition is redundant, since we are assuming normally-incident plane waves, which have their $\mathbf{B}$ fields parallel to the boundary of the conductor. However, $\mathbf{B}_i$ and $\mathbf{B}_r$ are companion fields to $\mathbf{E}_i$ and $\mathbf{E}_r$, propagating in air (or free space), so making use of Equation 1.16,

$$\mathbf{B}_i = \frac{E_{i0}}{c} \exp[i(k_0 z - \omega t)] \, \mathbf{e}_y$$

and

$$\mathbf{B}_r = -\frac{E_{r0}}{c} \exp[i(-k_0 z - \omega t)] \, \mathbf{e}_y = \frac{E_{i0}}{c} \exp[i(-k_0 z - \omega t)] \, \mathbf{e}_y.$$

In contrast to the reflection of the electric field, there is *no* change in phase for the magnetic field on reflection, as shown in Figure 5.7; this is consistent with the requirement for $\mathbf{E} \times \mathbf{H}$ to point in the direction of $\mathbf{k}$. The net $\mathbf{B}$ field is given by

$$
\begin{aligned}
\mathbf{B} &= \mathbf{B}_i + \mathbf{B}_r \\
&= \frac{E_{i0}}{c} \left(\exp[i(k_0 z - \omega t)] + \exp[i(-k_0 z - \omega t)] \right) \mathbf{e}_y \\
&= 2\frac{E_{i0}}{c} \cos(k_0 z) \exp[-i\omega t] \, \mathbf{e}_y \qquad \text{for } z \leq 0.
\end{aligned}
$$
(5.30)

$$\exp[i\theta] + \exp[-i\theta] = 2\cos\theta$$

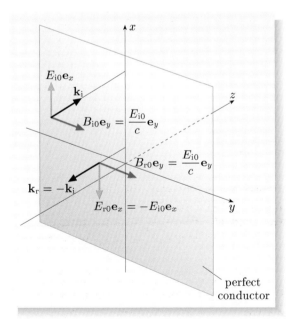

Figure 5.7 Incident and reflected fields at the boundary of a perfect conductor.

Notice that both the $\mathbf{E}$ and $\mathbf{B}$ fields include an exponential factor $\exp[-i\omega t]$, and *not* $\exp[i(\pm k_0 z - \omega t)]$. Consequently, there is no progressive change of phase with distance z, and therefore *no* propagation. In fact, instead of *travelling waves* for $\mathbf{E}$ and $\mathbf{B}$, we have *standing waves*. The physical fields are the real parts of

Figure 5.8 A standing wave excited on a string that is fixed at one end.

expressions in Equations 5.29 and 5.30, so

$$\mathbf{E}_{\text{phys}} = 2E_{\text{i0}} \sin(k_0 z) \sin(\omega t)\, \mathbf{e}_x \tag{5.31}$$

and

$$\mathbf{B}_{\text{phys}} = 2\frac{E_{\text{i0}}}{c} \cos(k_0 z) \cos(\omega t)\, \mathbf{e}_y. \tag{5.32}$$

The variation of the electric field is similar to the oscillation of a string that is clamped at one end, as you can see by comparing Figures 5.8 and 5.9a.

There is a $\pi/2$ phase difference between the time-dependence of the electric and magnetic fields at each value of $k_0 z$ in Figure 5.9, and this phase difference is also apparent from a comparison of Equations 5.31 and 5.32. As a result, the energy in any small volume oscillates in time and space between the $\mathbf{E}$ and $\mathbf{B}$ fields. The fields store energy but there is no net transport of energy in the standing wave.

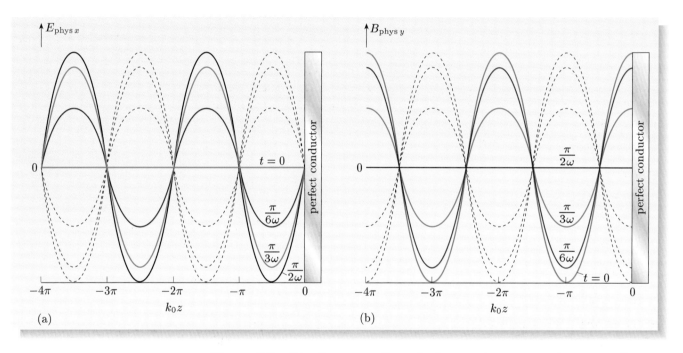

Figure 5.9 Standing waves formed when an electromagnetic wave strikes a perfectly conducting boundary at normal incidence: (a) electric field; (b) magnetic field. The fields are shown at intervals of $t = \pi/6\omega$. Check that these fields are consistent with Equations 5.31 and 5.32.

5.4   Oblique incidence

5.4.1   Reflection from a perfect conductor

Next we consider a plane wave incident at an angle θ_{i} on a perfect conductor, as shown in Figure 5.10. We shall then see what happens when waves are confined, first between parallel conducting surfaces and then within a waveguide formed from a hollow conducting tube of rectangular cross-section.

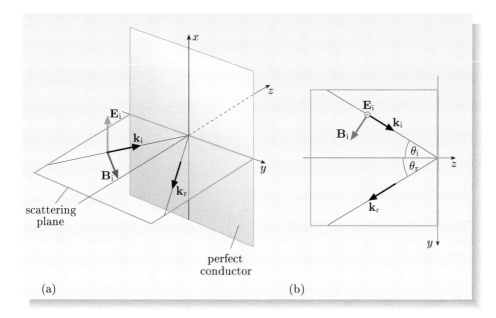

Figure 5.10 Oblique incidence and reflection from a perfect conductor for an electromagnetic wave that is polarized normal to the scattering plane. (a) 3D view; (b) the $x = 0$ (scattering) plane.

We choose axes so that the boundary of the perfect conductor is the plane $z = 0$ and the scattering plane is that in which $x = 0$. The case illustrated in Figure 5.10 has the electric field normal to the scattering plane so the magnetic field lies in the scattering plane. We can write the incident electric field as

$$\mathbf{E}_i = E_{i0} \exp[i(\mathbf{k}_i \cdot \mathbf{r} - \omega t)] \, \mathbf{e}_x,$$

and since

$$\mathbf{k}_i \cdot \mathbf{r} = k_{iy}y + k_{iz}z = k_i y \sin \theta_i + k_i z \cos \theta_i,$$

this can also be written as

$$\mathbf{E}_i = E_{i0} \exp[i(k_i y \sin \theta_i + k_i z \cos \theta_i - \omega t)] \, \mathbf{e}_x.$$

The reflected field is

$$\mathbf{E}_r = E_{r0} \exp[i(k_r y \sin \theta_r - k_r z \cos \theta_r - \omega t)] \, \mathbf{e}_x,$$

where I have been careful to reverse only the z-component of the spatial part of the phase, since the y-component is unchanged by the reflection. The incident and reflected wave are both in air, so

$$|\mathbf{k}_i| = |\mathbf{k}_r| = k_0 = \omega/c.$$

Since there is no electric field inside a perfect conductor, the component of the total field parallel to the boundary must be zero at $z = 0$. Hence, from our expressions for $\mathbf{E}_i$ and $\mathbf{E}_r$ we obtain

$$E_{i0} \exp[i(k_0 y \sin \theta_i - \omega t)] + E_{r0} \exp[i(k_0 y \sin \theta_r - \omega t)] = 0. \qquad (5.33)$$

● Explain how the following conclusions can be drawn from Equation 5.33.
(a) The angles of incidence and reflection must be the same.
(b) There is a phase change of π on reflection at a perfect conductor.

○ (a) Equation 5.33 must be true for all y, so $\sin \theta_r = \sin \theta_i$. (Don't forget that Figure 5.10 shows only a single incident ray. We are actually considering the reflection of a plane wave, which consists of an infinite number of parallel rays incident at all points on the boundary.)

(b) Equation 5.33 with $\theta_i = \theta_r$ requires $E_{r0} = -E_{i0}$ if it is to be true at every instant of time; the negative sign corresponds with a phase change of π, since $\exp[i\pi] = -1$.

Then we can write $E_0 = E_{i0} = -E_{r0}$ and $\theta = \theta_i = \theta_r$, so the total electric field is given by the real part of

$$\mathbf{E} = \mathbf{E_i} + \mathbf{E_r}$$
$$= E_0 \exp[i(k_0 y \sin\theta + k_0 z \cos\theta - \omega t)]\, \mathbf{e}_x$$
$$\quad - E_0 \exp[i(k_0 y \sin\theta - k_0 z \cos\theta - \omega t)]\, \mathbf{e}_x$$
$$= E_0 \left(\exp[ik_0 z \cos\theta] - \exp[-ik_0 z \cos\theta]\right) \exp[i(k_0 y \sin\theta - \omega t)]\, \mathbf{e}_x$$
$$= E_0\, 2i \sin(k_0 z \cos\theta) \exp[i(k_0 y \sin\theta - \omega t)]\, \mathbf{e}_x. \tag{5.34}$$

Notice that in contrast to Subsection 5.3.2, where we found a stationary wave for normal incidence ($\theta = 0$), in the case of oblique incidence ($\theta \neq 0$), there is now a propagating wave. In fact, the exponential term in Equation 5.34 shows that the wave propagates in the y-direction, *parallel to the conducting boundary*, with speed $\omega/(k_0 \sin\theta)$.

In this subsection, we have assumed that the electric fields of the incident and reflected waves are normal to the scattering plane. Another possibility is for the electric fields to lie in the scattering plane, and even more general electric fields could be resolved into components both in and normal to the scattering plane. However, we shall not analyse any of these situations here.

5.4.2 Propagation between perfectly conducting planes

We now use the results of the previous subsection to discover how waves propagate between two parallel conducting planes. This will provide us with an insight into propagation in waveguides. The situation I have in mind is shown in Figure 5.11. We already know that the electric field satisfying the boundary condition at $z = 0$ is given by Equation 5.34.

However, now the field also needs to satisfy the condition $E_{\parallel} = 0$ at $z = -a$, and this implies that

$$\sin(-k_0 a \cos\theta) = 0,$$

and hence

$$k_0 a \cos\theta = m\pi,$$

where m is any integer. In fact, we can limit ourselves to $m = 1, 2, 3, \ldots$; the case $m = 0$ can be discarded since this would imply $\theta = \pi/2$ and hence no reflection from the plane.

For a fixed frequency, and hence a fixed value of k_0, the boundary condition can be satisfied only for waves travelling at specific values of the angle θ, and these angles must satisfy

$$\cos\theta = \frac{m\pi}{k_0 a}. \tag{5.35}$$

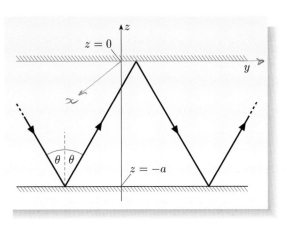

Figure 5.11 Plane wave propagation between two parallel, perfectly conducting planes at $z = 0$ and $z = -a$.

The different integer values of m correspond to different **modes** for propagation of waves between the conducting planes. For a given mode, you can see from

Equation 5.35 that as the free space wavenumber k_0 (and therefore the frequency) of the wave increases, the value of $\cos\theta$ decreases, and therefore the angle of incidence to the planes, θ, must increase.

It is important to note that although the electric field is in the x-direction, and the waves that are reflected back and forth between the planes travel at an angle θ to the z-direction, the term $\exp[\mathrm{i}(k_0 y \sin\theta - \omega t)]$ in Equation 5.34 indicates that changes in the field propagate in the y-direction. A wave is in effect guided by the conducting boundaries, and it has a wavenumber k_{gw} — the **guided-wave wavenumber** — given by

$$k_{\mathrm{gw}} = k_0 \sin\theta.$$

The **guided-wave wavelength** λ_{gw} is given by

$$\lambda_{\mathrm{gw}} = \frac{2\pi}{k_{\mathrm{gw}}} = \frac{2\pi}{k_0 \sin\theta} = \frac{\lambda_0}{\sin\theta}, \tag{5.36}$$

where λ_0 is the free space wavelength:

$$\lambda_0 = \frac{2\pi}{k_0} = \frac{2\pi c}{\omega}. \tag{5.37}$$

The phase speed of the waves in the y-direction can be deduced from Equation 5.34:

$$v_{\mathrm{phase}} = \frac{\omega}{k_0 \sin\theta} = \frac{\omega}{k_0 \sqrt{1 - \cos^2\theta}} = \frac{\omega}{k_0 \sqrt{1 - (m\pi/k_0 a)^2}}. \tag{5.38}$$

Note that this speed is *greater* than the phase speed in free space, $c = \omega/k_0$.

By contrast with the wave that propagates in the y-direction, the factor $\sin(k_0 z \cos\theta)$ in the expression for $\mathbf{E}$ in Equation 5.34 indicates that there is no propagation in the z-direction. Instead, the plane waves bouncing between the planes add together to form a standing wave pattern in the z-direction. If we denote the wavenumber and wavelength of these standing waves by k_{c} and λ_{c}, then

$$\lambda_{\mathrm{c}} = \frac{2\pi}{k_{\mathrm{c}}} = \frac{2\pi}{k_0 \cos\theta} = \frac{\lambda_0}{\cos\theta}. \tag{5.39}$$

The subscripts on λ_{c} and k_{c} stand for cut-off; the significance of this will become apparent shortly.

● Use Equations 5.35, 5.37 and 5.39 to show that

$$\lambda_{\mathrm{c}} = \frac{2a}{m}. \tag{5.40}$$

○ Starting with Equation 5.39 and then using Equations 5.35 and 5.37 in that order, we have

$$\lambda_{\mathrm{c}} = \frac{\lambda_0}{\cos\theta} = \lambda_0 \frac{k_0 a}{m\pi} = \frac{2\pi a}{m\pi} = \frac{2a}{m}.$$

The value of λ_{c} therefore depends on the mode m, but is independent of the frequency ω of the wave. For the $m = 1$ mode, $\lambda_{\mathrm{c}}/2 = a$ so one half-cycle of a standing wave fits between the planes; for $m = 2$, $\lambda_{\mathrm{c}} = a$ so two half-cycles of a standing wave fit between the planes and so on.

We can now use Equations 5.36 and 5.39 to express the electric field as the real part of either

$$\mathbf{E} = E_0 \, 2\mathrm{i} \sin(k_\mathrm{c} z) \exp[\mathrm{i}(k_\mathrm{gw} y - \omega t)] \, \mathbf{e}_x \tag{5.41}$$

or

$$\mathbf{E} = E_0 \, 2\mathrm{i} \sin\left(\frac{2\pi z}{\lambda_\mathrm{c}}\right) \exp\left[\mathrm{i}\left(\frac{2\pi y}{\lambda_\mathrm{gw}} - \omega t\right)\right] \mathbf{e}_x. \tag{5.42}$$

The parameters λ_gw, λ_c and λ_0 are not all independent. Since $\lambda_\mathrm{c} = \lambda_0 / \cos\theta$ and $\lambda_\mathrm{gw} = \lambda_0 / \sin\theta$, we can use the trigonometric identity $\cos^2\theta + \sin^2\theta = 1$ to derive the following important relationships between them.

$$\frac{1}{\lambda_\mathrm{gw}^2} = \frac{1}{\lambda_0^2} - \frac{1}{\lambda_\mathrm{c}^2}, \quad \text{or} \quad k_\mathrm{gw}^2 = k_0^2 - k_\mathrm{c}^2. \tag{5.43}$$

For a fixed plane separation a, a particular mode m has a wavelength for the standing wave in the z-direction given by $m\lambda_\mathrm{c}/2 = a$. For $\lambda_0 < \lambda_\mathrm{c}$ (and $k_0 > k_\mathrm{c}$), the value of λ_gw (and k_gw) is real, so there is a propagating wave in the y-direction. However, for $\lambda_0 > \lambda_\mathrm{c}$ (and $k_0 < k_\mathrm{c}$), the value of λ_gw (and k_gw) is imaginary, so there is an evanescent wave in the y-direction. We can now explain the reason for the subscript 'c': λ_c is the longest free space wavelength that can be propagated between the planes in a given mode (i.e. a given value of m), and is known as the **cut-off wavelength** for that mode. Each mode therefore has a minimum frequency — the **cut-off frequency** f_c — that can propagate between the planes, and this is given by $f_\mathrm{c} = c/\lambda_\mathrm{c} = (m/2a)c$.

Transverse modes

Figure 5.12 shows computed results for the electric and magnetic fields between the planes at three instants of time. On the left, the height of the three-dimensional surface represents E_x in the plane $x = 0$ in the region between the perfectly-conducting planes (given by Equation 5.41), and on the right the green vectors represent the magnetic field $\mathbf{B}$ at an array of points in the same plane between these planes (calculated by substituting the electric fields into Faraday's law). In the time interval $t = \pi/2\omega$ that elapses between parts (a) and (b) of Figure 5.12, and between (b) and (c), the guided wave advances a distance $\lambda_\mathrm{gw}/4$ in the y-direction.

Notice that the electric field has only an x-component, so the electric field is always transverse to the direction in which the guided wave is travelling — the y-direction. However, the direction of the $\mathbf{B}$ field at any point generally is not transverse to the propagation direction.

The waves we have described in this section are known as **transverse electric waves**, usually abbreviated to **TE waves**, and the corresponding modes are known as **TE modes**. This is because the electric field vector for these waves is always perpendicular to the direction of propagation. As the wave propagates, surface currents are induced in the boundaries to satisfy the boundary conditions for $H_\parallel$ and thereby sustain the wave.

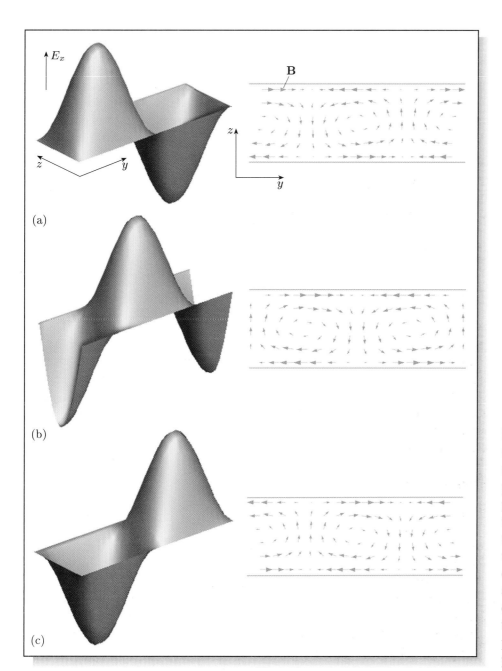

Figure 5.12 Electric field (left) and magnetic field (right) between two infinite, perfectly-conducting planes parallel to the $z = 0$ plane at three instants of time: (a) at $t = 0$, (b) at $t = \pi/2\omega$, (c) at $t = \pi/\omega$. The electric field is everywhere in the x-direction, and the magnetic field is everywhere perpendicular to the x-direction, but not perpendicular to the direction of propagation.

It is also possible to have waves with the magnetic field perpendicular to the direction of propagation, and these are known as **transverse magnetic waves**, or **TM waves**. The corresponding modes are known as **TM modes**. Induced surface charges ensure that the boundary conditions for $D_\perp$ are met for TM modes between parallel planes. It is even possible to have both the electric and magnetic fields perpendicular to the direction of propagation between two parallel planes, just like the free space propagation of plane waves.

For the remainder of this chapter we restrict our analysis and discussion to TE modes.

Group speed

We have already remarked on the fact that v_{phase} for guided waves between the two conducting planes exceeds the speed of light c (Equation 5.38). As we found in Chapter 4, this does not contradict the theory of special relativity because the energy and information in a wave travel at the *group speed* v_{group}, rather than the phase speed v_{phase}. The group speed of a guided wave depends on the dispersion, i.e. the variation of the phase speed with the frequency, and is given by

$$v_{\text{group}} = \frac{\mathrm{d}\omega}{\mathrm{d}k_{\text{gw}}}. \tag{5.44}$$

Using Equation 5.43, together with Equations 5.39 and 5.35, we see that

$$k_{\text{gw}} = \sqrt{k_0^2 - k_c^2} = \left[\frac{\omega^2}{c^2} - \left(\frac{m\pi}{a}\right)^2\right]^{1/2},$$

and therefore

$$\frac{\mathrm{d}k_{\text{gw}}}{\mathrm{d}\omega} = \frac{\omega}{c^2}\left[\frac{\omega^2}{c^2} - \left(\frac{m\pi}{a}\right)^2\right]^{-1/2} = \frac{\omega}{c^2 k_{\text{gw}}}.$$

Inverting this expression gives the group speed,

$$v_{\text{group}} = \frac{\mathrm{d}\omega}{\mathrm{d}k_{\text{gw}}} = \frac{c^2 k_{\text{gw}}}{\omega}, \tag{5.45}$$

and since $v_{\text{phase}} = \omega/k_{\text{gw}}$, we obtain

$$v_{\text{phase}} v_{\text{group}} = c^2.$$

From this result we can see that $v_{\text{group}} < c$, even though $v_{\text{phase}} > c$.

5.5 Waveguides

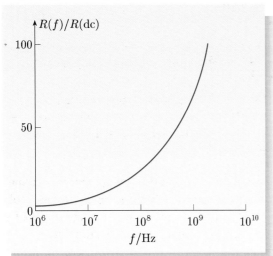

Figure 5.13 The factor by which the resistance of a wire of radius 1 mm increases with frequency due to the skin effect.

At low frequencies, alternating currents can be transmitted along wires made of good conductors (such as copper) without appreciable loss. However, as the frequency increases, the skin effect becomes more and more significant. At high frequencies, the skin depth is so small that the resistance of long wires becomes unacceptably high. Figure 5.13 illustrates the increase in resistance $R(f)$ of a wire with increasing frequency, relative to its value for direct current $R(\text{dc})$.

For very short conductors, the increased resistance may not be important, which is why integrated circuits can and do operate at very high frequencies (2 GHz and more). For very long distances, antennas are used to transmit broadcast signals through the air, avoiding ohmic losses as well as the cost of installing and maintaining long wires.

At intermediate distances, waves are often guided through space using structures made from dielectrics or conductors. We discussed a dielectric waveguide in the form of an optical fibre in

Chapter 4, and in Subsection 5.4.2 we showed that a simple structure formed by a pair of (infinite) parallel plane conductors was capable of guiding waves. However, it is more practical to use waveguides in the form of hollow conducting tubes of either rectangular or circular cross-section. Examples of sections of waveguides are shown in Figure 5.14.

(a)

(b)

Figure 5.14 (a) Straight section of waveguide, internal dimensions approximately $3.5\,\mathrm{cm} \times 1.7\,\mathrm{cm}$. (b) Twisted section of waveguide, internal dimensions about half those of the waveguide in (a). This rotates the polarization through a right angle.

In this final section, we shall discuss TE modes in a rectangular waveguide. This will enable us to specify suitable dimensions for a hollow tube that will efficiently guide electromagnetic pulses between an antenna and the ground station of an aviation radar system.

5.5.1 Propagation in a rectangular waveguide

A rectangular waveguide is formed by combining two orthogonal pairs of parallel conducting planes, as shown in Figure 5.15. By analogy with the simpler case of two parallel planes discussed in the previous section, we are interested in solutions of Maxwell's equations that propagate as waves in the y-direction and that satisfy the boundary conditions at the surface of the waveguide, in the planes $z = 0$, $z = a$, $x = 0$ and $x = b$. Instead of working through a formal derivation, we shall propose a general solution for the electric field that is consistent with the boundary conditions. We shall also identify conditions under which the general solution corresponds with a propagating **waveguide mode**.

The proposed solution is inspired by the results of the foregoing section:

$$E_x = E_{x0} \sin\left(\frac{m\pi z}{a}\right) \cos\left(\frac{n\pi x}{b}\right) \exp[\mathrm{i}(k_{\mathrm{gw}}y - \omega t)], \qquad (5.46)$$

$$E_y = 0, \qquad (5.47)$$

$$E_z = E_{z0} \cos\left(\frac{m\pi z}{a}\right) \sin\left(\frac{n\pi x}{b}\right) \exp[\mathrm{i}(k_{\mathrm{gw}}y - \omega t)], \qquad (5.48)$$

where m and n are integers characterizing different modes of propagation of waves in the guide.

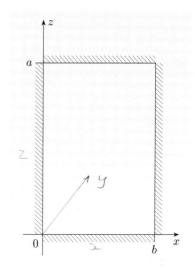

Figure 5.15 Cross-section of a rectangular waveguide.

Guided modes between $z = a$ and $z = 0$ are identical to those between $z = 0$ and $z = -a$.

Note that the symbol n is taking on its third meaning in this book — in expressions like $n\pi y/b$, it represents a specific integer.

● Explain why an electric field with components given by Equations 5.46–5.48 qualifies for the description TE.

○ The x- and z-components of the given field represent waves that travel in the y-direction, but E_y is zero, so the electric field is always transverse to the direction of propagation, which means that it is a *T*ransverse *E*lectric wave.

Notice that putting $n = 0$ removes the constraints of the boundaries at $y = 0$ and $y = b$, and this recovers the form of the electric field derived in the previous section. So the electric field (and the magnetic field) for the waveguide mode with $m = 1$ and $n = 0$ is identical to that shown in Figure 5.12.

Satisfying the boundary conditions

The boundary condition for the electric field is that its component parallel to each perfectly conducting plane must vanish (Section 5.3.2). We can see that this condition is satisfied by the proposed electric field in Equations 5.46–5.48, since:

- if n is an integer, the factor $\sin(n\pi x/b)$ ensures that $E_z = 0$ at $x = 0$ and $x = b$;

- if m is an integer, the factor $\sin(m\pi z/a)$ ensures that $E_x = 0$ at $z = 0$ and $z = a$.

Satisfying the wave equation

The factor $\exp[\mathrm{i}(k_{\mathrm{gw}}y - \omega t)]$ in the electric field in Equations 5.46–5.48 indicates that the waves propagate in the y-direction, but we specifically want to show that the electric field satisfies the wave equation in the air between the walls, that is,

$$\nabla^2 \mathbf{E} - \frac{1}{c^2}\frac{\partial^2 \mathbf{E}}{\partial t^2} = 0.$$

If the electric field $\mathbf{E}$ satisfies this wave equation, then the x-component of the electric field must satisfy a similar equation,

$$\nabla^2 E_x - \frac{1}{c^2}\frac{\partial^2 E_x}{\partial t^2} = E_x\left[-\left(\frac{m\pi}{a}\right)^2 - \left(\frac{n\pi}{b}\right)^2 - k_{\mathrm{gw}}^2 + \frac{\omega^2}{c^2}\right] = 0.$$

This is satisfied if

$$-\left(\frac{m\pi}{a}\right)^2 - \left(\frac{n\pi}{b}\right)^2 - k_{\mathrm{gw}}^2 + \frac{\omega^2}{c^2} = 0.$$

Since $\omega/c = k_0$, the wavenumber in free space or air, we can write this constraint as

$$k_{\mathrm{gw}}^2 = k_0^2 - \left(\frac{m\pi}{a}\right)^2 - \left(\frac{n\pi}{b}\right)^2. \tag{5.49}$$

The component E_z also satisfies the wave equation, subject to this same constraint.

Relating the amplitudes of the electric field components

The space enclosed by the guide contains air, which is essentially equivalent to free space, with no free charge and $\varepsilon = 1$. According to Gauss's law, Equations 5.46–5.48 must therefore specify a field with zero divergence. Let us see how that constrains the proposed solution.

Worked Example 5.2

What additional constraint is placed on the proposed electric field in Equations 5.46–5.48 by the requirement that it must satisfy Gauss's law?

Solution

Since there is no charge within the waveguide, Gauss's law reduces to $\mathrm{div}\,\mathbf{E} = 0$. In Cartesian coordinates,

$$\mathrm{div}\,\mathbf{E} = \frac{\partial E_x}{\partial x} + \frac{\partial E_y}{\partial y} + \frac{\partial E_z}{\partial z},$$

and

$$\frac{\partial E_x}{\partial x} = \left(\frac{-n\pi}{b}\right) E_{x0} \sin\left(\frac{m\pi z}{a}\right) \sin\left(\frac{n\pi x}{b}\right) \exp[\mathrm{i}(k_{\mathrm{gw}}y - \omega t)],$$

$$\frac{\partial E_y}{\partial y} = 0,$$

$$\frac{\partial E_z}{\partial z} = \left(\frac{-m\pi}{a}\right) E_{z0} \sin\left(\frac{m\pi z}{a}\right) \sin\left(\frac{n\pi x}{b}\right) \exp[\mathrm{i}(k_{\mathrm{gw}}y - \omega t)].$$

So for Gauss's law to be satisfied, we require

$$E_{x0}\frac{n\pi}{b} = -E_{z0}\frac{m\pi}{a},$$

or

$$E_{x0} = A\frac{m\pi}{a} \quad \text{and} \quad E_{z0} = -A\frac{n\pi}{b}, \tag{5.50}$$

where A is a constant determined by the amplitude of the guided wave.

Magnetic fields in the waveguide

The components of the companion magnetic field that is associated with the electric field in Equations 5.46–5.48 can be derived from Faraday's law, though we shall not do so here. The companion magnetic field satisfies the boundary condition $B_\perp = 0$ at the perfectly conducting surfaces of the waveguide, and the wavenumber for the propagating magnetic field satisfies exactly the same relationship as obtained for the x-component of the electric field (Equation 5.49).

5.5.2   TE modes in a rectangular waveguide

The proposed form for the electric field (Equations 5.46–5.48) satisfies Maxwell's equations in the space enclosed by the guide, and satisfies the boundary conditions at the perfectly conducting walls of the guide. The expressions for the field describe *travelling wave modes*. From Equation 5.49, we can see that k_{gw} is real for

$$k_0^2 \geq \frac{m^2\pi^2}{a^2} + \frac{n^2\pi^2}{b^2},$$

and if this condition is satisfied, there can be a wave propagating in the y-direction. If the condition is *not* satisfied, then k_{gw} is imaginary and the disturbance is evanescent in the y-direction.

The travelling wave modes are labelled as TE_{mn}. By convention, the first suffix (here called m) corresponds to the number of half wavelengths of a standing wave that fit into the *broader* dimension of the rectangular cross-section (in this case a), and the second suffix (here called n) corresponds to the number of half wavelengths that fit into the narrower dimension (in this case b). The allowed values of m and n are $m = 0, 1, 2, 3, \ldots$ and $n = 0, 1, 2, 3, \ldots$. Each TE mode has a cut-off frequency f_{mn} given by

$$f_{mn} = c\sqrt{\left(\frac{m}{2a}\right)^2 + \left(\frac{n}{2b}\right)^2} \tag{5.51}$$

below which the mode cannot propagate. The TE_{10} mode has the lowest cut-off frequency, and is known as the **fundamental mode**.

- Explain why $m = 0$, $n = 0$ is not a guided wave mode.

○ Although this would correspond to $f_{00} = 0$, i.e. no lower limit to the frequency, Equations 5.50 show that in this mode the electric field would be zero on all of the boundaries, and must therefore be zero everywhere within the waveguide. This is also clear from Equations 5.46–5.48.

Using Equation 5.51, it is possible to show that if the *aspect ratio* of the waveguide (i.e. a/b) is $2 : 1$, then we get the maximum possible range of frequencies over which *only* the TE_{10} mode propagates. This range is from the cut-off frequency of the fundamental mode, f_{10}, to twice this frequency, $2f_{10} = f_{20} = f_{01}$. For this reason, most rectangular waveguides have an aspect ratio of about $2 : 1$, and they are used in the frequency range where only the fundamental mode propagates.

5.5.3 Phase speed and group speed in a rectangular waveguide

- What is the phase speed of a waveguide mode?

○ The phase speed can be deduced from the exponential terms in Equations 5.46 and 5.48. It is $v_{\text{phase}} = \omega/k_{\text{gw}}$.

The guided-wave wavenumber is given by Equation 5.49, which can be written as

$$k_{\text{gw}} = \sqrt{\frac{\omega^2}{c^2} - \left(\frac{m\pi}{a}\right)^2 - \left(\frac{n\pi}{b}\right)^2}. \tag{5.52}$$

This indicates that $k_{\text{gw}} < \omega/c$, which means that $v_{\text{phase}} = \omega/k_{\text{gw}} > c$.

We can find the group speed from Equation 5.52, just as we did for propagation between parallel planes. The result is the same:

$$v_{\text{group}} = \frac{c^2 k_{\text{gw}}}{\omega} = \frac{c^2}{v_{\text{phase}}}. \tag{Eqn 5.45}$$

Thus the group speed is less than c, as required by special relativity.

To conclude this chapter, the following exercises investigate some of the parameters for waveguides that could be used in radar applications.

Exercise 5.5   A rectangular waveguide for a radar system has internal dimensions $0.16\,\text{m} \times 0.08\,\text{m}$. Show that it would transmit a $1\,\text{GHz}$ signal in a single TE mode.

Exercise 5.6   (a) Find the group speeds of TE_{10} and TE_{20} modes in a waveguide with dimensions $0.16\,\text{m} \times 0.08\,\text{m}$, for a frequency of $2.0\,\text{GHz}$.

(b) A $1\,\mu\text{s}$ signal pulse at this frequency is launched into a $100\,\text{m}$ length of this waveguide in such a way that its energy is divided equally between the TE_{10} and TE_{20} modes. Find the time separation of the two modes of the pulse when they arrive at the end of the guide.

(c) Suggest how the TE_{20} mode could be prevented from propagating. ■

You can reinforce your understanding of the skin effect and absorption of electromagnetic waves in metals by viewing the video sequence *Absorption of electromagnetic waves* on the course DVD.

Summary of Chapter 5

Section 5.1   The electric field of an electromagnetic wave in a conductor will drive current. A simple model of a conductor accounts for the motion of unbound electrons in a similar way to thc model for bound electrons in a dielectric in Chapter 4. This leads to an effective relative permittivity function $\varepsilon_{\text{eff}}(\omega)$ that exhibits three characteristic styles of behaviour. Well above the frequency $\omega_{\text{p}} = \sqrt{n_{\text{e}}e^2/m\varepsilon_0}$, the unbound electrons in a conductor cannot respond and electromagnetic waves pass unhindered. In the range between ω_{p} and the frequency of collisions between electrons and the lattice $(1/\tau_{\text{c}})$, electromagnetic waves will not propagate in a conductor but evanesce. At frequencies well below $1/\tau_{\text{c}}$, that is, where $\omega\varepsilon_0/\sigma \ll 1$, conduction currents dominate and energy is strongly absorbed from an electromagnetic field. Electric and magnetic fields effectively diffuse into a conductor at these frequencies:

$$\nabla^2\mathbf{E} = \mu_0\sigma\frac{\partial\mathbf{E}}{\partial t}.$$

The depth to which electromagnetic fields penetrate a conductor is characterized by the skin depth:

$$\delta = \frac{1}{k_{\text{imag}}} = \sqrt{\frac{2}{\mu_0\sigma\omega}}.$$

Section 5.2   Transmission and reflection of waves at the boundary of a conductor is determined by the boundary conditions for the fields. For a wave incident from material 1 onto the surface of conducting material 2, the conditions are:

$$B_{1\perp} = B_{2\perp}; \quad D_{2\perp} - D_{1\perp} = \sigma_{\text{f}}; \quad E_{1\|} = E_{2\|}; \quad H_{2\|} - H_{1\|} = i_{\text{s}},$$

where σ_{f} is the free surface charge density and i_{s} is the free surface current per unit length.

Section 5.3   When electromagnetic waves are normally incident on the surface of a conductor, the small fraction of energy transmitted through the surface is absorbed within the skin depth due to Joule heating. In conductors where the skin depth is small compared with other dimensions, it is reasonable to invoke a perfect conductor model, in which $\mathbf{E}$ and $\mathbf{B}$ are zero within the material, and the induced current and charge are restricted exactly to the surface.

The boundary conditions at the surface of a perfect conductor are $E_{\parallel} = 0$ and $B_{\perp} = 0$. Perfect conductors reflect all incident electromagnetic waves. Electric fields undergo a phase change of π on reflection from a perfect conductor, but the phase of magnetic fields is not affected by reflection.

Section 5.4   When a plane wave is incident on a perfect conductor, the superposition of the incident and reflected waves produces a standing wave pattern perpendicular to the surface and a travelling wave parallel to the surface. For the region between two parallel perfectly-conducting planes, the zero-electric-field boundary condition allows only wave modes that correspond to angles of incidence θ such that

$$\cos\theta = \left(\frac{m\pi}{k_0 a}\right), \quad \text{where } m = 1, 2, 3, \ldots.$$

Each of these modes has a standing wave pattern perpendicular to the planes, with wavenumber $k_c = k_0 \cos\theta$, or wavelength $\lambda_c = 2a/m$, and a travelling wave parallel to the planes, with wavenumber $k_{gw} = k_0 \sin\theta$. Waves with free space wavelength λ_0 greater than the cut-off wavelength $\lambda_c = 2a/m$, or equivalently waves with frequency less than the cut-off frequency $f_c = (m/2a)c$, are evanescent. For transverse electric (TE) modes, the electric field is perpendicular to the direction of propagation, but the magnetic field has a component in the direction of propagation. Energy is transmitted parallel to the planes at the group speed,

$$v_{\text{group}} = \frac{\mathrm{d}\omega}{\mathrm{d}k_{gw}} = \frac{c^2 k_{gw}}{\omega}.$$

The phase speed, $v_{\text{phase}} = \omega/k_{gw} = \omega/k_0 \sin\theta$, exceeds c, but the group speed is always less than c.

Section 5.5   Waveguides are hollow conductors within which there are solutions of Maxwell's equations that satisfy the boundary conditions and correspond to waves propagating along the guide. TE modes in a rectangular waveguide are characterized by two integers, m and n, which indicate the number of half cycles of standing wave that fit into the long and short dimensions of the guide cross-section. For each mode there is a cut-off frequency below which the mode cannot propagate, and for the TE_{mn} mode this is given by

$$f_{mn} = c\sqrt{\left(\frac{m}{2a}\right)^2 + \left(\frac{n}{2b}\right)^2}.$$

Achievements from Chapter 5

After studying this chapter, you should be able to do the following.

5.1   Explain the meanings of the newly defined (emboldened) terms and symbols, and use them appropriately.

5.2 Develop the model of dielectrics from Chapter 4 into a comparable model for conductors, and identify different behaviour in three different bands of frequency: $\omega \gg \omega_p$, $1/\tau_c \ll \omega < \omega_p$ and $\omega \ll 1/\tau_c$.

5.3 Set up Maxwell's equations for conducting media, derive the differential equation for electromagnetic waves in conducting media and solve the equation in the low-frequency regime.

5.4 Derive an expression for the skin depth, discuss its consequences and solve problems related to it.

5.5 Use the boundary conditions for (non-static) fields at a conducting surface to calculate the reflection and transmission coefficients for a wave at normal incidence.

5.6 Apply the boundary conditions for a wave having normal or oblique incidence at a perfect conductor. Show that there is a phase change of π between the incident and reflected electric fields, and that standing waves are formed for normal incidence.

5.7 Demonstrate propagation of electromagnetic waves between two parallel perfectly conducting planes, and calculate the wavelength for guided waves and the cut-off wavelength.

5.8 Explain what is meant by TE_{mn} modes in a rectangular waveguide, and for such waveguides explain the significance of a mode's cut-off frequency, group speed, phase speed and dispersion, and perform calculations involving these quantities.

Chapter 6   Plasmas

A **plasma** is a condition of matter containing an appreciable fraction of freely moving charged particles. By this I mean that there are sufficient of these charged particles to cause the electromagnetic properties of the medium to be significantly different from those of solids, liquids or gases. For this reason, plasmas are sometimes referred to as the *fourth* state of matter.

It is believed that most of the matter in the Universe is in the form of plasma, rather than gas or liquid or solid. This may come as a surprise to you, but our immediate environment is not typical of the Universe. The freely moving charged particles in a plasma (especially electrons) readily interact with electromagnetic fields, so plasmas in their various guises throughout the Universe exhibit interesting and important phenomena.

In Section 6.1 we shall briefly discuss the underlying nature of plasmas, from the medium of stars and interstellar matter to simple electrical discharges in the laboratory. The interaction of electromagnetic radiation with ionized gases is then investigated, initially through a development of the classical model that we have already applied to dielectrics and conducting media. The interaction of electromagnetic waves with the Earth's ionosphere is studied in Section 6.2 using this simple isotropic model. Then, to extend the model to wave phenomena in the magnetosphere and other magnetized plasmas, a steady magnetic field is introduced into the model and the assumption of isotropy is relaxed.

6.1   The nature of plasmas

In its most common usage, the term 'plasma' refers to a gas in which an appreciable fraction of the atoms and molecules have become ionized to create a mix of positive ions, negative electrons, and un-ionized neutral species. Many plasmas, such as the ionosphere and the electrically conducting gas in a fluorescent lamp, are only partially ionized. There are also many scenarios where plasmas are fully ionized, such as the high-temperature extra-terrestrial plasmas of stars, and also the plasmas generated on Earth for research into controlled thermonuclear fusion.

- ● Compare the conduction of electricity through a gaseous plasma and a solid metallic conductor.

- ○ In a plasma, charge is carried by free electrons and free ions; the motion of charges is impeded by collisions with other particles (gas molecules, electrons and ions). In a metal, the free electrons carry current by drifting through a fixed lattice of positive charge; collisions with the lattice impede motion and are responsible for electrical resistance.

The sea of conduction electrons that permeate the lattice of positively-charged atom cores in metals constitutes a plasma in which one charged species is immobile. There are also various other forms of plasma: populations of electrons, holes and dopant ions in semiconductors; gases of electrons and positrons; an exotic quark–gluon plasma. However, this chapter is concerned only with plasmas formed from ionized gas.

6.1.1 Plasmas sustained by thermal energy

In a gas at thermal equilibrium, the thermal kinetic energy of particles at absolute temperature T is proportional to $k_B T$, where k_B is the **Boltzmann constant** ($= 1.38 \times 10^{-23}$ J K^{-1}). The greater $k_B T$, the more likely it is that collisions between energetic particles will lead to electrons being knocked free from their parent atoms and molecules: this is thermally-driven ionization.

We can estimate the temperature at which hydrogen gas will become a thermally-ionized plasma, given that to liberate the electron from the ground state of a hydrogen atom requires 13.6 eV of energy. At room temperature, gaseous hydrogen exists as diatomic molecules, with a bond energy of 4.8 eV, so as the temperature is raised, the molecules will dissociate before significant ionization occurs. Thus it is appropriate to consider the thermal ionization of hydrogen atoms.

$1\,\mathrm{eV} \equiv 1.6 \times 10^{-19}\,\mathrm{J}$

Let the gas be at thermal equilibrium with temperature T. We can appeal to the statistics of the very large numbers of indistinguishable particles of any one species present in a given volume to determine the fraction of atoms with kinetic energy greater than E: it is proportional to the Boltzmann factor, $\exp(-E/k_B T)$. An appreciable fraction of hydrogen atoms will be ionized at temperatures for which $k_B T$ exceeds the ionization energy of an atom, that is,

$$T > \frac{13.6\,\mathrm{eV}}{k_B} = \frac{13.6 \times 1.60 \times 10^{-19}\,\mathrm{J}}{1.38 \times 10^{-23}\,\mathrm{J\,K^{-1}}}$$
$$= 1.6 \times 10^5\,\mathrm{K}.$$

So at around 10^5 K, a significant fraction of hydrogen atoms are ionized. The resultant plasma exhibits properties quite different from ordinary hydrogen gas. Looking to the example of our nearest star (Figure 6.1), we can see that there is a distinct boundary in its atmosphere where the physical properties of the gas change dramatically. At this boundary, spectroscopic measurements show that the temperature is about 10^5 K, suggesting that the dramatic change is, at least in part, related to a change from hydrogen being an un-ionized gas to being a plasma. All stars contain regions where temperatures are sufficient to ionize hydrogen.

Figure 6.1 (a) The Sun viewed in the visible part of the spectrum. Here we see emission from the photosphere, in which the un-ionized gas is at an effective temperature of about 5800 K. (b) The Sun imaged in X-rays. The photosphere appears dark in this image, and instead we see the hotter, outer part of the Sun, called the corona, with temperatures as high as 2×10^6 K so the hydrogen is fully ionized into a plasma. The thin dividing layer between the corona and the cooler photosphere is at a temperature of about 10^5 K.

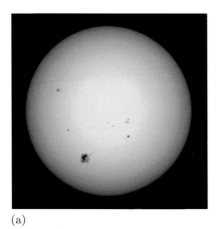

(a)

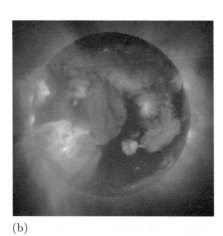

(b)

6.1.2 Plasmas sustained by radiation

Another way to turn a gas into a plasma is to bathe it in electromagnetic radiation that is energetic enough to ionize it. From previous studies of quantum mechanics, you may remember that the energy of a photon of wavelength λ is hc/λ, where h is Planck's constant ($h = 6.63 \times 10^{-34}\,\text{J s}$). So for $\lambda = 50\,\text{nm}$ (in the ultraviolet range) the energy is

$$\frac{hc}{\lambda} = \frac{6.63 \times 10^{-34}\,\text{J s} \times 3.00 \times 10^8\,\text{m s}^{-1}}{50 \times 10^{-9}\,\text{m}}$$

$$= 4.0 \times 10^{-18}\,\text{J}$$

$$\equiv \frac{4.0 \times 10^{-18}\,\text{J}}{1.60 \times 10^{-19}\,\text{J eV}^{-1}} = 25\,\text{eV}.$$

A single photon of $50\,\text{nm}$ radiation can ionize just about anything. Most stars are rich sources of ultraviolet radiation, so it is possible for a hydrogen plasma to form because it is near (in astronomical terms) to a star. Many instances of this can be seen in the night sky as nebulas, which themselves emit radiation when electrons and ions in the plasma recombine. The well-known Orion nebula is one example and is shown in Figure 6.2. Closer to home, incident ultraviolet radiation from the Sun ionizes a fraction of the atoms in the upper atmosphere of the Earth, so sustaining a plasma in the region known as the ionosphere.

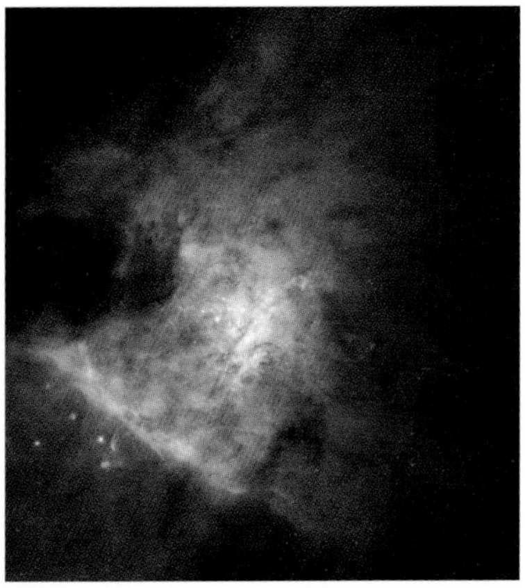

Figure 6.2 The Orion nebula, in which ultraviolet radiation from stars ionizes hydrogen gas to form a plasma. When electrons recombine with ions, photons are emitted and it is this emission that we see in this image.

6.1.3 Plasmas sustained by electrical energy

Lower down in the atmosphere, as well as in laboratories, factories and the home, plasmas can be created by electrical energy rather than by thermal or photonic energy. Charges accelerated in electric fields easily gain enough energy to ionize by collision: a field of $1\,\text{kV m}^{-1}$ will accelerate electrons to ionizing energies in a centimetre or so. Lightning and sparks provide ample evidence of this process. A power source is needed to sustain a plasma electrically for any significant time.

High-energy electrons are not easily brought into thermodynamic equilibrium by colliding with heavy atoms. However, there is a clear advantage in having plasmas far from equilibrium: the electrons can be readily sustained at temperatures equivalent to tens of thousands of kelvins (under which conditions they are potent ionizers) in gases that are cold. This means that you can have lamps that are brighter, but cooler, than incandescent bulbs — this is the basis of fluorescent lamps, neon signs and the high-intensity discharge lamps used in vehicle headlights.

You can also have chemical reactions promoted by the (hot) electrons of a plasma in gas that is barely above room temperature. This underlies the plasma-based etching and deposition of materials that has driven the miniaturization of microelectronics for the last thirty years or so (Figure 6.3). Plasmas are used to etch fine features in silicon during the manufacture of integrated circuits and microelectromechanical systems (MEMS). Areas that are to be etched are exposed to chemically-reactive species created in the plasma: for example, silicon is etched by plasmas made in gaseous fluorine compounds. Plasmas for materials processing and lighting applications are made in a variety of ways, but all of them use electromagnetism to get electrical energy into a gas, and the energetic particles then stimulate chemical and physical processes.

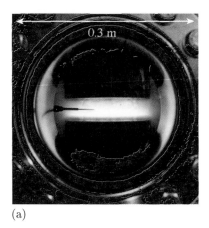

(a)

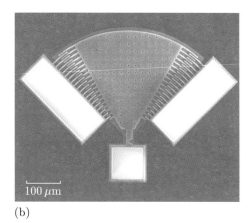

(b)

Figure 6.3 (a) The bright glow is from a low-pressure plasma, formed between the end-faces of two cylinders, excited by a radio frequency power supply. (b) A MEMS test structure that has been etched from a single piece of silicon using a plasma. The wedge shape is free to oscillate in the plane, being fixed to the square via a notched cantilever. Interdigitated combs provide electrostatic (capacitive) transducers to drive and sense displacement. The three white blocks have a thin metallic coating for electrical connections.

6.1.4 Plasmas sustained by multiple energy sources

Not all artificial plasmas are far from thermal equilibrium. A major international research programme has been underway for decades to harness the energy of nuclear fusion reactions. This is done by creating environments on Earth where thermonuclear fusion can be controlled. The particles in such plasmas have temperatures that reach millions of kelvins.

Holding such a hot plasma inside a vessel long enough for fusion reactions to occur calls for considerable ingenuity. Various schemes are in development, broadly based on two rival approaches — magnetic confinement and inertial confinement. The former uses magnetic bottles, while the latter uses high-intensity beams of light or particles. Heating matter to form a plasma at millions of kelvins even for a short time is not trivial either. So difficult is the challenge that just about anything is worth trying, provided that it couples energy into the plasma — drive large currents through it, shine high-intensity lasers at it, excite microwave resonances in it, launch a variety of electromagnetic waves within it, fire high-energy beams of particles at it, and so on.

6.1.5 The basic parameter space of plasma physics

Figure 6.4 shows the vast range of parameter space that characterizes all of the ionized gas plasmas described in this section. In this chapter we shall examine some of the interactions between electromagnetic fields and plasmas. To keep the task manageable, I am going to largely ignore the effects of thermal energy in plasmas. However, you should keep in mind how important the temperature axis can be in characterizing plasmas, as Figure 6.4 reveals.

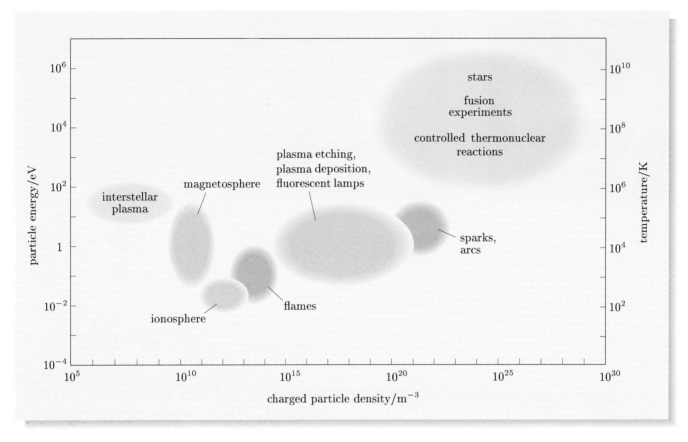

Figure 6.4   The location of a variety of plasmas in energy–density (or temperature–density) parameter space.

The first topic that we shall discuss is concerned with simple oscillations of charged particles, and we shall relate this behaviour to the classical LIH model of dielectrics and conductors discussed in previous chapters. Then the model is applied to the interaction of radio waves with the Earth's ionosphere. Next, the constraint of isotropy is abandoned in order to understand something about electromagnetic waves within plasmas in magnetic fields — here the Earth's magnetosphere is in the spotlight.

6.1.6   Plasma oscillations

Plasmas have a natural tendency to be neutral, since the charges in plasmas are free to move in response to Coulomb forces. Any unbalanced charge is the source of an electric field that tends to restore neutrality. This behaviour, which is similar to that of charge carriers in solid conductors, gives rise to a natural frequency of oscillation that characterizes the response of a group of electrons to any electrical disturbance. Let us see in more detail how this natural frequency comes about.

Consider a uniform plasma made up of electrons with number density n_e and an equal number density of positive ions, so that overall charge-neutrality exists. The thermal energy of the charged particles causes them to be constantly on the move, but this does not lead to a net displacement of charge, so I propose to ignore the thermal motion. Since there is no net charge, Gauss's law is satisfied if the electric field is zero, both in the plasma and outside it.

Let us consider what happens if all the electrons in a slab within the plasma are displaced relative to the positive ions by a small amount x in the direction perpendicular to the slab (Figure 6.5a). This displacement produces charge imbalances on the faces of the slab, which constitute surface charge densities $\sigma = \pm n_{\mathrm{e}} ex$. If Gauss's law is applied to the larger cylinder illustrated in Figure 6.5b, it can be shown that the electric field is zero outside the slab, so the field must be confined within the region between the surface charges. Applying Gauss's law to the smaller cylinder in the figure shows that the field within the slab is given by

$$\mathbf{E} = E_x \mathbf{e}_x = \frac{\sigma}{\varepsilon_0} \mathbf{e}_x = \frac{n_{\mathrm{e}} ex}{\varepsilon_0} \mathbf{e}_x.$$

Note that here we are using x to represent the x-component of the displacement of each of the electrons in the slab, not as a position coordinate.

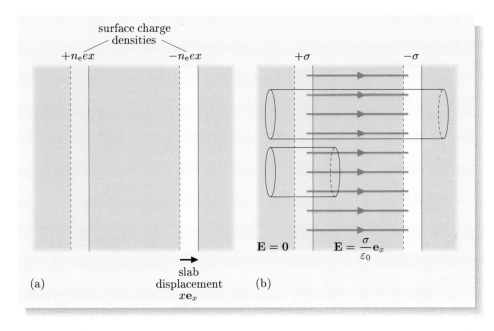

Figure 6.5 (a) The electrons in a plasma that were initially within the slab between the broken lines are displaced a small distance x, so that they are located between the solid lines. This leads to a thin layer containing no electrons (shown pink) and another layer containing an excess of electrons (shown blue). (b) Applying Gauss's law to the two cylinders shows that the layers of charge produce an electric field $E_x \mathbf{e}_x = (n_{\mathrm{e}} ex/\varepsilon_0) \mathbf{e}_x$ between them.

The electrons within the slab each experience a restoring force $-e E_x \mathbf{e}_x$, which pulls them back to their original positions. If the electrons are released at time $t = 0$, what follows is a coherent motion of the electrons, determined by the equation of motion

$$m \frac{\mathrm{d}^2 x}{\mathrm{d}t^2} = -e E_x = -\frac{n_{\mathrm{e}} e^2 x}{\varepsilon_0}.$$

The slab of electrons therefore undergoes a simple harmonic oscillation, with displacement $x = x_0 \cos \omega_{\mathrm{p}} t$, where the angular frequency ω_{p} is given by

$$\omega_{\mathrm{p}} = \sqrt{\frac{n_{\mathrm{e}} e^2}{m \varepsilon_0}}. \tag{6.1}$$

The quantity ω_{p} was first encountered in the dielectric model of Chapter 4, where, in anticipation of this result, I called it the **plasma frequency**. It is the natural (angular) frequency of the simple harmonic motion of a collection of electrons within the plasma about their equilibrium position following a simple electrostatic perturbation.

Energy must be put into the system to set up the initial displacement. A macroscopic electric field then exists in the region between the two faces of the

Plasma oscillations are a 'collective effect' because they involve the coherent motion of a group of particles.

slab. When released, the displaced charge accelerates, and the electric field vanishes as the displaced slab of electrons reaches its original position, swapping potential energy for kinetic energy and therefore going on to overshoot the equilibrium position. An electric field reappears, bringing the electrons back to rest but with the charges on the two faces of the slab reversed, and the electrons are pulled back again ... So the displaced electrons oscillate back and forth, just like a stretched and compressed spring. In this simple model, there is nothing that dissipates the energy, so the oscillation continues indefinitely.

6.1.7   A simple classical model of an isotropic plasma

In Chapter 4, I introduced a simple classical model of an LIH dielectric that led to an expression for a complex frequency-dependent dielectric function. In Chapter 5, I adapted this model to account for the linear response of an isotropic homogeneous conductor to a time-dependent electric field in terms of an analogous quantity that I called a complex relative permittivity function. As I shall show here, this model applies equally well to a plasma under conditions where the LIH assumptions are valid. We shall initially assume that there is no magnetic field; a magnetic field necessarily disrupts the notion of isotropy, since the motions of charges parallel to the field and perpendicular to the field are markedly different. We shall extend the model to cope with the presence of a magnetic field in Section 6.2.

The equations that describe electromagnetic waves in an ionized gas are Maxwell's equations for the fields, together with equations governing the motion of free charges. In principle, for a gaseous plasma, the statistical effects of temperature should be included. However, for the wave phenomena that are discussed in the contexts of this chapter, the thermal motion of the free charges does not have a primary influence on the behaviour. We shall therefore adopt a 'cold plasma' model, in which thermal effects are neglected.

- ● What constraint might be applied to the electric field of an electromagnetic wave to ensure that the interaction with a plasma remains linear?

- ○ The response would certainly be non-linear if the electric field were so strong that it caused the background gas to be further ionized. We shall suppose that the electric field is always sufficiently low to avoid that happening.

We can then characterize the plasma by a relative permittivity function $\varepsilon(\omega)$, just as we did for conductors in Chapter 5. The complex relative permittivity function for a conductor was shown to be

$$\varepsilon_{\mathrm{eff}}(\omega) = 1 - \omega_{\mathrm{p}}^2 \frac{1}{\omega^2 + i\omega/\tau_{\mathrm{c}}}. \qquad \text{(Eqn 5.9)}$$

We now examine $\varepsilon_{\mathrm{eff}}(\omega)$ when the conductor is a cold ionized gas, in the absence of a magnetic field. The collision frequency $1/\tau_{\mathrm{c}}$ is associated with collisions of electrons with other electrons, ions and the background un-ionized (neutral) atoms and molecules. In partially-ionized gases, it is collisions with the un-ionized particles that usually predominate, and $1/\tau_{\mathrm{c}}$ is proportional to the number density of neutral gas particles. In Chapter 5 we were concerned with the frequency of collisions between electrons and the heavy atom cores that make up a solid conductor, which have a number density of around $10^{28}\ \mathrm{m}^{-3}$. Gases at atmospheric pressure (at sea level) and at room temperature are about one thousand times less dense than this. In a plasma where the density of neutral gas atoms and molecules and the frequencies of interest are such that $1/\tau_c \ll \omega$, the so-called *collisionless regime*, the response to electromagnetic waves is described by

$$\varepsilon_{\text{eff}}(\omega) = 1 - \frac{\omega_p^2}{\omega^2}. \tag{6.2}$$

We shall use this collisionless model of the relative permittivity function throughout Section 6.2.

Waves above the plasma frequency

Equation 6.2 shows that if $\omega > \omega_p$, then the relative permittivity function is real and lies between zero and unity, i.e. $0 < \varepsilon_{\text{eff}} < 1$. Electromagnetic waves then propagate with a wavenumber given by

$$k = \frac{n\omega}{c} = \frac{\sqrt{\varepsilon_{\text{eff}}}\,\omega}{c}.$$

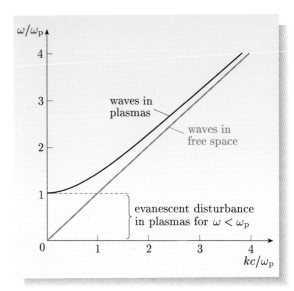

Figure 6.6 The dispersion diagram for electromagnetic waves in a linear isotropic homogeneous plasma, and in free space.

Substituting for $\varepsilon_{\text{eff}}(\omega)$ using Equation 6.2, we find that the wavenumber and frequency are related by the *dispersion relation*

$$\omega = \sqrt{\omega_p^2 + k^2 c^2}, \tag{6.3}$$

and this is plotted in Figure 6.6.

Worked Example 6.1

Compare the phase speed ($v_{\text{phase}} = \omega/k$) and the group speed ($v_{\text{group}} = \mathrm{d}\omega/\mathrm{d}k$) for plane electromagnetic waves in an LIH plasma when $\omega \geq \omega_p$.

Solution

Equation 6.3 gives the dispersion relation that links ω and k, from which it follows that

$$v_{\text{phase}} = \frac{\omega}{k} = \frac{\sqrt{\omega_p^2 + k^2 c^2}}{k}.$$

Using Equation 6.3, k can be eliminated, giving

$$v_{\text{phase}} = c\sqrt{\frac{\omega^2}{\omega^2 - \omega_p^2}}.$$

The group speed follows immediately from Equation 6.3, and again k can be eliminated:

$$v_{\text{group}} = \frac{\mathrm{d}\omega}{\mathrm{d}k} = \frac{kc^2}{\sqrt{\omega_p^2 + k^2 c^2}} = c\sqrt{\frac{\omega^2 - \omega_p^2}{\omega^2}}.$$

Essential skill

Finding phase and group speeds from a dispersion relation

These expressions show that high-frequency waves ($\omega \gg \omega_p$) travel at phase speed c, as if in free space, and the energy carried by high-frequency waves also travels as if in free space, since $v_{\text{group}} = c$.

Waves with frequencies just above ω_p have phase speeds that are much greater than c. However, the energy that they carry travels at speeds much less than c. Notice that $v_{\text{phase}} v_{\text{group}} = c^2$.

When $\omega = \omega_p$, the electrons just oscillate rather than enabling the propagation of a wave and the transport of energy.

Evanescent disturbances below the plasma frequency

There is more to be learnt from Equation 6.2. Notice that $\varepsilon_{\text{eff}} < 0$ if $\omega < \omega_p$. The wavenumber is then imaginary, so electromagnetic waves do not propagate, but are evanescent.

Essential skill

Using dispersion relations to determine the nature of disturbances

Worked Example 6.2

When a returning spacecraft re-enters the atmosphere, the shock wave and the friction that it generates lead to the ionization of gas molecules just ahead of it and around it. During the most intense phase of deceleration, radio communication signals cannot pass between the spacecraft and the ground. If the highest frequency communications band is in the region of 450 MHz, estimate a lower limit for the number density of the electrons in the plasma that surrounds a spacecraft during radio blackout.

Solution

If the frequency of the radio waves is greater than ω_p in the surrounding plasma, the waves will be able to propagate though it. At low plasma densities, this is always the case.

Communication is first cut off when the electron density reaches the value where $\omega_p = \sqrt{n_e e^2 / m \varepsilon_0}$ is equal to the maximum angular frequency for radio communication. Rearranging and evaluating:

$$n_e = (2\pi \times 4.50 \times 10^8 \, \text{s}^{-1})^2 \frac{9.11 \times 10^{-31} \, \text{kg} \times 8.85 \times 10^{-12} \, \text{F m}^{-1}}{(1.60 \times 10^{-19} \, \text{C})^2}$$

$$= 2.5 \times 10^{15} \, \text{m}^{-3}.$$

6.2 Waves in the Earth's ionosphere

The ultraviolet radiation from the Sun ionizes the upper layers of the Earth's atmosphere to create what is known as the ionosphere. The ionosphere extends above the Earth's surface from about 80 km to about 1500 km. Further out, shaped by the Earth's magnetic field and the solar wind, is the magnetosphere (see also Book 2, Chapter 6). These two environments blend continuously into each other, and throughout there are sufficient charged particles to classify the medium as plasma. The ionosphere and magnetosphere are the subject of much research interest, not least because they provide a huge natural plasma laboratory that we can readily probe through remote measurements from the ground and through measurements from within the plasma itself using spacecraft. Our increasing use of radio and satellite communications means that there is an increasing practical need to understand ionospheric and magnetospheric plasmas. We shall discuss ionospheric plasmas in this section and magnetospheric plasmas in Section 6.3.

6.2.1 The ionosphere

Figure 6.7 shows the structure of the atmosphere out as far as the ionosphere. Gases comprising the troposphere (lower parts of the atmosphere, in which we live) and the stratosphere (in which passenger jets cruise) are almost completely

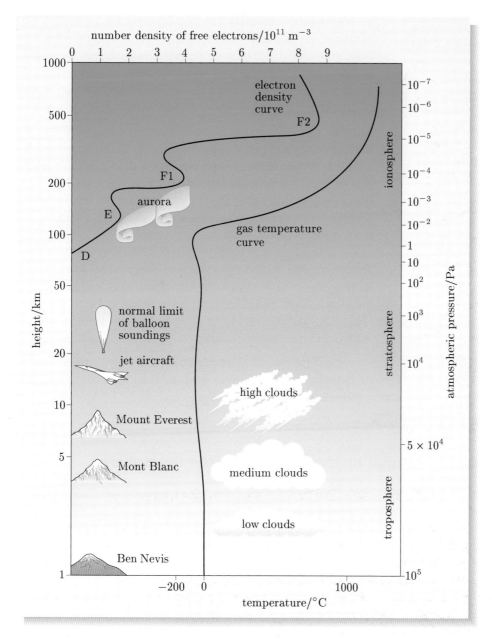

Figure 6.7 This figure shows the various named layers of the atmosphere on the right. The ionosphere generally describes the region that begins where the number density of charged particles exceeds about 10^{10} m^{-3} out to beyond the maximum density close to 10^{12} m^{-3}. Also shown is the temperature profile, which, together with the pressure, determines the local number density of gas atoms. Note that the pressure scale is neither linear nor logarithmic because of the dependence of pressure on both number density of gas atoms and temperature.

un-ionized, so the number density of free charges is too low for collective effects to prevail. Electromagnetic waves interact only weakly with the neutral molecules, and pass through these gases at very close to the vacuum speed of light. However, free charges in the ionosphere respond strongly to an electromagnetic wave, slowing it and possibly refracting it or even preventing its passage. For this reason, the ionosphere is particularly important for terrestrial radio communication.

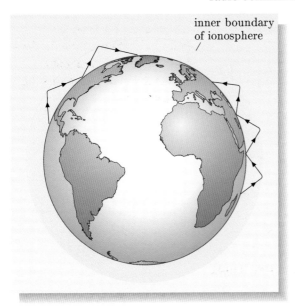

inner boundary of ionosphere

In 1901, Marconi first demonstrated that it was possible to send radio waves at around 800 kHz between points on the Earth's surface separated by thousands of miles. The first transatlantic radio message, transmitted almost 2200 miles between Cornwall and Newfoundland, was three short bursts, which is the letter 's' in Morse code. Communication over such long distances cannot be explained by line of sight propagation. Nor can it be explained by refraction arising from the vertical variation of the pressure of the atmosphere. It was suggested at that time that it was also unlikely to be a result of the diffraction of radio waves around the curvature of the Earth.

In 1902, a possible explanation of Marconi's long-distance transmissions was given independently by the American engineer Arthur Kennelly and the British physicist Oliver Heaviside. They proposed the existence of some kind of conducting region above the atmosphere. Such a layer might somehow reflect radio waves back down to great distances from the transmitter, as shown in Figure 6.8. The existence of the ionosphere was confirmed in the 1920s by Sir Edward Appleton, who carried out a series of experiments to explore its properties. His work on the ionosphere was recognized by the award of the 1947 Nobel prize for physics. The E-layer of the ionosphere (see Figure 6.7) is also said to be named after him, with D- and F-layers then being added on an alphabetical basis.

Figure 6.8 Kennelly and Heaviside proposed that reflections from a partially ionized layer high up in the atmosphere, and also from the 'conductor' constituted by the land or the sea, might explain Marconi's long-distance transmissions.

Let us see if we can work out for ourselves an explanation of how the ionosphere enables long-distance radio transmission. What we shall find turns out to account for modern practice, though it casts doubts on the interpretation of Marconi's original experiments.

6.2.2 Normal incidence: probing the ionosphere

According to the simple model of Subsection 6.1.7, electromagnetic waves will propagate freely in an isotropic homogeneous plasma so long as their frequency is such that $\omega > \omega_p$. Under these circumstances, a plane wave, polarized in the x-direction and travelling in the z-direction, is given by the real part of

$$\mathbf{E}(z,t) = E_0 \exp[\mathrm{i}(kz - \omega t)]\,\mathbf{e}_x. \tag{6.4}$$

The wavenumber k is given by

$$k = \frac{n\omega}{c} = \frac{\sqrt{\varepsilon_{\text{eff}}(\omega)}\,\omega}{c} = \frac{\sqrt{\omega^2 - \omega_p^2}}{c},$$

where we have used Equation 6.2 to substitute for ε_{eff}.

However, should the wave encounter a region where the electron number density is sufficiently high that ω_p exceeds ω, then the wave will not propagate because the wavenumber is imaginary. Inserting $k = ik_{\text{imag}}$ in Equation 6.4 shows the evanescent behaviour explicitly:

$$\mathbf{E}(z, t) = E_0 \exp[-k_{\text{imag}}z] \exp[-i\omega t]\,\mathbf{e}_x.$$

A similar situation was identified in Subsection 5.1.1 as the intermediate frequency regime in the response of solid conductors.

● What happens to the energy carried by a monochromatic electromagnetic wave through a plasma when the wave encounters a region in which $\omega_p > \omega$?

○ The evanescent wave does not transport energy, so the wave must undergo reflection at the place where $\omega_p = \omega$, taking all of the incident energy with it.

Exercise 6.1 Calculate the electron number density that would be sufficient to prevent the propagation of an electromagnetic wave at $800\,\text{kHz}$. Then use Figure 6.7 to estimate the maximum height to which such radiation could propagate.

Exercise 6.2 Suggest how the variation of electron number density with height shown in Figure 6.7 might be determined using radar techniques. ■

So, does reflection from the ionosphere explain Marconi's transatlantic transmission at $800\,\text{kHz}$? It does not. There are several weaknesses in the argument thus far. First, the simple model summarized in Equation 6.2 is for an LIH plasma. However, in the ionosphere, the plasma density generally increases with height between 80 and $500\,\text{km}$. Therefore we need to think carefully about whether the simple model remains valid up to the point where $\omega = \omega_p$, so that $n_e = m\varepsilon_0\omega^2/e^2$. From Figure 6.7 it is apparent that changes in the number density of electrons occur over a distance of many kilometres, which is much longer than the wavelength of most radio waves. (At $800\,\text{kHz}$ in free space, the wavelength is $0.38\,\text{km}$.) The departure from the LIH condition is therefore slight, so there should be no serious problem with using an LIH model for the plasma.

A second point of concern is that the frequency of Marconi's radio waves was so low that they would not have reached beyond the region marked in Figure 6.7 as the D-layer. Figure 6.9 shows the typical variations with height of the collision frequency and the daytime plasma frequency. The background gas density around the D-layer, though considerably less than at sea level, is not so low that it is appropriate to assume $\omega \gg 1/\tau_c$. We know from Chapter 5 that under such circumstances there is significant absorption of wave energy over a length scale characterized by the skin depth $\delta = \sqrt{2/\mu_0\sigma\omega}$. Around the D-layer, $\delta \sim 1\,\text{km}$. Maybe Marconi was fortunate and the attenuation of his signal was not too severe to prevent detection. More likely is the possibility of his message actually being carried inadvertently by a higher harmonic at $1600\,\text{kHz}$ or $2400\,\text{kHz}$.

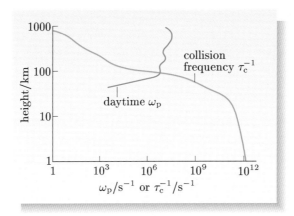

Figure 6.9   Typical variation with height of the collision frequency and the daytime plasma frequency in the ionospheric plasma.

● Given that propagating waves must have $\omega > \omega_p$, and given the data in Figure 6.9, above what height would it be safe to assume that $\omega \gg 1/\tau_c$?

○ From Figure 6.9, the frequency of collisions falls rapidly with increasing height, and $1/\tau_c \sim \omega_p$ at about 90 km. So above 100 km, say, $\omega_p \gg 1/\tau_c$ and it is reasonable to assume that for propagating waves $\omega \gg 1/\tau_c$.

Thirdly, we have so far neglected the fact that the edge of the ionosphere is gradual rather than sharp. In this case, the process of reflection at oblique incidence is more subtle than the sharp boundary reflections considered in earlier chapters. We look at this next.

6.2.3   Oblique incidence: long-distance radio transmission

It has been established that at sufficiently high altitude, the relative permittivity of the ionosphere for radio waves is given by Equation 6.2. The refractive index there is

$$n = \sqrt{\varepsilon(\omega)} = \sqrt{1 - \omega_p^2/\omega^2}. \tag{6.5}$$

Essential skill

Determining characteristics of wave propagation

Worked Example 6.3

Obtain an expression for the phase speed of radio waves in terms of the variation of electron number density with height, $n_e(h)$, and use it to show that wavefronts generally travel faster at higher altitude.

Solution

Using Equation 6.5 for the refractive index, the phase speed of waves with angular frequency ω is

$$v_{\text{phase}} = \frac{c}{\sqrt{\varepsilon(\omega)}} = \frac{c}{\sqrt{1 - n_e(h)e^2/(m\varepsilon_0\omega^2)}}.$$

Ignoring the bumps on the curve in Figure 6.7, $n_e(h)$ increases with height in the region of interest. Thus the speed at which wavefronts travel increases with altitude.

Imagine what happens to wavefronts as they head upwards into the ionosphere at an oblique angle. Those parts of any wavefront that are higher up will travel a little faster. Figure 6.10 illustrates the process and compares it with the formation of mirages, which are the result of an equivalent phenomenon at optical frequencies. In practice, the relatively gentle gradients of electron number density in the ionosphere cause radio waves to be refracted, bending their path so that they are in effect redirected towards the Earth. The process takes place somewhat below the height where the relative permittivity passes through zero (that is, where $\omega = \omega_p$).

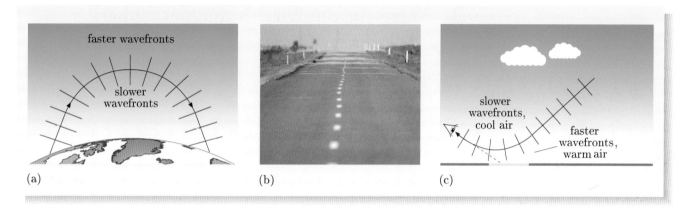

(a)   (b)   (c)

Figure 6.10   (a) Refraction in the ionosphere enables long-distance radio communication. (b) A mirage in which patches of sky light appear to come from the ground, as if reflected from a wet surface. (c) The continuous refraction of light that is responsible for mirages.

Whether you call this mechanism refraction or reflection depends on how closely you examine the process. From the surface of the Earth, the net effect has the major hallmark of reflection — the angle of incidence equals the apparent angle of reflection. From closer in, the process reveals the gradually increasing influence of the decreasing refractive index, which redirects the energy towards regions of higher refractive index.

Conditions in the ionosphere vary widely. There is a strong difference between night and day, as Figure 6.11 illustrates. Typically, the density at a particular height may vary by a factor of between 10 and 100. The primary cause of this is that only during daytime is there incident ultraviolet radiation from the Sun which not only ionizes the plasma, but also heats it, causing it to expand. Apart from this important 24-hour variation, there are effects caused by random solar activities impressed on systematic variations with periods of a year and about 11 years. (The Sun's activity, and so ultraviolet radiation, peaks roughly every 11 years.) There is also a measurable lunar period in the ionospheric density due to gravitational effects of the moon (analogous to ocean tides). All of these effects together cause a complicated time variability in the ionosphere's density structure. Conditions for radio communication follow suit, especially for the 24-hour and 11-year cycles, over which it seems as if the reflecting layers of the ionosphere are being raised and lowered, leading to substantial variability in radio reception.

Marconi knew none of this. If he had, he may well have chosen a higher frequency to be sure of a successful demonstration, but he might have been too daunted by the complexity of the overall process even to try. Ionospheric

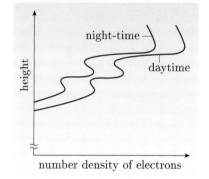

Figure 6.11   The number density of charged particles in the ionospheric plasma varies between night and day. At night, the height at which a given frequency is reflected is higher, and the range for signals at that frequency is consequently greater.

reflections are now routinely used across a range of radio frequencies between 3 and 30 MHz, but not normally as low as Marconi's 800 kHz.

Exercise 6.3   Radio frequency signals up to 30 MHz can be bounced off the ionosphere and the surface of the Earth to reach right round the globe, yet when directed straight upwards, signals above about 10 MHz or so, depending on the time of day, are not reflected. Explain this observation.   ■

6.3   Waves in the Earth's magnetosphere

In Chapter 6 of Book 2, we examined the motion of individual charged particles in the magnetosphere. Here we are concerned with electromagnetic waves propagating through the plasma constituted by those charges.

6.3.1   The magnetosphere

The magnetosphere is shown schematically in Figure 6.12. On its sunward side, there is a layer where the solar wind is rapidly decelerated as it encounters the Earth's magnetic field. This happens because the solar wind is itself a plasma and so its charged particles are forced to spiral tightly around the field lines and follow them around the Earth. In this way the Earth's magnetic field tends to shield the Earth from constant bombardment by charged particles from the Sun. This protection (and variations of it over time) may have played a part in the evolution of life on the Earth. It is known, for instance, that the Earth's magnetic field has reversed direction many times over the ages. During such a reversal, there is a period when the field is small and affords little protection from the solar wind.

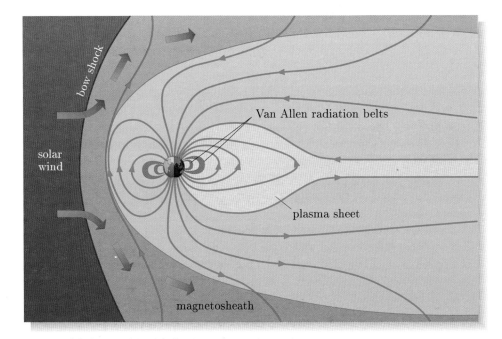

Figure 6.12   The magnetosphere is shaped by the magnetic field of the Earth, which is a dipole field that is being distorted by the incident solar wind.

The magnetosphere is continually affected by changes from within and without. From within, the ionospheric plasma carries the ring current (discussed in Book 2, Subsection 6.3.2) that causes variations in the Earth's magnetic field, which in turn disturbs the magnetosphere. On longer timescales, changes in the Earth's core can also change the Earth's magnetic field. The external disturbances are caused by the solar wind, which has fluctuations in density, magnetic field and composition originating from solar activity. Research into the magnetosphere can be conducted from the Earth's surface by measuring disturbances in the Earth's magnetic field and by detecting radio waves that originate in the magnetosphere. The spectrum of radio waves provides information about physical conditions in different parts of the magnetosphere because spectral features are often related to plasma frequencies and cyclotron frequencies. These frequencies can be used to provide quantitative estimates of number densities and magnetic field strengths in particular parts of the magnetosphere. In addition to this, we have much data from *within* the magnetosphere taken from spacecraft.

Some charged particles do penetrate the magnetosphere, however. Once inside, these follow the magnetic field lines until they arrive at the relatively strong fields near the Earth's magnetic poles, which act as magnetic mirrors. Depending on their pitch angle, particles will either be reflected back out into space, or pass through the magnetic mirror to reach lower layers of the Earth's atmosphere. When the solar wind contains a disturbance, i.e. a density and/or speed enhancement, many such particles will descend into polar regions. You can see one of the consequences in the aurora caused by these energetic particles exciting atoms and molecules in the upper atmosphere (Figure 6.13).

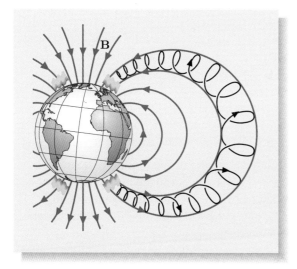

Figure 6.13 Auroras are caused by charged particles, which are following magnetic field lines, exciting atoms and molecules in the Earth's atmosphere in regions around the poles.

The closed field lines shown in Figure 6.12 are essentially magnetic bottles, in which charged particles bounce between poles until their pitch angle is altered by collisions with other particles, or by interaction with waves, leading to their escape. The trapping that occurs here causes the concentrations of charged particles that are known as radiation belts. There are two distinct belts, named after James Van Allen, the leader of the team that discovered them. The thin, inner belt (at about 1.5 Earth radii) is populated mainly by protons and electrons that arise from cosmic ray interactions (particles incident from all part of the Universe). The outer belt (3–4 Earth radii) is associated with trapped particles that originate in the solar wind. The number density of charged particles, trapped or otherwise, in the magnetosphere is in the range 10^{10}–$10^{12}\,\mathrm{m}^{-3}$.

● Calculate the range of plasma frequencies in the magnetosphere.

○ At the lower limit of particle number density,

$$\omega_\mathrm{p} = \sqrt{\frac{n_\mathrm{e}e^2}{m\varepsilon_0}} = \sqrt{\frac{10^{10}\,\mathrm{m}^{-3} \times (1.60 \times 10^{-19}\,\mathrm{C})^2}{9.11 \times 10^{-31}\,\mathrm{kg} \times 8.85 \times 10^{-12}\,\mathrm{F\,m}^{-1}}}$$
$$= 5.6 \times 10^6\,\mathrm{s}^{-1}.$$

The upper limit for the plasma frequency is $\sqrt{100}$ greater, so

$$5.6 \times 10^6\,\mathrm{s}^{-1} < \omega_\mathrm{p} < 5.6 \times 10^7\,\mathrm{s}^{-1}.$$

6.3.2   Whistler waves in the magnetosphere

The Earth's magnetic field profoundly affects the propagation of electromagnetic waves in the ionosphere and magnetosphere. A curious example of this is provided by **whistler waves**. The frequency of these electromagnetic waves ranges down to as low as $300\,\mathrm{Hz}$. They are short bursts of electromagnetic waves created by lightning strokes in one hemisphere and guided by the Earth's magnetic field up through the ionosphere, high into the magnetosphere, and back down to a region in the opposite hemisphere. The lower-frequency components travel slower than the higher-frequency components, so the electromagnetic crack of a lightning stroke gets smeared out over a few seconds after travelling several thousand miles. Sometimes whistlers bounce back and forth between hemispheres many times before being dissipated. Although they are electromagnetic waves, their low-frequency content is in the audio range, and they can be converted by audio electronic systems into audible sound waves. When this happens, they sound like a series of swishing sounds from high to lower audio frequencies. In this subsection the simple plasma model is developed to account for whistlers.

To do this, we must reconsider the classical model of the motion of a single electron that is driven by the electric field of an electromagnetic wave. Various forms of this model have been applied to LIH dielectrics (in Chapter 4), to conducting LIH solids (in Chapter 5), and to LIH plasmas (earlier in this chapter). So that we can study electromagnetic waves in magnetospheric plasma, a steady magnetic field, equivalent to that of the Earth, will now be included in the model. The plasma is still presumed to be homogeneous and its response to be linear, but the presence of the magnetic field means that the medium is no longer isotropic.

To model magnetospheric plasma in a local region, we include a constant magnetic field of magnitude B_0, aligned along the z-direction. It was shown in Chapter 4 that the magnetic field associated with the wave has a negligible effect compared with the electric field, but here we are adding a *steady* magnetic field. There is enough to discover without worrying about collisions, so I shall suppose that $1/\tau_\mathrm{c} \to 0$. Then the model equation of motion for a single free electron is

$$m\frac{\mathrm{d}^2\mathbf{r}(t)}{\mathrm{d}t^2} = -e\,\mathbf{E}(\mathbf{r}(t), t) - e\frac{\mathrm{d}\mathbf{r}(t)}{\mathrm{d}t} \times (B_0\mathbf{e}_z). \tag{6.6}$$

In the case that we shall consider here, the electron is driven by a travelling wave, polarized perpendicular to the steady magnetic field. The displacement of the electron can be assumed to be always much less than the wavelength of the wave, so that locally $\mathbf{E}(\mathbf{r}(t), t) \rightarrow \mathbf{E}(t)$.

Consider some point in space and time where $\mathbf{E}(t) = E_0(t)\,\mathbf{e}_y$ and $\mathbf{B} = B_0\mathbf{e}_z$, illustrated in Figure 6.14a. The electron is accelerated in the $-y$-direction by the electric force, $-eE_0\mathbf{e}_y$, and deflected in the plane perpendicular to the magnetic field by the magnetic component of the Lorentz force, $-e\mathbf{v} \times \mathbf{B}$. At a slightly later moment in time, the electric field of the wave will be different, and the direction of the magnetic force will have changed (Figure 6.14b), though it will still be perpendicular to the magnetic field and to the direction of motion. There are now some interesting possibilities:

- the electric field might be changing so rapidly that the displacement and deflection of an electron are small and repeatedly reversed, so that there is no induced polarization;

- the electric field might be changing so slowly that the combined effect of the fields $E_0(t)\,\mathbf{e}_y$ and $B_0\mathbf{e}_z$ leads to significant displacement of electrons in the x-direction as well as the y-direction;

- if the polarization of the wave were circular (see Subsection 1.3.5), then there is the possibility of a resonance between the frequency of the cyclotron motion, ω_c, and the rotation of polarization at the wave frequency, ω;

- if the polarization of the wave were circular, then the direction of rotation of the electric field vector would be important.

See Book 1, Chapter 3, and Book 2, Chapter 6, for a discussion of the cyclotron frequency $\omega_c = eB/m$. Note that here the subscript 'c' denotes 'cyclotron', whereas the subscript in τ_c denotes 'collision'.

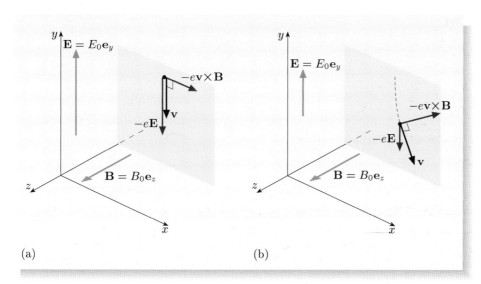

(a) (b)

Figure 6.14 (a) The Lorentz force, $-e(\mathbf{E} + \mathbf{v} \times \mathbf{B})$, guides an electron on a curved trajectory. (b) At a later instant in time, the electric force on the particle will have changed in magnitude, and the magnetic force will have changed in direction but will still be perpendicular to $\mathbf{v}$ and to $\mathbf{B}$.

● Calculate the value of the cyclotron frequency for electrons in the magnetosphere, where $B \sim 3 \times 10^{-4}\,\text{T}$.

○ $\omega_c = \dfrac{eB}{m} = \dfrac{1.60 \times 10^{-19}\,\text{C} \times 3 \times 10^{-4}\,\text{T}}{9.11 \times 10^{-31}\,\text{kg}} = 5 \times 10^7\,\text{s}^{-1}$.

This range of possibilities is in part a consequence of the inherent anisotropy imposed by the magnetic field. Before we analyse the situation further, I want to remind you of one of the characteristics of circular polarization.

Circularly polarized modes

In Chapter 1, two different forms of circular polarization were introduced. I am here going to describe them as being **left-handed (LH) circular polarization** and **right-handed (RH) circular polarization** according to how the electric vector rotates as the waves pass a fixed point in space. The electric field at $z = 0$ for a right-handed circularly polarized wave, travelling in the $+z$-direction, is given by the real part of

$$\mathbf{E}^{\mathrm{RH}}(0, t) = E_0 \exp[-\mathrm{i}\omega t] \, (\mathbf{e}_x + \mathrm{i}\mathbf{e}_y).$$

Since $\mathrm{i} = \exp[\mathrm{i}\pi/2]$, the phase of the y-component of the electric field is always ahead of that of the x-component by $\pi/2$. In a right-handed polarized wave, $E_y = \mathrm{i}E_x$, and the physical field is given by

$$\mathrm{Re}\{\mathbf{E}^{\mathrm{RH}}(0, t)\} = E_0 \, \mathrm{Re}\{\big(\cos(-\omega t) + \mathrm{i}\sin(-\omega t)\big)(\mathbf{e}_x + \mathrm{i}\mathbf{e}_y)\}$$
$$= E_0(\cos\omega t \, \mathbf{e}_x + \sin\omega t \, \mathbf{e}_y).$$

As shown in Figure 6.15, this leads to a steady rotation of the electric vector about the direction of propagation in the sense given by a right-hand grip rule, at the angular frequency of the wave.

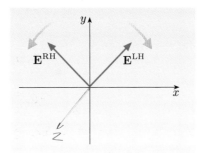

Figure 6.15   Rotation of the polarization direction for waves travelling in the z-direction.

The electric field of a left-handed wave has the opposite phase shift between the x- and y-components, with $E_y = -\mathrm{i}E_x$, and is the real part of

$$\mathbf{E}^{\mathrm{LH}}(0, t) = E_0 \exp[-\mathrm{i}\omega t] \, (\mathbf{e}_x - \mathrm{i}\mathbf{e}_y).$$

The physical field for a left-handed wave is given by

$$\mathrm{Re}\{\mathbf{E}^{\mathrm{LH}}(0, t)\} = E_0(\cos\omega t \, \mathbf{e}_x - \sin\omega t \, \mathbf{e}_y).$$

If equal amounts of RH and LH circular polarizations are added, the net result is a simple linear polarization. Conversely, any linear polarization can be thought of as a sum of equal portions of RH and LH waves.

A magnetized plasma responds differently to RH and LH waves, and when stimulated by a linearly polarized wave, the energy is transported in these RH and LH modes. Each mode has a corresponding relative permittivity function, as I shall now demonstrate.

Relative permittivity for RH and LH circularly polarized waves

Following the approach of Chapter 4, I shall first obtain an expression for the induced polarization of the medium in terms of the applied field and the displacement of an electron. Then the relative permittivity can be found by summing over all the electrons in any given volume.

For an electric field that has time-dependence $\exp[-\mathrm{i}\omega t]$, the equation of motion for a single electron, Equation 6.6, can be split into components as follows:

$$-\omega^2 x = -\frac{e}{m} E_x + (\mathrm{i}\omega y)\omega_\mathrm{c},$$

$$-\omega^2 y = -\frac{e}{m} E_y - (\mathrm{i}\omega x)\omega_\mathrm{c}.$$

Here we have used
$$(\mathrm{d}\mathbf{r}/\mathrm{d}t) \times \mathbf{e}_z = -\mathrm{i}\omega\mathbf{r} \times \mathbf{e}_z$$
$$= -\mathrm{i}\omega(x\mathbf{e}_x + y\mathbf{e}_y + z\mathbf{e}_z) \times \mathbf{e}_z$$
$$= -\mathrm{i}\omega(y\mathbf{e}_x - x\mathbf{e}_y).$$

Solving these simultaneous equations takes a few lines of careful algebra, and results in

$$x = \frac{e}{m\omega}\left(\frac{\omega E_x - \mathrm{i}\omega_\mathrm{c} E_y}{\omega^2 - \omega_\mathrm{c}^2}\right),$$

$$y = \frac{e}{m\omega}\left(\frac{\omega E_y + \mathrm{i}\omega_\mathrm{c} E_x}{\omega^2 - \omega_\mathrm{c}^2}\right).$$

So the displacement is

$$\mathbf{r} = \frac{e}{m\omega}\left(\frac{\omega E_x\mathbf{e}_x - \mathrm{i}\omega_\mathrm{c} E_y\mathbf{e}_x + \omega E_y\mathbf{e}_y + \mathrm{i}\omega_\mathrm{c} E_x\mathbf{e}_y}{\omega^2 - \omega_\mathrm{c}^2}\right).$$

Since we expect the system to be sensitive to circular polarization, it is worth looking at the displacement when the electric field is RH circularly polarized with $E_y = \mathrm{i}E_x$, and when it is LH circularly polarized with $E_y = -\mathrm{i}E_x$. Both of these lead to major simplifications:

$$\mathbf{r}^{\mathrm{RH}} = \frac{e\mathbf{E}^{\mathrm{RH}}}{m\omega(\omega - \omega_\mathrm{c})}, \tag{6.7}$$

$$\mathbf{r}^{\mathrm{LH}} = \frac{e\mathbf{E}^{\mathrm{LH}}}{m\omega(\omega + \omega_\mathrm{c})}. \tag{6.8}$$

There are n_e free electrons per unit volume, so the net polarization (remembering that an electron's charge is $-e$) created by an RH polarized wave is

$$\mathbf{P}^{\mathrm{RH}} = -n_\mathrm{e} e\mathbf{r}^{\mathrm{RH}} = -\frac{n_\mathrm{e} e^2}{m\omega(\omega - \omega_\mathrm{c})}\mathbf{E}^{\mathrm{RH}}.$$

Then from $\mathbf{D} = \varepsilon\varepsilon_0\mathbf{E} = \varepsilon_0\mathbf{E} + \mathbf{P}$, the relative permittivity for RH circularly polarized waves is

$$\varepsilon^{\mathrm{RH}}(\omega) = 1 + \frac{P^{\mathrm{RH}}}{\varepsilon_0 E^{\mathrm{RH}}} = 1 - \frac{\omega_\mathrm{p}^2}{\omega(\omega - \omega_\mathrm{c})}. \tag{6.9}$$

● Show that in the limit $\omega_\mathrm{c} \to 0$, the results of the simpler, magnetic field free, model of Subsection 6.2.1 is recovered from $\varepsilon^{\mathrm{RH}}$.

○ If $\omega_\mathrm{c} \to 0$, then $\varepsilon^{\mathrm{RH}} \to 1 - \omega_\mathrm{p}^2/\omega^2$, which is the same as the simpler result for isotropic plasmas in Subsection 6.2.1.

● To what does $\varepsilon^{\mathrm{RH}}$ reduce when ω greatly exceeds ω_c and ω_p?

○ If $\omega \gg \omega_\mathrm{c}$ and $\omega \gg \omega_\mathrm{p}$, then $\varepsilon^{\mathrm{RH}} \to 1$, reflecting the fact that at high frequencies the particles cannot 'follow' or resonate with the driving field.

Exercise 6.4 Show that an LH circularly polarized wave, $\mathbf{E}^{\mathrm{LH}}$, travelling in the direction of the field $B_0\mathbf{e}_z$, sees a medium with relative permittivity

$$\varepsilon^{\mathrm{LH}}(\omega) = 1 - \frac{\omega_\mathrm{p}^2}{\omega(\omega + \omega_\mathrm{c})}. \tag{6.10}$$

Exercise 6.5   Determine the relative permittivities of the circularly polarized waves $\mathbf{E}^{\mathrm{RH}}(z, t)$ and $\mathbf{E}^{\mathrm{LH}}(z, t)$ at the two frequencies $\omega = \omega_c/2$ and $\omega = 2\omega_c$, in a plasma for which $\omega_p = 2\omega_c$. Hence establish which waves propagate and at what speeds, and which are evanescent. ∎

Equations 6.9 and 6.10 show that a magnetized plasma has two relative permittivities, and therefore two propagation speeds, depending on the sense of circular polarization of the waves passing through it. In Section 3.5, calcite was given as an example of a birefringent material in which linearly polarized light can travel at two different speeds depending on its direction of polarization. For calcite, it is the crystal structure that causes the anisotropy. In the present case, the plasma is anisotropic because the magnetic field defines a special direction.

Whistling

Now let us see what our results say about whistlers. These are low-frequency electromagnetic waves ($1800\,\mathrm{s}^{-1} < \omega < 5000\,\mathrm{s}^{-1}$), so ω is very small compared to the values $\omega_c \sim 5 \times 10^7\,\mathrm{s}^{-1}$ and $\omega_p \sim 10^7\,\mathrm{s}^{-1}$ that we showed earlier are typical of the magnetosphere. In this limit, we are justified in replacing the terms $(\omega \pm \omega_c)$ in the expressions for $\varepsilon^{\mathrm{RH}}$ and $\varepsilon^{\mathrm{LH}}$ by $\pm \omega_c$. Then

$(800 Hz < \omega < 800 Hz)$

$$\varepsilon^{\mathrm{RH}}(\omega) \simeq 1 + \frac{\omega_p^2}{\omega\omega_c} \simeq \frac{\omega_p^2}{\omega\omega_c} \quad \text{and} \quad \varepsilon^{\mathrm{LH}}(\omega) \simeq 1 - \frac{\omega_p^2}{\omega\omega_c} \simeq -\frac{\omega_p^2}{\omega\omega_c}.$$

In this limit, $\varepsilon^{\mathrm{LH}}(\omega)$ is a negative real number, and since $n = \sqrt{\varepsilon}$, the associated refractive index is purely imaginary and the wave does not propagate. On the other hand, $\varepsilon^{\mathrm{RH}}(\omega)$ is real and positive, leading to a refractive index and wavenumber that are, respectively,

$$n^{\mathrm{RH}} = \sqrt{\frac{\omega_p^2}{\omega\omega_c}}, \tag{6.11}$$

$$k^{\mathrm{RH}}(\omega) = n^{\mathrm{RH}}(\omega)\frac{\omega}{c} = \frac{\omega_p}{c}\sqrt{\frac{\omega}{\omega_c}}. \tag{6.12}$$

So we can see that when bursts of electromagnetic waves are created by lightning strokes in one hemisphere, the phase speed of the components at audio frequencies is

$$v_{\mathrm{phase}} = \frac{c}{n^{\mathrm{RH}}(\omega)} = c\sqrt{\frac{\omega\omega_c}{\omega_p^2}}. \tag{6.13}$$

These bursts of waves are guided up and around by the Earth's magnetic field, and down to the antipode, with the higher frequencies arriving earlier due to their greater speed. When detected by an audio system, they sound like a descending whistle, lasting a few seconds.

Exercise 6.6   Find, in this low-frequency limit, the group speed of bursts of waves characterized by the dispersion relation in Equation 6.12, and compare it to the phase speed. ∎

6.3.3 The complete electromagnetic response

Figure 6.16a shows a plot of the complete dispersion relations for a plasma predicted by Equations 6.9 and 6.10 for a relatively weak magnetic field such that $\omega_p = 2\omega_c$. As we have discovered, there are three modes. At high frequencies, there are RH and LH circularly polarized waves, with dispersion diagrams that have shapes similar to that for an isotropic plasma, shown in Figure 6.6, but with minimum frequencies for propagating waves that are just above and just below ω_p. At low frequencies, only an RH polarized mode exists, and it is the very low frequency portion of this mode that constitutes the whistler.

Comparing Figures 6.6 and 6.16a, it is apparent that, in both cases, there is a range of frequencies for which there is no corresponding real value of the wavenumber — for these frequencies, only evanescent modes exist. However, in the presence of a steady magnetic field, electromagnetic waves can propagate at frequencies below the plasma frequency. This low-frequency mode can propagate up to the frequency where there is a resonance with the cyclotron motion. Strictly, in the analysis of the low-frequency regime, the motion of positive ions should also be included, though the ions are at least 1800 times more massive than the electrons, so their effects are confined only to very low frequency.

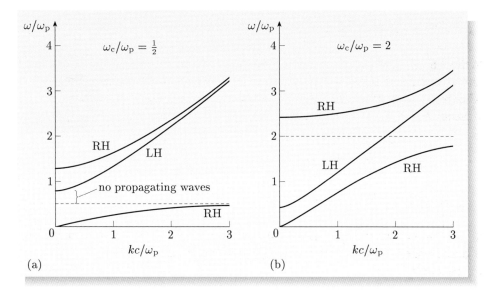

Figure 6.16 The dispersion diagram for RH and LH electromagnetic waves in a plasma within which there is (a) a relatively weak magnetic field such that $\omega_c = \omega_p/2$, and (b) a stronger magnetic field such that $\omega_c = 2\omega_p$. The broken lines correspond to $\omega_p = \omega_c$, which is the maximum frequency of the low-frequency RH mode.

Figure 6.16b shows the dispersion diagrams at a higher magnetic field, where the maximum frequency of the low-frequency mode, ω_c, is greater than the minimum frequency of the high-frequency modes. In this case, there is at least one propagating mode at any frequency. That is in marked contrast to the magnetic-field-free case of Figure 6.6, and this suggests a way of overcoming the radio blackout for re-entering spacecraft that was discussed earlier. The price to be paid is that the spacecraft must therefore carry the means to magnetize its surroundings: however, the weight penalty apparently is prohibitive, whereas a few minutes of radio silence is acceptable.

In the preceding analysis of electromagnetic modes in unbounded magnetized plasma, we assumed that the waves travel in the direction of the magnetic field. A more complete treatment should also consider the general case of waves that travel at an arbitrary angle to the local field. The result is an even greater variety of modes, all of which can transport electromagnetic energy through the magnetosphere and other magnetized plasmas. Including the effects of thermal energy of the particles adds even more detail, and yet more phenomena are uncovered if non-linear interactions in strong electric fields are considered. You may be relieved to learn that there is neither time nor space for these to be investigated here. Plasma physics is a vast subject, with relevance to many areas of astrophysics and engineering.

6.4   Making plasmas with electromagnetic waves

Plasmas are indeed exceedingly rich media in which to observe electromagnetic waves. The understanding of the different wave modes provides the basis of various measurements of the properties of a plasma and its environment. It also paves the way for developing new applications of laboratory plasmas.

In the opening section of this chapter, I described how plasmas can be sustained by supplying electrical energy. This underlies a range of applications, in particular the highly sophisticated schemes used in the etching and deposition of material on nanometre scales for semiconductor devices and microelectromechanical systems (MEMS). The plasmas that are used to do this are generally produced in low-pressure gases using either microwave or radio frequency (RF) power.

Steady-state plasmas can be sustained in a low-pressure vessel indefinitely, so long as the loss of charged particles at the surfaces of the vessel, where they recombine into neutral gas atoms, is continually offset by ionization in the volume of the gas. This requires electrical energy to be 'pumped in' to heat electrons to the temperature at which they are able to ionize atoms (tens of thousands of kelvins). One way to do this is to couple electromagnetic wave energy into the translational motion of electrons. We have already seen that low-frequency RH polarized waves can propagate in a magnetized plasma, and so carry energy into it. To conclude this chapter, we discuss two schemes that use RH polarized waves to sustain plasmas for technological applications, with the following parameters:

There are many other ways to sustain plasmas that do not require the presence of a steady magnetic field.

- electron temperature $T_e \sim 5 \times 10^4$ K — high enough to cause ionization and chemical reactions;

- $n_e > 10^{16}$ m^{-3} — greater number density means higher rates of reaction;

- $p < 100$ Pa — high enough to enable collisions to randomize electron energy, but not so high that charged particles collide before they have gained a significant amount of energy from electric fields.

6.4.1 Microwave ECR plasmas

One simple way to make a laboratory plasma is to inject microwaves into a closed vessel containing a static magnetic field and a low-pressure gas. If the frequency of the microwaves matches the cyclotron frequency — the frequency at which an electron traverses its cyclotron orbit in the static magnetic field — then the electric field of the microwaves is synchronized with the motion of the electrons, just as in a cyclotron. This means that the electrons absorb energy from the microwaves until they are scattered by collisions. This is known as **electron cyclotron resonance** (ECR).

● At what magnetic field strength does a 2.45 GHz RH polarized wave stimulate electron cyclotron resonance?

○ Rearranging $\omega_c = eB/m$, we obtain

$$B = \frac{2\pi f_c\, m}{e} = \frac{2\pi \times 2.45 \times 10^9\,\mathrm{s^{-1}} \times 9.11 \times 10^{-31}\,\mathrm{kg}}{1.60 \times 10^{-19}\,\mathrm{C}} \simeq 90\,\mathrm{mT}.$$

A field of that strength is easily obtained from electromagnets or even permanent magnets. To transfer the energy of cyclotron motion into electron heating, the energy of the gyrating electrons has to be randomized, and this occurs naturally when the electrons collide with gas molecules. If the frequency of collisions is such that $1/\tau_c \ll \omega_c$, the microwave field can accelerate electrons up to significant angular speeds over several cycles before collisions randomize their energy by knocking them out of synchronism. This enables energy to be transferred from the microwave field into the thermal energy of electrons.

● Use Figures 6.9 and 6.7 to estimate the pressure in air at which the electron collision frequency is $2\pi \times 2.45 \times 10^9\,\mathrm{s^{-1}}$, and hence suggest an operating pressure for a system that will heat electrons using microwaves.

○ Looking back to Figure 6.9, the height in the atmosphere where the frequency of collisions is $2.45 \times 10^9\,\mathrm{s^{-1}}$ is about 30 km. Then, referring to Figure 6.7, the corresponding pressure can be estimated to be about 1000 Pa. Operating at a pressure significantly lower than this will enable modest microwave fields to accelerate electrons over several cycles before the motion is randomized by collisions.

These two quick calculations are enough to specify approximate values for the magnetic field and pressure required for a so-called electron cyclotron resonance (ECR) plasma source for materials processing, of the type shown in Figure 6.17a. The electrons are heated by a combination of resonance and collisions, easily reaching a temperature $T_e \sim 5 \times 10^4\,\mathrm{K}$, under which circumstances the more energetic electrons are able to ionize the background gas. The electron and ion number densities can be sustained at around $10^{18}\,\mathrm{m^{-3}}$, which corresponds to $\omega_p \sim 6 \times 10^{10}\,\mathrm{s^{-1}}$. An operational system must also include a means to get the 2.45 GHz radiation from the waveguide into the plasma. Propagation comes to a halt where the cyclotron frequency in the local magnetic field is equal to the microwave frequency, at which point the microwave energy is resonantly absorbed. The important topic of matching waveguides and transmission lines to plasma loads could be the subject for another book.

6.4.2   Radio frequency helicon plasmas

A second approach to using RH polarized waves for plasma heating operates at lower frequency and does not need to achieve a resonant condition. The system is shown schematically in Figure 6.17b. Energy is coupled from a loop antenna wrapped on the outside of a glass tube. The excitation frequency is typically 13.56 MHz, a frequency set aside for scientific, technological and medical applications. There is an axial magnetic field that is sufficiently large that the cyclotron frequency ω_c is greater than this excitation frequency, that is, $\omega_c > 2\pi \times 13.56 \times 10^6 \, \mathrm{s}^{-1}$.

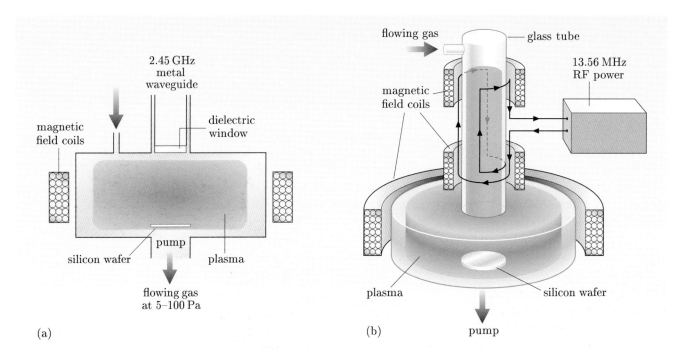

(a)

(b)

Figure 6.17   Plasma processing of silicon wafers. (a) An electron cyclotron resonance plasma source. (b) A helicon plasma source.

The detail of how a plasma first forms when the RF power is turned on is rather complicated and would take us away from the topic of waves. Therefore let us just suppose that a plasma has been produced somehow, and we can then see how energy can be coupled into the plasma to sustain it.

The changing RF magnetic field created by RF excitation of the antenna structure in Figure 6.17b excites the RH polarized wave mode that, at audio frequency, we identified in Subsection 6.3.2 with whistler waves. In the present context, the frequency is well above the audio range, and the wave is said to be a **helicon mode**, vividly capturing the helical motion of the electric field of a circularly polarized wave. As the wave propagates down into the main chamber, it loses energy through collisional damping of the electrons that are accelerated in the electric field of the wave. This transfers energy to the electron population, heating it up to a temperature $T_e \sim 5 \times 10^4 \, \mathrm{K}$ or more, such that the electron and ion number densities can be sustained at around $10^{19} \, \mathrm{m}^{-3}$, which corresponds to an electron plasma frequency $\omega_p = 2 \times 10^{11} \, \mathrm{s}^{-1}$. That is an order of magnitude greater than number densities in an ECR source, so processes like plasma etching and thin film deposition, which proceed in proportion to electron number density, are relatively fast in helicon sources.

Summary of Chapter 6

Section 6.1   Plasmas are ionized gases comprising electrons, ions and neutral atoms and molecules. They are neutral overall, and the density of free charges is such that there is strong coupling between the charges; as a result, the properties of plasmas are markedly different from those of neutral gases. Thermal energy, radiation and electrical energy can all contribute to sustaining the ionized condition of a plasma. Plasmas exist in stars, in the interstellar medium and around the Earth in the ionosphere and the magnetosphere, as well as in artificial and natural electrical discharges. The effective temperature of the particles in a plasma, especially the electrons, can be equivalent to tens of thousands of kelvins, though heavier particles are often considerably cooler.

The characteristic resonance frequency for oscillations in a plasma, known as the plasma frequency, is given by

$$\omega_{\mathrm{p}} = \sqrt{\frac{n_{\mathrm{e}} e^2}{m \varepsilon_0}}.$$

Treating a plasma as a linear isotropic homogeneous gaseous conductor, and neglecting thermal motion of the constituent particles, leads to an expression for the relative permittivity function that is analogous to that of an ordinary conductor. If the background gas pressure is low enough, that is, $1/\tau_{\mathrm{c}} \ll \omega$, then

$$\varepsilon_{\mathrm{eff}}(\omega) = 1 - \frac{\omega_{\mathrm{p}}^2}{\omega^2}.$$

Electromagnetic waves in LIH plasmas can propagate only if $\omega > \omega_{\mathrm{p}}$. At lower frequencies, the solutions of Maxwell's equations are evanescent.

Section 6.2   The model developed in Section 6.1 is applicable to the ionospheric plasma. The ionosphere reflects normally-incident electromagnetic waves at a height where the plasma frequency equals the wave frequency. The plasma frequency corresponding to the maximum electron number density in the ionosphere is about 10 MHz, so waves above this frequency can be transmitted through the ionosphere into space. The ionosphere is a near perfect reflector of obliquely-incident electromagnetic waves for frequencies up to about 30 MHz, and this accounts for the long range of radio transmissions between 5 and 30 MHz.

Section 6.3   A steady magnetic field makes a plasma anisotropic. The magnetic component of the Lorentz force leads to a sensitivity to circularly polarized waves, with left- and right-handed polarizations provoking a different response from the plasma. The relative permittivity functions for circularly polarized waves travelling parallel to the magnetic field are

$$\varepsilon^{\mathrm{RH}}(\omega) = 1 - \frac{\omega_{\mathrm{p}}^2}{\omega(\omega - \omega_{\mathrm{c}})} \quad \text{and} \quad \varepsilon^{\mathrm{LH}}(\omega) = 1 - \frac{\omega_{\mathrm{p}}^2}{\omega(\omega + \omega_{\mathrm{c}})},$$

in which ω_{c} is the electron cyclotron frequency, eB/m.

A plasma in a steady magnetic field is able to support propagating electromagnetic waves at frequencies below the plasma frequency (the lower limit for propagation in LIH plasmas). Whistler waves, which propagate in the Earth's magnetosphere, are an example of the RH polarized mode at low frequency.

Section 6.4   Various methods exist for producing laboratory plasmas that are sustained by energy absorbed from the low-frequency mode of RH circularly polarized electromagnetic waves. Electron cyclotron resonance can be used directly to couple microwave energy into a plasma in a magnetic field. Another method couples radio frequency electromagnetic waves into the helicon mode of a magnetized plasma. As the wave travels, its energy is transferred to the plasma's particles through collisional damping.

Achievements from Chapter 6

After studying this chapter you should be able to do the following.

6.1   Explain the meanings of the newly defined (emboldened) terms and symbols, and use them appropriately.

6.2   Give examples of plasmas sustained by thermal energy, by radiation and by electric fields.

6.3   Show that the bulk displacement of electrons in a plasma has a natural frequency, ω_p.

6.4   Develop the model of conductors in Chapter 5 to describe linear, isotropic and homogeneous plasmas and identify different behaviour above and below the plasma frequency, based on the collisionless regime ($1/\tau_c \ll \omega$).

6.5   Apply the collisionless plasma model to the interaction of electromagnetic waves with plasmas, in particular the interaction of radio waves with the ionosphere at normal and oblique incidence.

6.6   Show that in the presence of a steady magnetic field, the LIH assumption is invalid and the response of electrons to electromagnetic waves is determined by RH and LH circularly polarized modes.

6.7   Use expressions for the relative permittivity of RH and LH circularly polarized modes to account for so-called whistler waves in the Earth's magnetosphere.

6.8   Describe how electromagnetic wave energy can be used to sustain laboratory plasmas.

Chapter 7   Seeing clearly

In this final chapter, two contrasting topics will be investigated as a means of consolidating the material presented in earlier chapters. One topic is concerned with ordinary dielectric phenomena and is based around the biological tissue that forms the cornea of the mammalian eye. The aim is to account for its high transparency to light. The second topic relates more to conducting media and is based on a simple waveguide structure surrounded by a plasma. The aim is to explain how such a structure can be used to measure the number density of free electrons in the plasma formed by an electrical discharge in a low-pressure gas.

7.1   The cornea

The **cornea** is a window that passes light from a scene into an eye (Figure 7.1). It has several important duties. It provides a tough resilient layer to protect the interior of the eye from damage. Its surface is optically smooth and curved, and acts as the front surface of a fixed lens, which, when fine-tuned by the variable lens within the eye, forms images on the retina. The cornea is over 90% transparent to light with free space wavelengths between 400 and 750 nm, yet it is opaque to damaging ultraviolet light owing to dielectric absorption mechanisms similar to those discussed in Chapter 4.

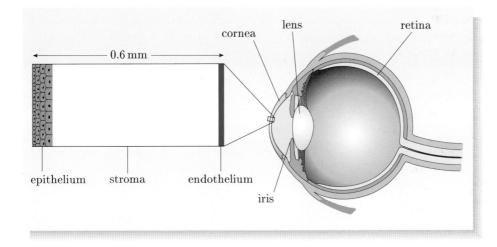

Figure 7.1   A cross-section through the eye is shown on the right. An expanded view of a cross-section through the cornea is shown on the left. The epithelium at the front surface of the tissue, and the endothelium at the back, protect and nourish the cornea. The stroma contains about 250 layers, or lamellae, each containing parallel strands of collagen.

7.1.1   The microstructure of the cornea

The physical composition of a material at a scale between the atomic and that visible in optical microscopes is generally described as its *microstructure*. At a microstructural level, corneal tissue is similar to that of the 'white' of the eye (the sclera) and, in varying degrees, to skin, tendons, ligaments, and even bone. What all these have in common is that they are composites based on a soft matrix material strengthened by many long narrow strands of protein called **collagen fibrils**, or just **fibrils** for short. The strength of fibrils along their length approaches that of steel. However, whereas skin, tendon and bone are quite opaque (though thin sections are translucent), the cornea is almost perfectly transparent. In this section we shall show that this remarkable property of transparency can be traced back to the size and spatial distribution of fibrils in the cornea.

It is important to distinguish between **transparency** and **translucence**. You can see clearly the details of an image through a transparent material, like a normal pane of glass, whereas you can see only overall lightness and darkness through a translucent material, like a pane of frosted glass.

● What characteristics are required for a material to have a high transparency?

○ First, it must not absorb significant amounts of light. Second, it must not reflect or scatter significant amounts of light. Scattering here includes processes like Rayleigh scattering (Chapter 2) and refraction (Chapter 4) at rough dielectric interfaces.

In general terms, the corneas of all mammals are similar, but the details vary from species to species. The human cornea is about to 0.6 mm thick, and is made up of several sections (Figure 7.1). The sections at the front and back provide protection and sustenance. But the middle section, or **stroma**, comprises some 90% of the corneal thickness and dominates the question of corneal transparency.

Exercise 7.1   Compare the thickness of the human cornea to a mid-range wavelength of visible radiation. ■

The stroma is made up of about 250 layers, each roughly 2.4×10^3 nm in thickness. A single layer, or **lamella**, consists of many long collagen fibrils, each about 30 nm in diameter, embedded in a gel-like, transparent matrix of aqueous protein. Within a given lamella, the fibrils are arranged essentially parallel to one another and to the lamella surface. The lamellae themselves are arranged something like the pages in a book, but in a roughly cross-ply manner, and consequently the overall structure is very stable and strong. The micrograph in Figure 7.2 shows parts of three adjacent lamellae.

Owing to the parallel arrangement of fibrils within it, a single lamella is birefringent, having different optical properties for light polarized parallel and perpendicular to its fibrils. However, variations in orientation of the fibrils in different lamellae tend to smear out this asymmetry over the full thickness of a cornea, making mammalian eyes largely insensitive to the polarization of light.

Exercise 7.2   Using Figure 7.2, compare the average separation between the centres of two fibrils, and the thickness of a single lamella, with a mid-range wavelength of light. ■

A model cornea

To model the propagation of light in the cornea, it is sufficient to ignore many subtle details of its structure. The fibrils can be treated as identical, parallel rods of a dielectric material, each with diameter 30 nm, which is small compared to the wavelength of light. The fibrils are embedded in a uniform dielectric matrix substance, with a spacing of about 50 nm between centres of nearest-neighbour fibrils. The dielectric rods and the matrix have different relative permittivities. A lamella comprises fibrils aligned in a sheet that is several wavelengths

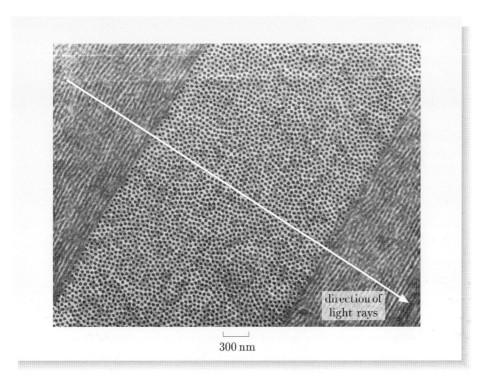

Figure 7.2   High-magnification transmission electron micrograph of the corneal stroma showing parts of three adjacent lamellae. The fibrils in the central lamella are coming directly out of the page; those in the adjacent lamellae lie roughly parallel to the page.

(~ 2400 nm) in total thickness. There are many lamellae across the thickness of the cornea, with fibril alignments changing abruptly from one lamella to the next. The model cornea is about twelve hundred wavelengths from front to back (~ 0.6 mm).

There is considerable overall order in the microstructure of the cornea. Elsewhere in the body, no such orderly use of collagen fibrils occurs; instead, their arrangement is disordered, even tangled, and their radii are larger and more variable. Such disordered assemblies of collagen do provide strength, but not transparency. The next section considers how it is that a highly-ordered microstructure endows corneas with transparency.

7.1.2   Light scattering in the cornea

Painstaking experiments have revealed that the matrix material of the cornea has a relative permittivity of 1.81 at optical frequencies, while that of the fibrils is 2.17. You should recall from Chapter 3 that electromagnetic energy is reflected from boundaries between dielectric media with different refractive indices, and that differences in refractive index arise from differences in relative permittivity that in turn come from differences in polarizability. The aim of this subsection is to demonstrate how the cornea remains highly transparent, even though it contains several thousand fibrils across its thickness, each of which is a potential scatterer.

Scattering by a single fibril in the matrix

The first question to explore in more detail is how a single fibril, immersed in a transparent matrix, scatters light. We discussed a similar problem in Section 2.5 in connection with Rayleigh scattering by gas molecules in the atmosphere. In that case, a fraction of the electromagnetic energy incident on an isolated gas molecule is re-radiated when the molecule is polarized by the electric field of a passing wave. The re-radiation of energy is a consequence of the induced oscillating dipole, and the radiation follows the spatial pattern of the radiation from a Hertzian dipole (Figure 2.11).

Consider first radiation that is polarized *parallel* to the fibril axis.

● Why might an isolated fibril *in empty space* cause Rayleigh-like scattering?

○ Rayleigh scattering is normally associated with small (sub-wavelength) particles. A small-diameter fibril may well behave in a manner similar to Rayleigh scattering, at least in two dimensions. When a fibril is polarized by the electric field of a passing electromagnetic wave, the induced dipole will re-radiate energy as a line source rather than the point source of normal Rayleigh scattering.

● Why might an isolated fibril *in a transparent matrix* cause scattering?

○ The matrix and the fibril are polarized by the electric field of a passing electromagnetic wave. In a continuous dielectric, the induced polarization slows the propagation of a wave as the molecules coherently interact with the wave. However, because the fibril has a different polarizability from that of the matrix, the molecules in the fibril and in the matrix respond differently to the wave, so the fibril re-radiates energy radially.

● What must be the pattern of radiation scattered by a long fibril when polarized along its axis by an incoming wave?

○ By symmetry, the amplitude of the radiation must be independent of the azimuthal angle around the fibril axis, and can depend only on the radius r from the axis, as shown in the radiation pattern in Figure 7.3a.

● How will the radiated electric and magnetic fields scale with radius?

○ By reasoning similar to that in Subsection 2.4.3, in the absence of absorption, the radiated power crossing any cylindrical surface coaxial with the fibril must be independent of its radius. The area of a cylindrical surface is proportional to its radius r, so the magnitude of the Poynting vector must fall off as $1/r$. The magnitude of the Poynting vector is proportional to the square of the field magnitudes, so the electric field and the magnetic field must both be proportional to $1/\sqrt{r}$.

Figure 7.3   The patterns of the radiation scattered by an isolated fibril from a plane wave that has k perpendicular to the axis of the fibril. (a) Incident polarization parallel to the fibril axis. (b) Incident polarization transverse to the axis. The amplitude of the field of the scattered wave for any azimuthal angle is proportional to the distance from the fibril axis to the cylindrical surface in that direction.

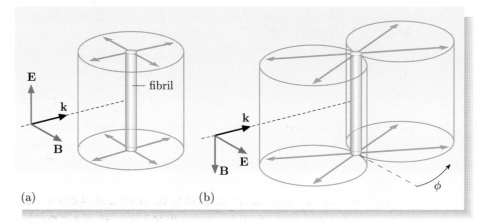

So a single fibril immersed in the matrix material certainly scatters light. The process can be quantified in terms of a scattering cross-section by adapting the procedure we used in Chapter 2 in connection with the scattering of light by gas atoms in the upper atmosphere.

- First, determine the strength of the induced dipole caused by the incident electric field, using the relative permittivity to estimate the polarizability.

- Next, adapt the simple Hertzian dipole model to the geometry of a fibril by integrating over a fibre comprising many co-aligned Hertzian dipoles, and obtain the form of the radiation fields.

- Finally, divide the total power radiated by the fibril by the magnitude of the Poynting vector for the incident wave, to obtain an effective scattering cross-section.

We shall not carry through those calculations here. Instead, I shall tell you the result. The scattering cross-section of a fibril is less than one thousandth of the physical cross-section it presents to an incident wave, which is Ld for a fibre of length L and diameter d. The details of the scattering depend on the size of a fibril compared with the wavelength of the light, and also on the disparity in relative permittivity between the matrix and the fibril.

For incident polarization *transverse* to the fibril axis, rather than parallel to the axis, analysis shows that the scattered field again includes a radiation term with $1/\sqrt{r}$ dependence, so the magnitude of the Poynting vector has a $1/r$ dependence. However, the field amplitude also depends on the azimuthal angle ϕ, as can be seen in the radiation pattern in Figure 7.3b. The general pattern of radiation in a plane perpendicular to the fibril axis is reminiscent of a single Hertzian dipole; the amplitude is zero in the direction of polarization, and has its maximum values in directions perpendicular to the polarization. The scattering cross-section for transverse polarization is comparable with that for polarization parallel to the fibril axis.

So any one fibril does not, in practice, scatter a significant fraction of the incident light. This allows us to ignore the complication of multiple scattering — since such a tiny fraction is scattered by any one fibril, we do not need to worry about the subsequent scattering of scattered light. However, since the cornea has thousands of fibrils across its thickness, overall there could still be an appreciable amount of scattering of energy from the main wave. Therefore the fact that the cornea has a very high transparency needs further careful explanation.

Scattering by a single-layer fibril grating

The next level of sophistication considers the scattering of an incoming wave by a monolayer of regularly-spaced fibrils, lying side by side in a plane perpendicular to the path of an incident wavefront. We have already established that the spacing d of the fibrils is such that $d \ll \lambda$, so within the layer, very many are stimulated simultaneously and synchronously by the incoming wave. This situation is quite different from Rayleigh scattering of light by gas molecules in the atmosphere, where the scattering objects are much more widely spaced, and their separations cover a wide range of values.

For simplicity, only the case of polarization parallel to the fibril axis is discussed here. Figure 7.4 illustrates how the regular spacing within a layer of scatterers (the fibrils) affects the scattering process. In Figure 7.4a it is assumed that the fibrils are spaced exactly one wavelength apart. Then the radiation that is scattered sideways from one fibril reaches the neighbouring fibril delayed in phase by exactly 2π relative to the radiation scattered by that neighbour. There would therefore be constructive interference of scattered radiation within the layer of fibrils, so overall some of the incident energy would be diverted in this sideways direction. The rest of the energy would be propagated forwards, with wavefronts parallel to the layer of fibrils; at distances from the layer that are much greater than the wavelength, the wavefront would be planar.

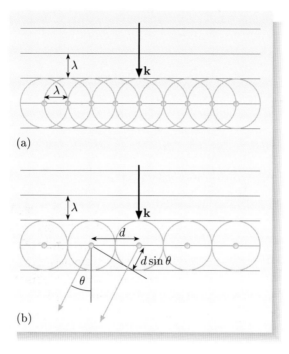

Figure 7.4 (a) Scatterers spaced at $d = \lambda$, when simultaneously excited, produce radiation that is exactly in phase in the sideways directions. (b) For wider spacings, energy is diffracted at those angles that satisfy the condition $n\lambda = d\sin\theta$.

Table 7.1 Angles of diffraction, θ, for scatterers with a uniform spacing $d = 2\lambda$.

Order n	θ/rad	θ/degree
0	0	0
1	0.524	30
2	1.571	90
≥ 3	–	–

By the same token, an optical microscope cannot 'see' fibrils and lamellae — the image in Figure 7.2 is from an electron microscope.

Wider spacings between the fibrils will lead to constructive interference at particular angles to the layer of scatterers, as shown in Figure 7.4b. This is now just a **diffraction grating**, and the directions along which the energy of the wave is diffracted are defined by

$$n\lambda = d\sin\theta, \tag{7.1}$$

where n is an integer specifying the order of diffraction. For example, if $d = 2\lambda$, Equation 7.1 has the solutions shown in Table 7.1.

● Fibrils in the cornea have a spacing of $d \simeq 0.1\lambda$, as shown in Figure 7.2. What orders of diffraction are possible?

○ Since $\lambda/d \simeq 10$, the only real solution to Equation 7.1 is the so-called zero-order solution, with $n = 0$, $\theta = 0$ (or π).

The fibrils are spaced more closely than a wavelength, and their arrangement in the lamellae is highly regular (though not as perfect as found in crystalline substances). As a result, a layer of fibrils does not diffract significant amounts of wave energy away from the forward direction. That is good news for the cornea. It means that even though the cornea is criss-crossed with layers of strengthening fibrils, their size and disposition is such that, in effect, any one layer is 'invisible'.

The overall effect

The complete story should now look at the effect of there being many layers of fibril gratings. However, we shall not go any further, because we have already found the key features that underlie the transparency of the cornea. The cornea is transparent to light because it neither absorbs nor scatters light. Other collagen-based tissue is, at best, only translucent, because the microstructure lacks the order and regularity required for transparency. It turns out that the cornea is opaque to ultraviolet radiation because specific molecules absorb radiation in this region of the spectrum; Chapter 4 discussed absorption in dielectrics.

The cornea's cross-ply structure of strengthening fibrils in a transparent matrix is transparent overall because of the various factors that are summarized in the following exercise.

Exercise 7.3   List the factors that together render the cornea transparent in spite of its complicated microstructure of collagen fibrils in a transparent medium.   ■

7.2   Guided waves and plasma density

The second topic in this chapter concerns guided waves and plasmas. It was noted in Chapter 6 that an important application of electrically-sustained laboratory plasmas is in the etching and deposition of thin films. An important parameter for such processing plasmas is the number density of free electrons, since it is electrons that stimulate chemical reactions in plasmas and that sustain the ionized state. The goal of this section is to explain a technique of measuring electron number density in a cold collisionless plasma, using some of the electromagnetic wave phenomena introduced in Chapter 6.

● In Chapter 6, how does the number density of electrons enter into the discussion of electromagnetic waves in plasmas?

○ The electron number density n_e appears in connection with the plasma frequency,

$$\omega_p = \sqrt{n_e e^2 / m \varepsilon_0}.$$
(Eqn 6.1)

This in turn comes from considering the polarization response of a plasma.

The plasma frequency enters expressions for the relative permittivity function for unmagnetized and magnetized plasmas, $\varepsilon_{\text{eff}}(\omega)$. In particular, for a cold collisionless plasma in a weak magnetic field, where $\omega_p \gg \omega_c$, $\omega \gg \omega_c$,

$$\varepsilon_{\text{eff}}(\omega) = 1 - \omega_p^2 / \omega^2.$$
(Eqn 6.2)

Under these circumstances, the dispersion relation for plasma waves is

$$\omega = \sqrt{\omega_p^2 + k^2 c^2}.$$
(Eqn 6.3)

So if the plasma frequency is determined from wave propagation experiments, then the electron number density can be calculated by using Equation 6.1.

An example of this is discussed in Subsection 6.2.2. Electromagnetic waves propagate up through the ionosphere as long as their frequency exceeds the plasma frequency, but are reflected at the height where the plasma frequency exceeds the wave frequency. If waves of a certain frequency are reflected at a particular height in the ionosphere, then the plasma frequency at that height is equal to the wave frequency, and the number density of the electrons at that height can be calculated from this plasma frequency.

Another way of using electromagnetic waves to determine electron number density in a plasma combines a simple waveguide with the dielectric response of a plasma (Equation 6.2). This is the case studied here; the waveguide in question looks like a hairpin and it resonates at frequencies that depend on the relative permittivity function for the plasma that surrounds it.

7.2.1 A hairpin resonator

In Chapter 5 we discussed waveguides that were formed by a pair of perfectly-conducting infinite parallel planes and by a perfectly-conducting hollow rectangular tube. Within these waveguides we found solutions of Maxwell's equations that are waves with the electric field transverse to the direction of propagation (TE modes), and it was noted that transverse magnetic (TM) modes are also possible. In Chapter 2 we identified wave solutions of Maxwell's equations for free space in which electric and magnetic fields are simultaneously transverse to the direction of propagation — these are TEM waves.

It turns out that although TEM modes do not arise in hollow-section conducting waveguides, they are allowed in certain other waveguide structures. In particular, a pair of conductors in a coaxial configuration, or a pair of parallel wires, can guide electromagnetic waves in a TEM mode. The forms of the electric and magnetic fields in such waveguides are essentially the same as the static fields that you encountered in Book 2, and they are illustrated in Figure 7.5. When the space between the coaxial conductors, or the space around the pair of wires, is empty, the phase speed of the TEM waves is c, the speed of light in a vacuum. However, when the conductors are embedded in a dielectric material, the TEM waves travel in the dielectric with a phase speed $c/\sqrt{\varepsilon}$, where ε is the relative permittivity of the dielectric.

Figure 7.5 (a) Electric and magnetic fields between coaxial conductors connected at one end across a source of electrical energy. (b) Electric and magnetic fields around parallel wires connected at one end across a source of electrical energy.

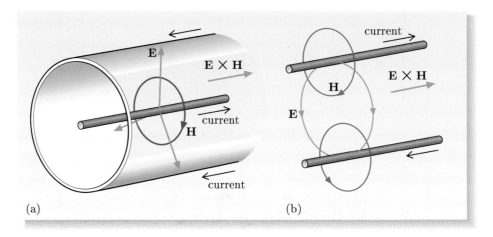

(a)

(b)

Here we are particularly interested in the parallel wire configuration because I want to consider the electromagnetic characteristics of a hairpin — you will see why in a moment. Figure 7.6a shows a rectangular loop of conductor with one short side left open, and in the present context this structure will be referred to as a hairpin.

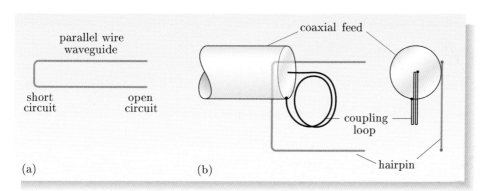

Figure 7.6 (a) A wire hairpin, which acts as a transmission line with a short circuit at one end and an open circuit at the other. (b) A small loop placed near the closed end of the hairpin enables electromagnetic coupling between the loop and the hairpin.

To discover the electromagnetic characteristics of the hairpin, we need to supply it with electromagnetic energy. An easy way to do this is by means of a wire loop placed near the closed end, as shown in Figure 7.6b. A time-varying current in the loop creates a time-varying magnetic field that encircles the wire at the closed end; according to Faraday's law, this induces a time-varying emf (and a time-varying current) in the hairpin. Likewise, any current in the hairpin induces an emf in the loop. The loop and hairpin are effectively primary and secondary windings of a transformer, and the coupling between them is more effective at smaller separation and higher frequency.

A similar loop arrangement can be used to couple energy into a hollow waveguide.

Having established that parallel wires support TEM wave modes, and that a simple loop will couple energy onto the hairpin, it should be no surprise to learn that this arrangement is an effective way to stimulate an electromagnetic wave that travels along the length of the hairpin. In fact, the wave travels through the space around the hairpin, guided by the structure. At any discontinuity, such as a sudden change in dielectric, the wave energy will be shared between reflected and transmitted components. This is precisely analogous to the behaviour of plane waves at dielectric boundaries, which was discussed in Chapter 3. On reaching the open end of the hairpin, the waves are also reflected.

Vacuum resonance

A hairpin behaves in a similar way to an organ pipe that is open at one end and closed at the other. Both will support waves, and both can be excited into resonance when their lengths correspond with an odd number of quarter-wavelengths, as shown in Figure 7.7.

● Suppose that a hairpin, length L, is surrounded by empty space and is excited via a loop by a variable-frequency oscillator. What is the longest wavelength that could lead to a resonance?

○ The longest wavelength is when the hairpin length equals one quarter-wavelength, that is, when $L = \lambda/4$.

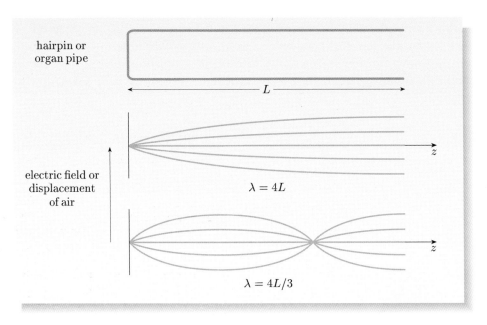

Figure 7.7   Both a hairpin and an organ pipe can support standing waves. For the hairpin, they are TEM waves. For the organ pipe, they are waves of longitudinal displacement of gas molecules. In both cases, the standing waves have a node at the closed end and an antinode at the open end.

Thus in empty space, the lowest resonant frequency for the hairpin, known as the **fundamental frequency**, is given by

$$f_0 = \frac{c}{4L}. \tag{7.2}$$

Figure 7.8 shows a practical hairpin arrangement and the associated circuitry, together with its measured frequency response. This circuitry comprises a variable-frequency oscillator, a directional coupler and a diode detector, which measures the strength of the signal reflected back from the hairpin. In general, the hairpin reflects most of the signal it receives. However, at resonance, a standing wave builds up along its length, and the strength of the reflected signal drops sharply because the standing wave radiates energy into the surrounding space.

Exercise 7.4   Calculate the frequency of the fundamental resonance in a vacuum for a hairpin that is 25.0 mm in length.   ■

Dielectric resonance

A hairpin structure can, in principle, be used to determine the relative permittivity of any LIH material that surrounds it. The length of the hairpin determines the frequency at which the measurement is made.

● Suppose that the hairpin, surrounded by a dielectric with relative permittivity ε, is excited via the loop by a variable-frequency oscillator. What is the fundamental resonant frequency $f_{\mathrm{res,\,d}}$?

○ By extension of Equation 7.2, the resonance for a hairpin in a dielectric occurs when

$$f_{\mathrm{res,\,d}} = \frac{c}{4L\sqrt{\varepsilon}} = \frac{f_0}{\sqrt{\varepsilon}}. \tag{7.3}$$

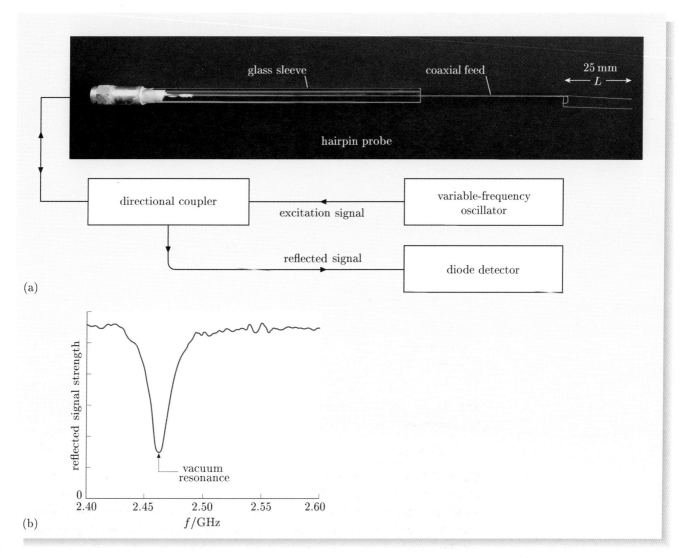

(a)

(b)

Figure 7.8 (a) A wire hairpin coupled via a loop to a coaxial cable, which is connected to a variable-frequency oscillator via a directional coupler. The directional coupler enables the reflected wave to be sampled by a diode detector. (b) The frequency response of the hairpin in a vacuum.

Surrounding a hairpin structure with a dielectric material shifts the resonances to lower frequencies, since $\varepsilon > 1$ (at least for ordinary dielectrics) and so the phase speed in the dielectric is less than in a vacuum.

Exercise 7.5 Calculate the fundamental resonant frequency for a hairpin that is 25.0 mm in length, when immersed in transformer oil for which $\varepsilon = 2.20$ at frequencies in the GHz range.

Exercise 7.6 Suggest how one might use a hairpin structure to determine the relative permittivity of transformer oil at 100 MHz.

Transformer oil is an insulating liquid that is used to cool power transformers.

185

7.2.2   Measuring plasma density with a hairpin

Plasmas are not ordinary dielectrics because the electrons in them are free rather than bound. In Chapter 6 it was shown that in gases at low pressure, the relative permittivity function for a cold collisionless plasma is

$$\varepsilon_{\text{eff}}(\omega) = 1 - \frac{\omega_{\text{p}}^2}{\omega^2}. \qquad \text{(Eqn 6.2)}$$

In terms of the frequency $f = \omega/2\pi$ and $f_{\text{p}} = \omega_{\text{p}}/2\pi$, this is equivalent to

$$\varepsilon_{\text{eff}}(f) = 1 - \frac{f_{\text{p}}^2}{f^2}. \qquad (7.4)$$

Plasma resonance

● Suppose that a hairpin structure is immersed in a cold collisionless plasma, and is excited via a loop by a variable-frequency oscillator. Derive an expression for the fundamental resonant frequency $f_{\text{res, p}}$ in terms of f_0 and f_{p}.

○ Combining Equations 7.3 and 7.4, the fundamental resonance in a plasma is

$$f_{\text{res, p}} = \frac{c}{4L\sqrt{\varepsilon}} = \frac{f_0}{\sqrt{\varepsilon_{\text{eff}}(f_{\text{res, p}})}} = \frac{f_0}{\sqrt{1 - f_{\text{p}}^2/f_{\text{res, p}}^2}}.$$

This simplifies to

$$f_{\text{res, p}}^2 = f_{\text{p}}^2 + f_0^2, \qquad (7.5)$$

which shows that the resonant frequency in a plasma is shifted *above* the resonant frequency in a vacuum, in contrast to the behaviour in ordinary dielectrics. Figure 7.9 shows resonance curves for a hairpin in a vacuum and in plasmas with a range of number densities.

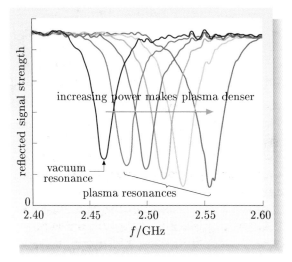

Figure 7.9   The frequency response of a hairpin, measured using a variable-frequency source, in a vacuum and in a plasma formed by the electrical breakdown of nitrogen at low pressure. Increasing the electrical power supplied to the plasma increases the electron number density, causing the resonance to shift to higher frequencies.

We can rearrange Equation 7.5 to give

$$f_p^2 = f_{res,p}^2 - f_0^2. \qquad (7.6)$$

This suggests that the plasma frequency in the medium around the hairpin can be deduced from the vacuum and plasma resonant frequencies. Since f_p is related to the number density of free electrons, the hairpin therefore provides a means of measuring the local electron number density in a cold collisionless plasma. That is exactly what we set out to do in this section, so the task is complete.

Exercise 7.7   Show that the electron number density in a plasma can be related to the vacuum and plasma resonances of a hairpin structure through the following equation:

$$n_e = \frac{4\pi^2 m \varepsilon_0}{e^2} \left(f_{res,p}^2 - f_0^2 \right). \qquad (7.7)$$

Exercise 7.8   A hairpin structure, which has a resonant frequency in a vacuum of 2.50 GHz, is found to resonate at 3.15 GHz when immersed in the plasma formed by the electrical breakdown of argon at low pressure. Estimate the electron number density in the plasma, stating any necessary assumptions.

Exercise 7.9   A hairpin structure in a vacuum radiates energy when excited by an oscillator via a coupling loop; it radiates most at resonance. Show, on the basis of the simple classical model of an isotropic plasma given in Chapter 6, that a hairpin in a plasma can also be expected to radiate energy into the surrounding space when at resonance. ∎

Summary of Chapter 7

Section 7.1   The mammalian cornea is made up of a composite dielectric formed from collagen fibrils in a transparent matrix medium. The fibrils are packed into lamellae, and within each lamella the fibrils are essentially parallel to each other and to the lamella surface. The spacing between fibril centres is about one tenth of a typical mid-range optical wavelength. The thickness of a lamella is about five wavelengths, and the thickness of the cornea is about twelve hundred wavelengths.

Owing to differences in relative permittivity between fibrils and the matrix, an isolated fibril scatters incident electromagnetic radiation. The scattering cross-section is, however, very small; a fibril scatters less than 0.1% of the radiation that is incident upon it. Each layer of fibrils in a lamella effectively forms a diffraction grating, but since the spacing between fibrils is less than one wavelength, only zero-order diffraction occurs. This means that overall the fibrils are not 'visible' — they do not, as a whole, scatter light, because they are arranged as arrays of almost identical, low cross-section scatterers, packed at sub-wavelength separation. As a consequence, the cornea is highly transparent.

Section 7.2   A pair of parallel wires can guide TEM waves through surrounding dielectric material. A straight-sided hairpin can therefore be modelled as a resonant structure on which TEM standing wave modes can be excited. The fundamental resonance occurs when the length of the hairpin corresponds to one quarter of the wavelength of a TEM wave.

When surrounded by an ordinary dielectric material, the resonant frequency of the hairpin is decreased. However, in a plasma, the presence of free electrons gives rise to a relative permittivity ($\varepsilon = 1 - f_\mathrm{p}^2/f^2$) that causes the resonance to shift to higher frequency. The frequency shift can be simply related to the number density of free electrons in the plasma.

Achievements from Chapter 7

After studying this chapter you should be able to do the following.

7.1 Explain the meanings of the newly defined (emboldened) terms and symbols, and use them appropriately.

7.2 Apply concepts from earlier chapters, including electromagnetic waves in free space, electromagnetic wave generation and scattering, reflection and refraction at dielectric interfaces, dispersion and absorption in bulk dielectrics, reflection and absorption at conductor boundaries, and electromagnetic waves in plasmas, to new scenarios.

7.3 Explain how the microstructure of a cornea leads to its high transparency to light.

7.4 Explain how a hairpin resonator can be used to measure the number density of free electrons in a cold collisionless plasma, and perform calculations related to such measurements.

Solutions to exercises

Ex 1.1 The values for the wavenumber k and the angular frequency ω can be determined from the relationships $k = 2\pi/\lambda$ and $\omega = 2\pi f = 2\pi/T$, and the wave types are deduced from Figure 4 in the Introduction to this book.

Wave type	Wavenumber k/m^{-1}	Angular frequency ω/s^{-1}
FM radio	2.09	6.28×10^8
Microwave	105	3.14×10^{10}
Ultraviolet	52.4×10^6	1.57×10^{16}

Ex 1.2 The *speed* follows from simply multiplying frequency f and wavelength λ, which is equivalent to, though slightly quicker than, converting to angular frequency ω and wavenumber k and then evaluating the ratio ω/k, so

$$v = 1200 \times 10^3\,\text{Hz} \times 250\,\text{m} = 3.0 \times 10^8\,\text{m s}^{-1}.$$

A wave with the form $A_0 \sin(kz - \omega t + \phi)$ travels in the positive z-direction. This can be demonstrated by noting that at position $z = 0$ and time $t = 0$, the displacement of the wave is $A_0 \sin \phi$. At the same place a short time Δt later, the displacement of the wave is $A_0 \sin(\phi - \omega\,\Delta t)$, and the reduction in the phase of the wave indicates that the wave has shifted in the direction of increasing z.

Ex 1.3 If we write $g(z - vt) = g(u)$, where $u = z - vt$, then

$$\frac{\partial g}{\partial z} = \frac{\mathrm{d}g}{\mathrm{d}u}\frac{\partial u}{\partial z} = g'(u) \times 1 = g'(z - vt),$$

$$\frac{\partial g}{\partial t} = \frac{\mathrm{d}g}{\mathrm{d}u}\frac{\partial u}{\partial t} = g'(u) \times (-v) = -v\,g'(z - vt),$$

where we use the notation $g'(u)$ to represent $\mathrm{d}g/\mathrm{d}u$. The second derivatives are

$$\frac{\partial^2 g}{\partial z^2} = \frac{\mathrm{d}(g'(u))}{\mathrm{d}u}\frac{\partial u}{\partial z} = g''(u) = g''(z - vt),$$

$$\frac{\partial^2 g}{\partial t^2} = \frac{\mathrm{d}(-v\,g'(u))}{\mathrm{d}u}\frac{\partial u}{\partial t} = (-v)^2 g''(u)$$
$$= (-v)^2 g''(z - vt),$$

where $g''(u)$ means $\mathrm{d}^2 g/\mathrm{d}u^2$. So

$$\frac{\partial^2}{\partial z^2} g(z - vt) - \frac{1}{v^2}\frac{\partial^2}{\partial t^2} g(z - vt) = 0,$$

and similarly

$$\frac{\partial^2}{\partial z^2} g(z + vt) - \frac{1}{v^2}\frac{\partial^2}{\partial t^2} g(z + vt) = 0,$$

so functions like $g(z \pm vt)$ satisfy the wave equation.

Ex 1.4 We can write $A(z, t)$ as

$$A(z, t) = A_0 \cos\left[k\left(z - \frac{\omega}{k}t\right) + \phi\right].$$

This is a function of $(z - vt)$, with $v = \omega/k$. In this case the d'Alembert function is $g(u) = A_0 \cos(ku + \phi)$.

Ex 1.5 Write

$$\mathbf{B}(\mathbf{r}, t) = B_x(\mathbf{r}, t)\,\mathbf{e}_x + B_y(\mathbf{r}, t)\,\mathbf{e}_y + B_z(\mathbf{r}, t)\,\mathbf{e}_z$$

and substitute into Equation 1.10 using the fact that $\mathbf{e}_x$, $\mathbf{e}_y$ and $\mathbf{e}_z$ are constants, and therefore independent of position *and* time:

$$\nabla^2 B_x(\mathbf{r}, t)\,\mathbf{e}_x + \nabla^2 B_y(\mathbf{r}, t)\,\mathbf{e}_y + \nabla^2 B_z(\mathbf{r}, t)\,\mathbf{e}_z$$
$$= \varepsilon_0\mu_0\left(\frac{\partial^2 B_x(\mathbf{r}, t)}{\partial t^2}\,\mathbf{e}_x + \frac{\partial^2 B_y(\mathbf{r}, t)}{\partial t^2}\,\mathbf{e}_y \right.$$
$$\left. + \frac{\partial^2 B_z(\mathbf{r}, t)}{\partial t^2}\,\mathbf{e}_z\right).$$

Using Equation 1.9, and equating the x-components on each side,

$$\frac{\partial^2 B_x(x, y, z, t)}{\partial x^2} + \frac{\partial^2 B_x(x, y, z, t)}{\partial y^2} + \frac{\partial^2 B_x(x, y, z, t)}{\partial z^2}$$
$$= \varepsilon_0\mu_0\frac{\partial^2 B_x(x, y, z, t)}{\partial t^2}.$$

There are similar equations for the y- and z-components of $\mathbf{B}$. Comparison with Equation 1.2 confirms that this is a three-dimensional wave equation with the phase speed equal to $1/\sqrt{\varepsilon_0\mu_0}$. Taking the three components together, we have a three-dimensional vector wave equation.

Ex 1.6 Starting with Equation 1.6, one could carry out an analysis very similar to that used in the text to derive Equation 1.10, but if we make the formal exchanges $\mathbf{B} \to -\varepsilon_0\mu_0\mathbf{E}$ and $\mathbf{E} \to \mathbf{B}$ in the four Maxwell's equations, then they are *unchanged*. This means that we can make the same exchanges (actually, we need only the first) in Equation 1.10, which is itself based on three of Maxwell's equations, and this gives Equation 1.11 directly.

Ex 1.7   Using Faraday's law, $\operatorname{curl} \mathbf{E} = -\partial \mathbf{B}/\partial t$,

$$\operatorname{curl} \mathbf{E} = \begin{vmatrix} \mathbf{e}_x & \mathbf{e}_y & \mathbf{e}_z \\ \dfrac{\partial}{\partial x} & \dfrac{\partial}{\partial y} & \dfrac{\partial}{\partial z} \\ g(z+ct) & 0 & 0 \end{vmatrix}$$

$$= \left(\frac{\partial}{\partial z} g(z+ct) \right) \mathbf{e}_y.$$

So we have to solve $g'(z+ct)\,\mathbf{e}_y = -(\partial/\partial t)\mathbf{B}(z,t)$. By the same reasoning as that leading to Equation 1.15, we find

$$\mathbf{B}(z,t) = -\frac{1}{c}\, g(z+ct)\,\mathbf{e}_y.$$

Ex 1.8

$$\mathbf{B}^{(\mathrm{circ})}(z,t)$$
$$= \frac{1}{c}\, \mathbf{e}_z \times \mathbf{E}^{(\mathrm{circ})}(z,t)$$
$$= \frac{E_0}{c} \exp[\mathrm{i}(kz - \omega t + \phi)]\,(\mathbf{e}_z \times \mathbf{e}_x + \mathrm{i}\mathbf{e}_z \times \mathbf{e}_y)$$
$$= \frac{E_0}{c} \exp[\mathrm{i}(kz - \omega t + \phi)]\,(\mathbf{e}_y - \mathrm{i}\mathbf{e}_x).$$

Ex 1.9   Instead of Equation 1.26, the electric field is given by

$$\mathbf{E}(z,t) = E_0 \exp[\mathrm{i}(kz - \omega t + \phi)]\,\mathbf{e}_x$$
$$+ E_0 \exp[\mathrm{i}(kz - \omega t + \phi - \pi/2)]\,\mathbf{e}_y.$$

Since $\exp(-\mathrm{i}\pi/2) = \cos(-\pi/2) + \mathrm{i}\sin(-\pi/2) = -\mathrm{i}$, the electric field for this wave is

$$\mathbf{E}_{\mathrm{phys}} = \operatorname{Re}\{\mathbf{E}(z,t)\}$$
$$= \operatorname{Re}\{E_0 \exp[\mathrm{i}(kz - \omega t + \phi)]\,(\mathbf{e}_x - \mathrm{i}\mathbf{e}_y)\}.$$

Comparison with Equation 1.27 indicates that we again have circular polarization, but the electric field rotates in the opposite sense.

Ex 1.10   From Equation 1.34,

$$\overline{N} = \tfrac{1}{2}\varepsilon_0 (E_0)^2 c = 10^{-12}\ \mathrm{W\,m^{-2}}.$$

Inserting values for the constants $\varepsilon_0 = 8.85 \times 10^{-12}\ \mathrm{F\,m^{-1}}$ and $c = 3.00 \times 10^8\ \mathrm{m\,s^{-1}}$ gives $E_0 \simeq 30\ \mu\mathrm{V\,m^{-1}}$, which is a readily detectable signal.

Ex 2.1   The magnitude of $\delta\mathbf{l} \times \mathbf{r}$ is $r\,\delta l \sin\theta$, where θ is the angle between $\delta\mathbf{l}$ and $\mathbf{r}$. So the magnitude of the oscillating field $\delta\mathbf{B}(\mathbf{r},t)$ would be proportional to r^{-2}.

A magnetic field associated with radiation from a point source must be proportional to r^{-1} (so that its square falls off as r^{-2}), so a magnetic field based on the Biot–Savart law does not account for radiation.

Ex 2.2   We require

$$\frac{(\omega/c)(k)}{r} \gg \frac{k}{r^2} \quad \text{and} \quad \frac{(\omega/c)(k)}{r} \gg \frac{1}{r^3},$$

which are both satisfied if

$$r \gg \frac{\lambda}{2\pi}.$$

Not surprisingly, this requirement for the radiation field to predominate is identical to that obtained from considering the magnetic field.

Ex 2.3   Consider the expression

$$\mathbf{E}^{(\mathrm{rad})}(r,\theta,t) = \omega\eta\,\frac{\sin\theta}{r}\sin(kr - \omega t)\,\mathbf{e}_\theta$$

(Equation 2.20). When $r \gg \lambda$ (say $r \sim 100\lambda$), the value of r will hardly change over several spatial cycles of the wave; furthermore, $\sin\theta$ is approximately constant across a small area transverse to the direction of travel. So the amplitude of the wave is very nearly constant and

$$\mathbf{E}^{(\mathrm{rad})}(r,t) \simeq E_0 \sin(kr - \omega t)\,\mathbf{e}_\theta,$$

which looks like an equation for a plane wave.

Ex 2.4   (a) The wavelength is $\lambda = 2\pi c/\omega = 22\ \mathrm{m}$, which is consistent with this being a Hertzian dipole, since $\delta l = 0.10\ \mathrm{m}$. The far field region, where the radiation fields dominate, extends beyond about twice λ, say $50\ \mathrm{m}$.

(b) $\overline{W}$ is given by

$$\frac{\mu_0 \omega^2 I_0^2 (\delta l)^2}{12\pi c}$$
$$= 4\pi \times 10^{-7}\ \mathrm{T\,m\,A^{-1}}$$
$$\times (2\pi \times 13.56 \times 10^6\ \mathrm{Hz} \times 1.0\ \mathrm{A} \times 0.10\ \mathrm{m})^2$$
$$\div (12\pi \times 3.00 \times 10^8\ \mathrm{m\,s^{-1}})$$
$$= 8.1\ \mathrm{mW}.$$

Ex 2.5   Figure 2.7 shows that waves radiated by an oscillating dipole in directions perpendicular to the dipole's axis are polarized parallel to the dipole's axis, and Figure 2.11 indicates that the maximum signal strength occurs in directions perpendicular to the dipole's axis. The receiving antenna structures in Figure 8b are especially sensitive to electric fields parallel to the short horizontal elements, so the television signals must be horizontally polarized. Also, the antennas need to point towards the transmitter so that these short elements are parallel to the transverse electric field.

Ex 2.6   The angular frequency is given by

$$\omega = 2\pi c/\lambda$$
$$= 2\pi \times 3.00 \times 10^8 \, \text{m s}^{-1}/(520 \times 10^{-9} \, \text{m})$$
$$= 3.6 \times 10^{15} \, \text{s}^{-1}.$$

Using this value of ω in Equation 2.31, together with the previously calculated value for α_{air}, we obtain

$$\sigma = \frac{(2.2 \times 10^{-29} \, \text{m}^3)^2 \times (3.6 \times 10^{15} \, \text{s}^{-1})^4}{6\pi \times (3.00 \times 10^8 \, \text{m s}^{-1})^4}$$
$$\simeq 5 \times 10^{-31} \, \text{m}^2.$$

Ex 2.7   You could rework the calculation based on Equations 2.31 and 2.34, but alternatively you could simply scale the result for the scattering length for green light ($\lambda = 520 \, \text{nm}$), which was calculated in the text to be 80 km. The scattering length is inversely proportional to σ, which means that it is proportional to ω^{-4}, and hence to λ^4. Thus the scattering length for red light is about $80 \, \text{km} \times (650/520)^4 \simeq 200 \, \text{km}$.

Ex 3.1   The parameters for the dielectric are obtained by replacing c by c/n, as shown in the table below.

	Free space	Dielectric
frequency	$\omega/2\pi$	$\omega/2\pi$
phase speed	c	$v = c/\sqrt{\varepsilon} = c/n$
wavenumber	$k_0 = \omega/c$	$k = \omega/v = n\omega/c$
wavelength	$\lambda_0 = 2\pi/k_0$	$\lambda = 2\pi/k = \lambda_0/n$

Ex 3.2   Replace ε_0 by $\varepsilon\varepsilon_0$, and c by c/n, in Equation 1.34 for the time-averaged Poynting vector in free space:

$$\overline{\mathbf{N}} = \tfrac{1}{2}\varepsilon_0 E_0^2 c \, \widehat{\mathbf{k}} \quad \rightarrow \quad \overline{\mathbf{N}} = \tfrac{1}{2}\varepsilon\varepsilon_0 E_0^2 \frac{c}{n} \, \widehat{\mathbf{k}}.$$

The result of Equation 3.4 is recovered immediately.

Ex 3.3   Collecting the expressions for the magnetic fields $\mathbf{B}_\text{i}$, $\mathbf{B}_\text{r}$ and $\mathbf{B}_\text{t}$, and using $\mathbf{H} = \mathbf{B}/\mu_0$ at $z = 0$, gives

$$\frac{n_1}{\mu_0 c} E_{\text{i}0} \exp[\text{i}(-\omega t)] \, \mathbf{e}_y - \frac{n_1}{\mu_0 c} E_{\text{r}0} \exp[\text{i}(-\omega t)] \, \mathbf{e}_y$$
$$= \frac{n_2}{\mu_0 c} E_{\text{t}0} \exp[\text{i}(-\omega l)] \, \mathbf{c}_y.$$

The time-dependence cancels since the same exponential factor appears in each term. The factors $1/(\mu_0 c)$ and $\mathbf{e}_y$ also cancel, leaving

$$n_1 E_{\text{i}0} - n_1 E_{\text{r}0} = n_2 E_{\text{t}0},$$

which rearranges to Equation 3.13.

Ex 3.4   The simplest way to eliminate $E_{\text{r}0}$ from Equations 3.12 and 3.13 is to add the equations:

$$2E_{\text{i}0} = \left(1 + \frac{n_2}{n_1}\right) E_{\text{t}0}.$$

Hence

$$\frac{E_{\text{t}0}}{E_{\text{i}0}} = \frac{2n_1}{n_1 + n_2}.$$

Then, to eliminate $E_{\text{t}0}$, multiply Equation 3.12 by n_2/n_1 and subtract Equation 3.13 from it:

$$E_{\text{i}0}\left(\frac{n_2}{n_1} - 1\right) + E_{\text{r}0}\left(\frac{n_2}{n_1} + 1\right) = 0.$$

Hence

$$\frac{E_{\text{r}0}}{E_{\text{i}0}} = \frac{n_1 - n_2}{n_1 + n_2}.$$

Ex 3.5   Conservation of energy is assured if the incident power is equal to the sum of transmitted and reflected power, as asserted by Equation 3.18. Expanding the term $(n_1 - n_2)^2$ in Equation 3.17 and combining it with Equation 3.16 gives the required result:

$$R + T = \frac{n_1^2 - 2n_1 n_2 + n_2^2}{(n_1 + n_2)^2} + \frac{4n_1 n_2}{(n_1 + n_2)^2}$$
$$= \frac{n_1^2 + 2n_1 n_2 + n_2^2}{(n_1 + n_2)^2} = 1.$$

Ex 3.6   The task is to evaluate the reflectance when $n_1 = 1$ and $n_2 = 1.5$, using Equation 3.17:

$$R = \frac{(1 - 1.5)^2}{(1 + 1.5)^2} = \left(\frac{0.5}{2.5}\right)^2 = 0.04.$$

This means that 4% of the power is reflected. It follows that in any fixed interval of time, 4% of the incident energy is reflected.

It does not matter from which side the light crosses the boundary, owing to the squaring of the terms in the expression for the reflectance.

Comment: 96% of light is transmitted across an air–glass interface at normal incidence, which means that a sheet of glass is only 92% transparent, since in passing through one sheet a wave encounters two interfaces, and $0.96^2 = 0.92$. Neglecting multiple reflections, eight sheets are enough to just about halve the transmitted intensity ($0.92^8 = 0.51$).

Ex 3.7 At normal incidence, $\cos\theta_i = \cos\theta_t = 1$, so Equations 3.26 and 3.27 simplify to

$$\frac{E_{t0}}{E_{i0}} = \frac{2n_1}{n_1 + n_2} \quad \text{and} \quad \frac{E_{r0}}{E_{i0}} = \frac{n_1 - n_2}{n_1 + n_2},$$

as given in Equations 3.14.

Ex 3.8 Air–glass:

$$\theta_B = \tan^{-1}(n_{glass}/n_{air})$$
$$= \tan^{-1}(1.5)$$
$$= 0.98 \text{ radians.}$$

This is about 0.31π radians, or $56°$.

Glass–air:

$$\theta_B = \tan^{-1}(n_{air}/n_{glass})$$
$$= \tan^{-1}(1/1.5)$$
$$= 0.59 \text{ radians.}$$

This is about 0.19π radians, or $34°$.

Ex 3.9 The Brewster angle will offer close to optimal transmission — for an air–glass interface that is about $56°$. The reflection ratios at an air–glass interface for 'isp' and 'nsp' polarizations are small and slowly varying at small angles of incidence. At larger angles, as Figure 3.11a shows, $|r_{nsp}|$ increases slightly as $|r_{isp}|$ decreases to zero at the Brewster angle. The value of t_{isp} at this point must be unity. Now, if the front and back surfaces of the window are parallel, refraction at the air–glass interface means that the angle with which the light is incident on the glass–air interface will be $\sin^{-1}(\sin 56°/1.5) = 34°$. According to the previous exercise, this is the Brewster angle for the glass–air interface, so there is minimal reflection here also.

Comment: It is no accident that the light striking the first interface at its Brewster angle appears also to strike the second surface at its Brewster angle — it is built into the equations.

Ex 3.10

$$\theta_{crit} = \sin^{-1}(n_{air}/n_{water})$$
$$= \sin^{-1}(1/1.3) = 0.9 \text{ radians} \approx 50°.$$

Ex 3.11 As indicated in Figure 3.12, the scattering plane for reflection of sunlight from a horizontal surface is vertical. The light reflected from a horizontal surface will be predominantly polarized in the direction normal to the scattering plane. So polarizing filters oriented to pass light polarized in the vertical plane will block most of the reflected light.

Ex 3.12 First, the choice of a cladding with a *lower* refractive index than the core is an essential requirement for total internal reflection to occur, so that the energy is contained within the higher refractive index core. Second, the smallness of the difference in refractive index means that the critical angle will be large, favouring the propagation of energy *along* the fibre.

Ex 4.1 From Equation 4.5, $\omega_p = \sqrt{n_e e^2 / m\varepsilon_0}$, so

$$n_e = \omega_p^2 \times \frac{m\varepsilon_0}{e^2}$$
$$= (1.12 \times 8.8 \times 10^{15}\,\text{s}^{-1})^2$$
$$\times \frac{9.11 \times 10^{-31}\,\text{kg} \times 8.85 \times 10^{-12}\,\text{F m}^{-1}}{(1.60 \times 10^{-19}\,\text{C})^2}$$
$$= 3.1 \times 10^{28}\,\text{m}^{-3}.$$

Comment: This is equivalent to about one bound electron per atom. Other electrons will have different effective spring constants and will make contributions to the dielectric function with different natural frequencies. Bear in mind that we have used a simple classical model, and we should not expect quantitative agreement with data for real materials.

Ex 4.2 When $\varepsilon_{imag} \ll \varepsilon_{real}$, Equation 4.12 simplifies directly to

$$n_{real} = \sqrt{\varepsilon_{real}}.$$

For n_{imag}, we first rewrite Equation 4.13 as

$$n_{imag}^2 = \frac{-\varepsilon_{real} + \varepsilon_{real}\sqrt{1 + (\varepsilon_{imag}/\varepsilon_{real})^2}}{2}.$$

When $\varepsilon_{imag} \ll \varepsilon_{real}$, the square root can be approximated by $1 + \frac{1}{2}(\varepsilon_{imag}/\varepsilon_{real})^2$, so

$$n_{imag} = \varepsilon_{imag}/2\sqrt{\varepsilon_{real}}.$$

Ex 4.3 From Figure 4.5, $\varepsilon_{real}(\omega_{blue}) = 2.37$ and $\varepsilon_{real}(\omega_{red}) = 2.30$. From Figure 4.4, $\varepsilon_{imag}(\omega_{blue}) = 0.73$ and $\varepsilon_{imag}(\omega_{red}) = 0.28$. Therefore, using Equation 4.12,

$$n_{real}(\omega_{blue}) = 1.56 \quad \text{and} \quad n_{real}(\omega_{red}) = 1.52,$$

so $v_{blue} = c/1.56 = 1.92 \times 10^8\,\text{m s}^{-1}$,

$$v_{red} = c/1.52 = 1.97 \times 10^8\,\text{m s}^{-1}.$$

Ex 4.4 The angle at which an observer, on looking up, sees most blue light is about $(180 - 140)° = 40°$ to the direction of the incident sunlight, and the angle for most red light is $42°$. Thus the bow subtends an angle of about $2°$, with blue closer to the ground.

Ex 4.5 At the first interface, taking the refractive index of air as unity, Snell's law reads

$$\sin\theta_i = n_{real}(\omega)\sin\theta_t,$$

where θ_i is the angle of incidence at the first air–glass interface, which is the same for all frequencies. Figure 4.8 implies that the refractive index for glass, $n_{real}(\omega)$, is larger for higher (bluer) frequencies than it is for the lower (redder) frequencies, because θ_t is smaller for blue light than it is for red. The refractive index varies smoothly between the red and blue extremes, giving the intermediate spread of colours. In the given geometry, the second interface increases the degree of dispersion.

Ex 4.6 Phase and group speeds will be different when $\omega_0\,n'(\omega_0)$ is significant compared with $n(\omega_0)$ (see Equation 4.27). Since $n = \sqrt{\varepsilon}$, it is likely that this will occur where ε_{real} is beginning to curve (see Figure 4.4). The region close to the resonance, where ε and n are changing rapidly with frequency, is excluded from the discussion by the condition $\varepsilon_{imag} \ll \varepsilon_{real}$, but clearly here too the group and phase speeds can be expected to be different.

Ex 4.7 First note that $\varepsilon_{imag} \ll \varepsilon_{real}$, so $k_{imag} \simeq \varepsilon_{imag}\,\omega/2c\sqrt{\varepsilon_{real}}$. Also, $c/\omega = \lambda_0/2\pi$. The absorption length is then

$$k_{imag}^{-1} \simeq \frac{2c}{\omega}\frac{\sqrt{\varepsilon_{real}}}{\varepsilon_{imag}}$$

$$= \frac{2\lambda_0}{2\pi}\frac{\sqrt{\varepsilon_{real}}}{\varepsilon_{imag}}$$

$$= \frac{600\times10^{-9}\,\mathrm{m}}{\pi}\frac{\sqrt{1.50}}{2.00\times10^{-5}}$$

$$= 12\,\mathrm{mm}.$$

Ex 4.8 The field is attenuated by absorption in the quartz — there is an exponential decay of field strength with distance by a factor of $\exp(-k_{imag}z)$. So we need to determine k_{imag}. Since ε_{imag} is small compared to ε_{real},

$$k_{imag} = \frac{\varepsilon_{imag}}{2\sqrt{\varepsilon_{real}}}\frac{\omega}{c}. \qquad \text{(Eqn 4.34)}$$

At $30\,\mathrm{MHz}$, $\omega = 60\pi\times10^6\,\mathrm{s}^{-1}$. Inserting values into Equation 4.34 gives

$$k_{imag} = \frac{8.6\times10^{-4}}{2\sqrt{4.3}}\frac{60\pi\times10^6\,\mathrm{s}^{-1}}{3\times10^8\,\mathrm{m\,s}^{-1}}$$

$$= 1.3\times10^{-4}\,\mathrm{m}^{-1}.$$

Recall that when $\delta \ll 1$, $\exp(\delta) \simeq 1 + \delta$, so with $z = 10^{-2}\,\mathrm{m}$,

$$\exp(-k_{imag}z) = \exp(-1.3\times10^{-4}\times10^{-2})$$

$$\simeq 1 - 1.3\times10^{-6}.$$

This shows that the signal amplitude is attenuated by a little over one part per million in passing through the quartz window.

Ex 4.9 From Section 4.4, the absorption length, k_{imag}^{-1}, can be expressed as $c/n_{imag}\omega$ (Equation 4.34). Since $\omega/c = 2\pi/\lambda_0$, this can also be expressed as

$$\text{absorption length} = k_{imag}^{-1} = \lambda_0/2\pi n_{imag}.$$

Data for n_{imag} can be read from Figure 4.15, and are shown in Table 4.3, along with calculated values of the absorption length.

Table 4.3 Absorption lengths for water.

λ_0/nm	n_{imag}	Absorption length/m
100	0.7	2×10^{-8}
500	3×10^{-9}	30
1000	3×10^{-6}	0.05

Note how strongly ultraviolet radiation is attenuated.

Ex 4.10 (a) The log scale makes it difficult to read values for n_{imag} from Figure 4.17, but you should be able to see that the tabulated values are consistent with the data in the graph.

(b) The relative intensity of the signal after travelling distance z is given by $\exp(-2k_{imag}z)$, and from Equation 4.34,

$$k_{imag} = \omega n_{imag}/c = 2\pi n_{imag}/\lambda_0.$$

So

$$\text{relative intensity} = \exp(-4\pi n_{imag}z/\lambda_0),$$

and the values calculated for the three wavelengths are shown in the third column of Table 4.4.

Table 4.4 Imaginary part of the refractive index and relative intensity after travelling 1 km through amorphous silica for light of three wavelengths.

λ_0/nm	$n_{\text{imag}}/10^{-11}$	Relative intensity
480	3	0.5
585	1	0.8
630	0.6	0.9

Thus, in addition to severe dispersion, the original pulse suffers appreciable absorption, and this is more pronounced at the blue end of the visible spectrum.

Ex 5.1　(a) The two terms in Equation 5.11 are equal in magnitude when $\omega\varepsilon_0 = \sigma$, or $\omega = \sigma/\varepsilon_0$. For copper,

$$\omega = \frac{5.8 \times 10^7\,\Omega^{-1}\,\text{m}^{-1}}{8.85 \times 10^{-12}\,\text{F}\,\text{m}^{-1}} = 6.6 \times 10^{18}\,\text{s}^{-1}.$$

Comment: Note that this implies that the conductivity term certainly dominates for metals throughout the low-frequency range, where $\omega \ll 1/\tau_{\text{c}} \sim 10^{13}\,\text{s}^{-1}$.

For seawater,

$$\omega = \frac{5\,\Omega^{-1}\,\text{m}^{-1}}{8.85 \times 10^{-12}\,\text{F}\,\text{m}^{-1}} = 5.6 \times 10^{11}\,\text{s}^{-1},$$

so the conductivity term dominates only for $\omega < 10^{10}\,\text{s}^{-1}$ (about 1 GHz).

(b) For graphite, the ratio $\sigma/\omega\varepsilon_0$ at $\omega \sim 10^{10}\,\text{s}^{-1}$ is

$$\frac{1 \times 10^5\,\Omega^{-1}\,\text{m}^{-1}}{10^{10}\,\text{s}^{-1} \times 8.85 \times 10^{-12}\,\text{F}\,\text{m}^{-1}} \sim 10^6.$$

This means that the conductivity term dominates.

Ex 5.2　(a) Use Equation 5.18. At 50 Hz, $\omega = 100\pi\,\text{s}^{-1}$, giving

$$\delta = \left(\frac{2}{\mu_0\sigma\omega}\right)^{1/2}$$

$$= [2/(4\pi \times 10^{-7}\,\text{T}\,\text{m}\,\text{A}^{-1} \times 5.8 \times 10^7\,\Omega^{-1}\,\text{m}^{-1}$$

$$\times\ 100\pi\,\text{s}^{-1})]^{1/2}$$

$$= 0.0093\,\text{m}.$$

At 50 MHz, the frequency is higher by a factor of 10^6, so

$$\delta = \sqrt{\frac{1}{10^6}} \times 0.0093\,\text{m} = 9.3 \times 10^{-6}\,\text{m}.$$

At 50 THz, the frequency is higher again by a factor of 10^6, so

$$\delta = \sqrt{\frac{1}{10^6}} \times 9.3 \times 10^{-6}\,\text{m} = 9.3 \times 10^{-9}\,\text{m}.$$

The free space wavelengths are given by $\lambda_0 = c/f$. At 50 Hz, $\lambda_0 = 6 \times 10^6\,\text{m}$, at 50 MHz, $\lambda_0 = 6\,\text{m}$, and at 50 THz, $\lambda_0 = 6 \times 10^{-6}\,\text{m}$, so at all of these frequencies $\delta \ll \lambda_0$.

(b) At a wavelength of 3000 m, the frequency is 10^5 Hz, giving

$$\delta = [2/(4\pi \times 10^{-7}\,\text{T}\,\text{m}\,\text{A}^{-1} \times 5\,\Omega^{-1}\,\text{m}^{-1}$$

$$\times\ 2\pi \times 10^5\,\text{s}^{-1})]^{1/2}$$

$$= 0.7\,\text{m}.$$

At a wavelength of 3000 km, the frequency is reduced by a factor of 10^3, so

$$\delta = \sqrt{10^3} \times 0.71\,\text{m} \simeq 20\,\text{m}.$$

Comment: This shows that in order to communicate by radio with submarines when submerged, the lowest possible frequencies must be used. Achieving efficient radiation at such low frequencies requires the use of antennas that are several kilometres in length!

Ex 5.3　The frequency of electromagnetic waves with a free space wavelength of 3 m is $f = c/\lambda_0 = 10^8$ Hz. The distance characterizing the penetration of the radiation is the skin depth, $\delta = \sqrt{2/\mu_0\sigma\omega}$, so

$$\delta = [2/(4\pi \times 10^{-7}\,\text{T}\,\text{m}\,\text{A}^{-1} \times 5.8 \times 10^7\,\Omega^{-1}\,\text{m}^{-1}$$

$$\times\ 2\pi \times 10^8\,\text{s}^{-1})]^{1/2}$$

$$= 6.6 \times 10^{-6}\,\text{m}.$$

From Equation 5.28, the transmittance is

$$T = 2\sqrt{\frac{2\varepsilon_0\omega}{\sigma}}$$

$$= 2\sqrt{\frac{2 \times 8.85 \times 10^{-12}\,\text{F}\,\text{m}^{-1} \times 2\pi \times 10^8\,\text{s}^{-1}}{5.8 \times 10^7\,\Omega^{-1}\,\text{m}^{-1}}}$$

$$= 2.8 \times 10^{-5}.$$

Comment: This result shows why a thin sheet of a good conductor provides excellent shielding for radio frequencies — a tiny fraction of the incident power enters the conductor, and this energy is almost completely absorbed over a few skin depths (here $\simeq 10^{-5}\,\text{m}$).

Ex 5.4　Inspection of the expression given for the reflectance suggests that $R \to 1$ as $\sigma \to \infty$. So the most effective reflector will be that with the highest conductivity, that is, silver:

$$R = 1 - T$$
$$= 1 - 2\sqrt{\frac{2\varepsilon_0\omega}{\sigma}}$$
$$= 1 - 2[2 \times 8.85 \times 10^{-12}\,\text{F m}^{-1} \times 2\pi$$
$$\times 1.4 \times 10^9\,\text{s}^{-1}/6.1 \times 10^7\,\Omega^{-1}\,\text{m}^{-1}]^{1/2}$$
$$= 1 - 0.0001$$
$$= 0.9999.$$

Ex 5.5 The cut-off frequency for the TE_{mn} mode in the waveguide is

$$f_{mn} = c\sqrt{\left(\frac{m}{2a}\right)^2 + \left(\frac{n}{2b}\right)^2}. \qquad \text{(Eqn 5.51)}$$

The lowest frequency that will propagate is that for which f_{mn} is a minimum, and since a is the longer dimension, this is the mode with $m = 1$ and $n = 0$. Then

$$f_{10} = c\frac{m}{2a}$$
$$= 3.00 \times 10^8\,\text{m s}^{-1} \times \frac{1}{2 \times 0.16\,\text{m}}$$
$$= 0.94\,\text{GHz}.$$

So the waveguide would transmit a 1 GHz signal in the TE_{10} mode. The next highest cut-off frequencies are for the TE_{20} and TE_{01} modes, both of which have a cut-off frequency of $2f_{10} = 1.88\,\text{GHz}$. This cut-off frequency is above 1 GHz, so the only possible TE mode for a 1 GHz signal is the TE_{10} mode.

Ex 5.6 (a) From Equation 5.45, $v_{\text{group}} = c^2 k_{\text{gw}}/\omega$. So, taking $n = 0$ in Equation 5.52 yields

$$v_{\text{group}} = \frac{c^2}{\omega}\sqrt{\frac{\omega^2}{c^2} - \left(\frac{m\pi}{a}\right)^2} = c\sqrt{1 - \frac{m^2 c^2}{4f^2 a^2}}.$$

Substituting $f = 2 \times 10^9$ Hz, $a = 0.16$ m, we find

$$v_{\text{group}} = c\left(1 - \frac{m^2 \times (3.00 \times 10^8\,\text{m s}^{-1})^2}{4 \times (2.0 \times 10^9\,\text{Hz})^2 \times (0.16\,\text{m})^2}\right)^{1/2}$$
$$= c\,(1 - 0.22\,m^2)^{1/2}.$$

For TE_{10}, $m = 1$, yielding $v_{\text{group}} = 2.65 \times 10^8\,\text{m s}^{-1}$.

For TE_{20}, $m = 2$, yielding $v_{\text{group}} = 1.04 \times 10^8\,\text{m s}^{-1}$.

(b) Times for pulses in the TE_{10} and TE_{20} modes to travel 100 m to the end of the guide are 0.38 μs and 0.96 μs, respectively, a difference of 0.58 μs.

Comment: This would cause significant distortion of a 1 μs pulse.

(c) The way to stop the TE_{20} mode propagating would be to ensure that the operating frequency is below the cut-off f_{20} for the TE_{20} mode. For $a = 0.16$ m,

$$f_{20} = c\frac{m}{2a}$$
$$= 3.00 \times 10^8\,\text{m s}^{-1} \times \frac{2}{2 \times 0.16\,\text{m}}$$
$$= 1.88\,\text{GHz}.$$

The TE_{20} mode could be cut off by reducing the operating frequency below 1.88 GHz, or by reducing the width a of the guide so that $f_{20} > 2$ GHz.

Ex 6.1 At the limit of propagation, $\omega_p = \omega$, from which it follows that $n_e = m\varepsilon_0\omega^2/e^2$, so

$$n_e = 9.11 \times 10^{-31}\,\text{kg} \times 8.85 \times 10^{-12}\,\text{F m}^{-1}$$
$$\times (2\pi \times 8.0 \times 10^5\,\text{Hz})^2$$
$$\div (1.60 \times 10^{-19}\,\text{C})^2$$
$$= 8.0 \times 10^9\,\text{m}^{-3}.$$

Reading from Figure 6.7, this electron number density is exceeded by a height of about 80 km, right at the lower limit of the ionosphere, so radio waves at 800 kHz would certainly not penetrate the ionosphere beyond 100 km.

Ex 6.2 The electron number density profile in the ionosphere can be measured by sending pulses of energy at specific frequencies vertically upwards. Then the arrival time of the echo is determined by the height at which the signal frequency equals the local plasma frequency (at which point the signal energy is reflected).

Ex 6.3 The 10 MHz limit relates to pure reflection at the place where $\omega = \omega_p$, which defines a critical electron number density. At normal incidence, the greatest electron number density in the ionosphere will reflect radiation with frequency below about 10 MHz, and anything of higher frequency goes straight through. However, waves that are obliquely incident on the ionosphere can be redirected towards the Earth without having to encounter the critical density. The waves are turned around gradually by refraction. On returning to the Earth's surface, the waves encounter land or ocean with sufficient conductivity to reflect a significant fraction of the incident energy (as discussed in Chapter 5).

Ex 6.4 The LH wave excites a displacement given by Equation 6.8. This differs from the RH case only in the substitution of $+\omega$ for $-\omega$. This follows through into the expression for relative permittivity, which is given by Equation 6.9 with $\omega(\omega - \omega_c)$ replaced by $-\omega(-\omega - \omega_c)$, which equals $\omega(\omega + \omega_c)$.

Ex 6.5 From Equations 6.9 and 6.10, with $\omega_p = 2\omega_c$, we find:

$$\varepsilon^{RH}(\omega_c/2) = +17,$$
$$\varepsilon^{LH}(\omega_c/2) = -13/3,$$
$$\varepsilon^{RH}(2\omega_c) = -1,$$
$$\varepsilon^{LH}(2\omega_c) = +1/3.$$

So for $\omega = \omega_c/2$, the wave with right-handed polarization propagates with phase speed $c/\sqrt{17}$, but the left-handed polarization has a negative permittivity and therefore is exponentially damped and does not propagate.

For $\omega = 2\omega_c$, the rôles are reversed: $\mathbf{E}^{LH}$ propagates, but $\mathbf{E}^{RH}$ does not. The phase speed of $\mathbf{E}^{LH}$ in this case is $\sqrt{3}c$, which exceeds the speed of light in a vacuum.

Ex 6.6 From Equation 6.12,

$$v_{group} = \frac{d\omega}{dk^{RH}} = \left(\frac{dk^{RH}}{d\omega}\right)^{-1}$$
$$= 2c\sqrt{\frac{\omega\omega_c}{\omega_p^2}} = 2v_{phase}.$$

Ex 7.1 The cornea is about $0.6\,\text{mm} = 600\,\mu\text{m}$ thick. The visible spectrum spans 400–750 nm — so taking $500\,\text{nm} = 0.5\,\mu\text{m}$ for ease of calculation as a mid-range wavelength, the cornea is about 1200 wavelengths thick.

Ex 7.2 A 300 nm scale bar is shown in Figure 7.2. That distance seems to incorporate maybe five or six fibrils, giving an average separation between centres of roughly 50 nm. This is one tenth of a convenient mid-range wavelength of 500 nm. The thickness of the middle lamella in the figure corresponds to about eight of the 300 nm scale bars, so a typical width for a lamella is about 2400 nm, which amounts to about five mid-range wavelengths.

Ex 7.3

- The fibrils are virtually identical.

- The fibrils are arranged in arrays with a high degree of regularity (though this does not need to be perfect).

- The scattering cross-section of fibrils is very small because the fibrils are small compared with the wavelength of visible light, and their relative permittivity is not too different from that of the matrix (so multiple scattering is negligible).

- The spacing of the fibrils is less than the wavelength of light, so only zero-order diffraction occurs when electromagnetic waves encounter any particular layer of fibrils.

Ex 7.4

$$f_0 = \frac{c}{4L} = \frac{3.00 \times 10^8\,\text{m s}^{-1}}{4 \times 0.0250\,\text{m}} = 3.00\,\text{GHz}.$$

Ex 7.5

$$f_{res,\,d} = \frac{c}{4L\sqrt{\varepsilon}} = \frac{3.00 \times 10^8\,\text{m s}^{-1}}{4 \times 0.0250\,\text{m} \times \sqrt{2.20}}$$
$$= 2.02\,\text{GHz}.$$

Since the given value of the relative permittivity is specified for GHz frequencies, this calculation is valid.

Ex 7.6 First choose the dimensions of the hairpin to give a vacuum resonance in the range of interest, say at 250 MHz:

$$L = \frac{c}{4f_0} = \frac{3.00 \times 10^8\,\text{m s}^{-1}}{4 \times 2.50 \times 10^8\,\text{Hz}} = 0.300\,\text{m}.$$

Then construct a hairpin with this length, and determine its actual resonant frequency in a vacuum, f_0. Next, immerse the hairpin in the transformer oil, and sweep the excitation down from f_0 to find the new resonance, $f_{res,\,d}$. The relative permittivity at $f_{res,\,d}$ is then found by rearranging Equation 7.3:

$$\varepsilon = \left(\frac{f_0}{f_{res,\,d}}\right)^2.$$

If the resonant frequency $f_{res,\,d}$ differs appreciably from 100 MHz, a little iteration may be required to adjust the hairpin's length so that it resonates in the oil at 100 MHz.

Ex 7.7 Combining Equations 6.1 and 7.6, and remembering that $\omega = 2\pi f$, gives directly

$$n_e = \frac{m\varepsilon_0}{e^2}\omega_p^2 = \frac{4\pi^2 m\varepsilon_0}{e^2}f_p^2$$
$$= \frac{4\pi^2 m\varepsilon_0}{e^2}\left(f_{res,\,p}^2 - f_0^2\right).$$

Ex 7.8 Assuming that the plasma is sufficiently cold and collisionless for the simple relative permittivity function of Equation 6.2 to be valid, Equation 7.7

relates electron number density to resonant frequencies. So

$$n_{\mathrm{e}} = \frac{4\pi^2 m \varepsilon_0}{e^2} \left(f_{\mathrm{res,\,p}}^2 - f_0^2 \right)$$

$$= \frac{4\pi^2 \times 9.11 \times 10^{-31}\,\mathrm{kg} \times 8.85 \times 10^{-12}\,\mathrm{F\,m^{-1}}}{(1.60 \times 10^{-19}\,\mathrm{C})^2}$$

$$\times \left(3.15^2 - 2.50^2 \right) \times 10^{18}\,\mathrm{Hz^2}$$

$$= 4.6 \times 10^{16}\,\mathrm{m^{-3}}.$$

Ex 7.9 Although electromagnetic waves cannot propagate in an unmagnetized plasma at frequencies below the plasma frequency (see Chapter 6), according to Equation 7.5, the resonance always occurs at a frequency *above* the plasma frequency. Therefore the hairpin at resonance will always excite electromagnetic waves in surrounding plasma.

Acknowledgements

Grateful acknowledgement is made to the following sources:

Figure 1: © CuboImages srl/Alamy; *Figure 2:* Farkas, I., Helbing, D. & Vicsek, T. (2002) 'Mexican waves in an excitable medium', *Nature* **419**, 12 September 2002. © Nature Publishing Group; *Figure 3a:* VLA http://chandra.harvard.edu/photo; *Figure 3b:* NASA/CXC/SAO/Rutgers/J.Hughes; *Figure 3c:* MDM Observatory http://chandra.harvard.edu/photo; *Figures 5a, b, & c:* Courtesy of Colin Gagg, Open University; *Figure 5d:* Per-Magnus Heden/pixonnet.com/Alamy; *Figure 5e:* Keith Kent/Science Photo Library; *Figure 6:* Science Photo Library; *Figure 7:* Courtesy of Professor David Coutts, University of Oxford (photo taken by Stuart Bebb, Oxford Photographic Unit); *Figure 8b:* © Directphoto.org/Alamy;

Figure 2.1: © David Martyn Hughes/Alamy; *Figures 2.13 & 2.14:* Courtesy of Professor Nicholas Braithwaite, Open University; *Figure 2.15:* Susumu Nishinaga/Science Photo Library;

Figure 3.1a: © Robert Harding Picture Library/Alamy; *Figure 3.1b:* John McFarlane/Science Photo Library; *Figure 3.1c:* Bsip Bajande/Science Photo Library; *Figures 3.2 & 3.15:* Courtesy of Professor Nicholas Braithwaite, Open University;

Figure 4.7: © James Davis Photography/Alamy;

Figure 5.1: Martin Dohrn/Science Photo Library; *Figure 5.14:* Courtesy of Mike Levers, Open University;

Figure 6.1a: NASA; *Figure 6.1b:* ISAS/NASA; *Figure 6.2:* NASA/C. R. O'Dell and S. K. Wong (Rice University); *Figure 6.3a:* Courtesy of Professor Nicholas Braithwaite, Open University and Bill Graham, Queens University, Belfast; *Figure 6.3b:* Courtesy of Joao Gomes, Open University; *Figure 6.10b:* Photolibrary.Com (Australia);

Figure 7.2: Giraud, J. P. et al. (1975) 'Statistical morphometric studies in normal human and rabbit corneal stroma', *Experimental Eye Research* **21**, 1975, Academic Press (London) Limited; *Figure 7.8a:* Courtesy of Alec Goodyear, Open University.

Every effort has been made to contact copyright holders. If any have been inadvertently overlooked the publishers will be pleased to make the necessary arrangements at the first opportunity.

Index

Items that appear in the Glossary have page numbers in **bold type**. Ordinary index items have page numbers in Roman type.